Industrial Engineering And Management

Industrial Engineering And Management

Kaushik Kumar
B.Tech (Mech. Engg.), MBA, Ph.D.
Birla Institute of Technology-Mesra, Ranchi

Divya Zindani
B. Tech (Mech Engg.), M.E. (Mech. Engg.)
Birla Institute of Technology-Mesra, Ranchi

ISBN: 978-93-89633-19-1

Edition: 2019

Printed at: Shree Maitrey Printech Pvt. Ltd., Noida

Preface

Industrial engineering deals with the optimization of different processes, systems or organizations. As such it involves the use of different physical, mathematical and social principles together with the methods of engineering design to predict and hence to optimize the results obtained from the different complex processes or systems.

The scope of industrial engineering management is as vast as to include a wide array of sub-specialties such as operations research, manufacturing engineering, production engineering, management science, etc. Thus the importance of learning the different principles, methods and techniques to achieve the objective of optimization, the role of industrial engineering and management can be realized truly.

Keeping in view the importance of the subject, this book has been designed to explain the different aspects related to the principles of optimizing the complex systems and processes of an organization. The book is intended for all the engineering and management students across the country. The authors have tried to include each and every aspect of the subject and therefore the book caters to the syllabus of the different universities and colleges across the country.

The book is divided into **fifteen sections. Section I** provides a brief introduction on industrial engineering and management and its prospects. **Section II** deals with the productivity and the ways to increase it by the discussion on work study in the subsequent chapters of the section. Continuing on the aspect of productivity enhancement, **Section III and Section IV** are devoted to method study and work measurement through time study.

The role of entrepreneurs is truly important in nation building. **Section V** throws light on the entrepreneurial development. The different chapters in this section discuss the theories on entrepreneurship and the different government policies for small scale industries.

Section VI discusses the different aspects of inspection and statistical quality control. This section of the book covers the aspects of Total Quality Management, role of inspection and the statistical quality control. Discussion on production planning and control is provided in **Section VII** of the book.

One of the key elements to success of any organization lies in the proper plant location and its layout. **Section VIII** of this book illuminates the readers with the different objectives and importance of plant location as well as decisions regarding its layout.

Section IX is related to job evaluation and wages concerned with the employees of an organization. The chapters in this section introduce the notion of job evaluation, the different methods to job evaluation and aspects of wages. **Section X** provides a brief overview of the different industrial legislations concerning an organization.

Section XI provides an understanding of one of the important aspects of the value analysis and its different stages.

Role of a leader, the domains of leadership have been highlighted in **Section XII** of the book. **Section XIII** gives a brief introduction on the methods of optimization and project management. **Section XIV** elaborates on industrial safety whereas the last section of the book, i.e., **Section XV** deals with Engineering Economics elaborating the concepts and principles of Replacement and Maintenance Analysis and Inventory Control and its models.

Utmost care has been taken to remove any mistakes and misprints in the textbook. Yet some of them might have inadvertently crept in which will be refined in the future editions.

We are grateful to all quality managers whose kind contribution helped in bringing this to the present form. Our efforts will come to a level of satisfaction if the students from different universities across the nation with industrial engineering and management as one of the subjects gets benefited.

Kaushik Kumar and Divya Zindani
Birla Institute of Technology - Mesra
National Institute of Technology - Silchar

Acknowledgements

It is with immense pleasure that we begin to write this section. If not the reason for this being the last section we wanted to fill in, it is the pure pleasure of thanking every single heart that helped us get to this stage.

We acknowledge the blessings of the almighty without which this would not have been possible.

Our deepest gratitude goes to our family for their unflagging love and support throughout our lives; this work was simply impossible without them. Their dedication, love and persistent confidence in us, had taken the load off our shoulder and allowed us to concentrate towards writing this book.

We would like to thank all our teachers for preparing us for this long journey.

We owe huge thanks to all our technical reviewers. All their efforts helped to make this book complete and we couldn't have done it without them.

We would also like to thank all our friends from different parts of the country and abroad for wishing us luck towards this venture.

Finally, we would like to thank everybody who was important to the successful realization of this book, as well as expressing our apology that we could not mention personally one by one.

Kaushik Kumar and Divya Zindani

Birla Institute of Technology – Mesra

National Institute of Technology – Silchar

Contents

Section III: Method Study

Section IV: Work Measurement

Section XII: Leadership

Section XIII: Operations Research

Section XIV: Industrial Safety

Section XV: Engineering Economics

SECTION I
INTRODUCTION TO INDUSTRIAL ENGINEERING

1
Introduction

1.1 INTRODUCTION

The branch of engineering that deals with the optimization of different complex processes, systems and organizations is known as **Industrial Engineering.** Engineers in this field aim to eliminate or reduce the unwanted elements that do not generate any value. The engineers are called **industrial engineers** and reduce the wastage of time, materials, money, man-hours and other related resources to optimize the different processes. The Institute of Industrial and Systems Engineers defines the role of industrial engineers as to figure out the ways in which the different things can be done better and also the engineering systems to produce goods and services with improved productivity and quality.

Industrial engineering predicts, evaluates and specifies the results that will be obtained from the different complex processes. The objective to do so is accomplished through the development, implementation and improvement of different integrated systems. The integrated systems may be systems of money, people, information, knowledge, equipment, energy and so on. Further, the different mathematical, social sciences and physical models too constitute the integrated systems. The improvement and implementation of different systems is done in coherence with the principles and different methods of engineering design. In most jurisdictions, industrial engineering is a discipline subject to professional engineering licensure. However, the underlying principles of industrial engineering overlap with the different business-oriented disciplines, say for instance, operations management.

The different terms that can be used to define Industrial Engineering are operations research, manufacturing engineering, systems engineering, management science, production engineering, safety engineering and so on. This depends on the nature of sub-specialties involved.

1.2 HISTORY AND DEVELOPMENT OF INDUSTRIAL ENGINEERING

Origins

Industrial Revolution

The roots of the field of industrial engineering date back to the era of the industrial revolution. This is also a general consensus amongst the different historians. The mass production of different products was made possible because of the generated economies of scale. The economies of scale was generated as a result of the different technologies that mechanized the traditional manual operations in different industries. These were the textile industries producing flying shuttle, and the industries producing spinning jenny and most importantly the steam engines.

Specialization of Labour

Many of the technological innovators of the industrial revolution were motivated by the concept of division of labour introduced by Adam Smith in his treatise, "The Wealth of Nations". The concept of the "invisible hand" of capitalism accompanied with that of the "division of labour" motivated the innovators to establish the factory system. The first integrated machine manufacturing facility was established because of the efforts of James Watt and Matthew Boulton. The different concepts such as cost control systems were implemented to reduce the waste and increase the productivity.

The concept of division of the job into smaller elements and its effect, time involved in performing a specific task and the advantages to be gained by the performance of repetitive jobs were introduced by Charles Babbage. He has penned down his concepts in a book "Economy of Machinery and Manufacturers" after visiting the different factories in England and the United States in the early 1800s.

Interchangeable Parts

The concept to mass production of individual parts for their use in any finished product was introduced by Eli Whitney and Simeon North. This concept is known as the interchangeability of parts. They introduced it in their manufacturing of muskets and pistols. The concept led to the significant reduction in the need for skills from specialized workers.

Pioneers

The father of Industrial Engineering discipline is Frederick Taylor. He published books in early 1900s: "Shop Management" and "The Principles of Scientific Management" marking the beginning of Industrial Engineering. Fredrick Taylor led to methods for improvements in work efficiency. The methods were on improving the way of performing the job, developing of certain standards to perform the job and to set time standards to reduce the time required to carry out the work. A high level of predictability and precision for the manual tasks was established by the Taylor's contribution to "Time study".

The human motion was categorized into eighteen basic elements by Frank Gilbreth and Lilian Gilbreth. The two were the other cornerstones of the Industrial Engineering movement. The basic elements were known as therbligs. The concept of therbligs led to the design of jobs by analysts without the knowledge of the time required to do a job. A much broader field of ergonomics was born as a result of these developments.

A chart outlining the different actions of the organization and the relationships between them was developed in 1912 by Henry Laurence Gantt. The chart is known as the Gantt chart.

Assembly lines: moving car factory of Henry Ford (1913) accounted for a significant leap forward in the field. Ford reduced the assembly time of a car more than 700 hours to 1.5 hours. In addition, he was a pioneer of the economy of the capitalist welfare ("welfare capitalism") and the flag of providing financial incentives for employees to increase productivity.

Comprehensive quality management system (total quality management or TQM) developed in the forties was gaining momentum after World War II and was part of the recovery of Japan after the war.

Modern Practice

In 1960 to 1975, with the development of decision support systems in supply such as the material requirements planning (MRP), you can emphasize the timing issue (inventory, production, compounding, transportation, etc.) of industrial organization. Israeli scientist Dr. Jacob Rubinovitz installed the CMMS programme developed in IAI and Control-Data (Israel) in 1976 in South Africa and worldwide.

In the seventies, with the penetration of Japanese management theories such as Kaizen and Kanban, Japan realized very high levels of quality and productivity. These theories improved issues of quality, delivery time, and flexibility. Companies in the West realized the great impact of Kaizen and started implementing their own continuous improvement programmes.

In the nineties, following the global industry globalization process, the emphasis was on supply chain management, and customer-oriented business process design. Theory of constraints developed by an Israeli scientist Eliyahu M. Goldratt (1985) is also a significant milestone in the field.

1.3 PROSPECTS

Industrial engineers are expected to have employment growth of 14 per cent over the projections decade, faster than the average for all occupations. As firms look for new ways to reduce costs and raise productivity, they increasingly will turn to industrial engineers to develop more efficient processes and reduce costs, delays, and waste.

This focus should lead to job growth for these engineers, even in some manufacturing industries with declining employment overall. Because their work is similar to that done in management occupations, many industrial engineers leave the occupation to become managers. Numerous openings will be created by the need to replace industrial engineers who transfer to other occupations or leave the labour force.

SECTION II
PRODUCTIVITY AND WORK STUDY

2

Productivity

2.1 DEFINITION OF PRODUCTIVITY

One can define productivity as the ratio of output to input. Putting in equation form we have the following:

$$\text{Productivity} = \frac{\text{Output}}{\text{Input}}$$

The definition of productivity as mentioned is ubiquitous and therefore is applicable to a sector of economy or the economy as a whole. It is the measure of the degree of extraction of output from a given input. The equation seems to be simple for ***tangible*** output and input parameters. However, the calculation of productivity becomes tedious when the input and output are ***intangibles***. We take an example of a potter to help in gaining the understanding of the difference one has in measuring tangibles versus that of intangibles.

- Let the number of pots produced by a potter be 400 per month. After a few months he was say able to produce 500 pots per month using the same equipment. If one measures the productivity in terms of number of pots produced then one can easily find an increment of 25 per cent.
- Let us now assume that, for some reason the potter had to reduce the price of a pot from Rs 2 to Rs 1.80. Then by selling 400 pots earlier at a price of Rs 2, his total value of output was 400×2 = Rs 800. For the new price of Rs 1.80 a pot his output value comes out be 500×1.8 = Rs 900. Therefore, now the value of output has changed from Rs 800 to Rs 900. Hence, the productivity gain is $\frac{900 - 800}{800} = 12.5$ per cent. The input is same in both the cases of price.

From the above two examples one can make some simple observations. In the first case, productivity was measured for the output that was measured in terms of number of pots produced while in the second case it was the monetary terms that were used to measure the output. Thus, the nature of input and output will differ for measuring the productivity. The nature depends on what one is interested in measuring. Another simple observation that can be made also infers the difference between ***production*** and ***productivity***. In the first case there was increase in production of about 25%, however the productivity as measured in terms of monetary value increased to about 12.5% only. Thus, there is a wide difference between increased production and increased productivity.

- Now, suppose the potter spends Rs 6000 to buy one oil fired kiln. The potter decides to amortize this investment spanning over a period of 10 years. This amounts to Rs 600 investment per year or Rs 50 per month. Apart from the investment on the fire kiln the potter also requires a monthly expenditure of Rs 50 on the oil. The total investment thus amounts to Rs 100 per month. The potter sells a total of 500 pots at the price of Rs 1.80 per pot. So the total output in monetary terms amounts to Rs 900. From this will be deducted the monthly expenditure on amortization of the oil kiln and the oil. Therefore, the monetary gain is Rs 900 - Rs 100, i.e., Rs 800. If this figure is compared with the one of producing 400 pots and selling at the rate of Rs 2, there is no improvement in the monetary gain. Thus, one can say that the productivity has not improved.

But if one looks from the perspective of the potter, the quality of the product has improved using oil fired kiln. This resulted in lesser rejections and thus increasing consumer satisfaction. Due to this the potter was able to increase the price of the product in the latter stage thereby gaining on monetary terms. Secondly, the potter had the satisfaction of the ease and comfort of use of the production assembly thus giving the potter the work satisfaction. Both the output and input are *intangible* in this case. Thus, productivity gains become more difficult to measure accurately because of these intangible factors and because of the time lag that needs to be estimated until users' satisfaction will permit an increase in price of the pots produced in the new kiln. This simple example helps to show that the factors affecting productivity in an organization are many, and often interrelated. Many people have been misled into thinking of productivity exclusively as the productivity of labour, mainly because labour productivity usually forms the basis for published statistics on the subject. It also becomes evident how, in a community or a country, improving productivity or extracting the best possible yield from the available resources does not mean exploitation of labour but the harnessing of all available resources to stimulate a higher rate of growth that can be used for social betterment, a higher standard of living and an improved quality of life. In this book, however, we will restrict ourselves to productivity issues and more specifically to work study as it applies to the individual enterprises.

2.2 QUALITY OF LIFE AND PRODUCTIVITY

The world population saw an increase of about 250 per cent in 2000 in comparison to the year 1950, i.e., the population increased from 2.5 billion in 1950 to around 6.2 billion in 2000. The population of developing countries contributes most towards this increasing population, i.e., around 90 per cent. In the year 2012 the world population stood at 7.06 billion, developing countries contributing around 97% towards this increase. The developing countries are finding it difficult to provide for the basic needs to this growing population. Food, clothing, shelter, security, health and essential services together form basic needs of population. One should have access to enough food so that energy required for living and day-to-day working can be generated. To protect one from the adverse weather conditions and to ensure body cleanliness, adequate clothing is required. To look after oneself in the old age and sickness, safety from violence and protection, and need of security can't be ignored. Shelter equipped with certain household equipment that can provide for protection under healthy conditions forms another part of the basic needs. Further, the needs of safe drinking water, sanitation to ensure good health also plays a pivotal role in ensuring better quality of life. Education, means of transport, medical services are some of the key basic needs of the population that makes a population better-off. The aspiration to increase the quality of life for the better-off population increases. The quality of life is increased with the raise in standard of living. This is foreseen as an improvement in the quality of these basic needs, and in the range and quantity available so that a person exerts the option of choice among various alternatives, for example in housing, clothing or food. Human aspirations also extend to a desire for a healthier and cleaner environment, cultural activities, the ability to have and make use of leisure time in an enjoyable manner, and an income that would allow a person to support these various endeavours. The return from resources must be maximized or the ***productivity*** should be improved by any nation in order to raise the standard of living. This can also ensure progressive growth in the economy and aid the nations to sustain a better quality of life.

2.3 PRODUCTIVITY IN AN ENTERPRISE

There are a number of external and internal factors that affect the productivity in an individual enterprise. The internal factors are the number of deficiencies in the operation and functioning of an enterprise. Availability of raw materials, of skilled labour, existing infrastructure, taxation and tariff policies of the government, interest rates, availability of capital, and adjustment measures applied by the government to the economy or to some of its specific sectors, are some of the external factors that affect the productivity of an enterprise. Employer finds it difficult to control the aforementioned external factors.

The output and input factors in an enterprise

Products or services rendered are the output of any enterprise. It is the value, the numbers of a product that define the output in any manufacturing enterprise. The conformity of the product to the predetermined quality standards also determines the output in any manufacturing concern. For enterprises such as a travel agency or a public transport company, the output is in terms of services rendered. The number of customers or the quantity of cargo carried per kilometer by any transport company is the services rendered and hence the output of such an enterprise. On the other hand for any travel agency, the services rendered and hence its output will be the value of tickets sold or average value of tickets per customer, and so on. Consumers' or users' satisfaction is of utmost importance to both the manufacturing concern as well as for the service enterprise. Thus, be it a manufacturing concern or any service enterprise, the feedback in the form of product rejection is of utmost importance.

For producing any output, an enterprise needs to dispose of certain inputs. These may include land and buildings, materials, energy, machine and equipment and last but not the least human resources. Land and buildings are required at convenient location so that products can be produced. Materials that can be converted into products to be sold, both as raw materials or auxiliary materials such as solvents or other chemicals and paints needed in the process of manufacturing and packaging material. Energy in its various forms such as electricity, gas, oil, or solar power affects output of any enterprise. Machines and equipment necessary for the operational activities of the enterprise, including those intended for transport and handling, heating or air conditioning, office equipment, computer terminals and the like. Men and women trained to perform the operational activity, to plan and control, to buy and sell, to keep track of accounts and to perform other operations such as maintenance or administrative and secretarial jobs. Another factor of production or input is that of capital which, while not explicitly defined here, is implicitly included since it is used to finance the purchase of land, machinery, equipment, materials and labour, and to pay for the services rendered by human resources. The use which is made of all these resources combined determines the productivity of the enterprise.

2.4 THE TASK OF MANAGEMENT

The management of an enterprise is responsible for seeing that the enterprise resources mentioned above are combined in the best possible way to achieve the highest productivity. In any concern larger than a one-person business (and to some extent even in a one-person business), harnessing and coordinating these resources and balancing one resource against another is the task of the management. If the management fails to do what is necessary, the enterprise will fail in the end. In such a case, the five resources become uncoordinated – like the efforts of five horses without a driver. The enterprise – like a driverless coach – moves forward jerkily, now held up for lack of material, now for lack of equipment, because machines or equipment are badly chosen and even more badly maintained, or because energy sources are inadequate or employees unwilling to contribute their best. Fig. 2.1 illustrates this management function.

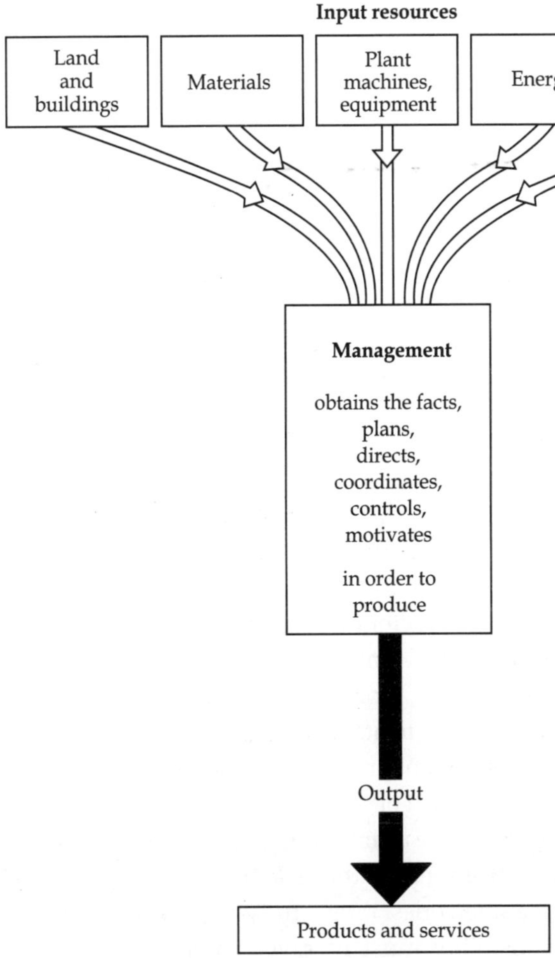

Fig. 2.1: Role of the management in coordinating the resources of an enterprise.

In its quest for higher productivity, an efficiency-minded management acts to influence either one or both of the two factors, the output (i.e., products and services) or the input (i.e., the five resources at its disposal). Thus, the management may be able to produce a larger quantity of, and/or better-quality or higher-value, products or services with the same input, or it may achieve a better result by changing the nature of the input such as investing in advanced technology, information systems and computers or by using an alternative source of raw material or energy. It is rare, however, that one manager or a small team of top managers can by themselves attend to the normal running of an enterprise and at the same time devote enough thinking and energy to the various issues involved in improving productivity. More frequently they will rely on specialists to assist them in this task, and among them is the work study practitioner.

3
Work Study

3.1 IMPORTANCE OF WORK STUDY

Ever since human effort was first organized on a large-scale, improvements and investigations at the workplace have been carried out by good managers. As such there is nothing new in improvising and investigating operations at the workplace. Notable advancements in this field have been made by the managers having outstanding abilities. However, there is lack of supply of competent managers with outstanding capability in any country to look after the task of improvement and investigation at the workplace. It is where the need of work study is realized. Work study consists of systematic procedures that aid even the less competent managers to achieve better results than the less systematic approaches adopted by the more competent ones. Work study investigates the problem in a systematic way. Further, the development of solution to the problem under consideration is also systematic. However, the procedure is time consuming. Therefore, the job of making work studies should be separated from that of the task of the management. This becomes a necessity for all firms barring the small ones. Work study requires continuous observation of an activity and such a responsibility must be given to someone who can do so by undertaking it full time. Further, any alteration in any of the procedures and for its effectiveness requires the information to be accurate. This can be achieved only through careful and continuous observation. Because of the condition of continuous observation, even the capable managers with their material and human problems can't afford to devote enough time and that too without any interruptions to study an activity in a working area or in any factory floor. Therefore, people from staff position could be chosen over the ones in line position. This is because people in line positions exercise direct supervisory authority over the ranks below them. While on the other hand staff appointees are strictly advisers with no power or authority to put their recommendations into operation. Their function is to provide expert information. One can say that service to management and supervision is accomplished by the tool of work study.

There are reasons behind making work study a valuable tool of the management. Some of the reasons have been summarized below.

- The productivity of an operating unit or a plant can be improvised by undertaking work study. This can be done by reorganization of work. The work study does so with involvement of little or no capital expenditure on facilities and equipment.
- Work study is a systematic approach for increasing the productivity of an enterprise. Due to this systematic approach, it's ensured that no factors are overlooked affecting the operation of an enterprise. This helps in proper evaluation and thus alteration in the existing work method. Further, due to availability of almost all the facts about the operation, development of new method becomes much easier, which then can be implemented effectively to increase the productivity of any enterprise.
- Work study leads to effective planning and control of production activities. This becomes easier through work study as it sets standards of performance.
- Hazardous operations are exposed by using work study. This can lead to the improvement of safety and working conditions at the workplace. Also new safer methods for performing the operations can be developed efficiently.
- Proper work method adopted through efficient work study leads to savings which continues as long as the operation continues to function in the improved form.
- Work study is a ubiquitous tool that can be applied everywhere. It can be applied to manufacturing shops. Apart from plant operations it can be applied in offices, laboratories, stores and even to service industries that looks after wholesale and retail distribution, restaurants, farms, to name a few.
- It requires little or no capital and is therefore relatively cheap and easy to apply.
- Work study is ***one of the most penetrating tools of investigation available to the management.*** It leads to alteration in work methodology and hence increased efficiency of any organization. By doing so it considers all the factors that influence the working of the organization and hence its efficiency. Thus, it exposes the weaknesses of all the factors that directly or indirectly affect the efficiency of the organization.

The last point is further illustrated using an example. There may be a case where due to improper scheduling of materials supply, the machine remains idle and hence the production time is wasted. One could observe that the production time may be wasted because of lack of maintenance of the machinery, due to which breakdown of the machinery took place. Hence, one can say that, it was failure on the part of material control and the maintenance engineer due to which the production time was wasted. Further, on observing the role of production planning and marketing policy, the work study manager may observe that constant resetting of machine was required if the production was run for short batches of product. Therefore, while observing one activity of production time, the factors that were affecting it were exposed and hence steps to correct these could be taken in a systematic way. The example clearly illustrates the penetrating ability of the work study tool.

However, work study also exposes people in the working environment while exposing the shortcomings of the activities. Therefore, work study should be handled properly and is often referred to as surgeon's knife. Work study may lead to animosity of management and workers alike if not handled with care. This will affect the productivity and hence the efficiency of the enterprise. Further, managers and supervisors, though trained, find it difficult for them to apply work study continuously and thus have failed to achieve the savings and improvements in the long run. Thus, besides being systematic, it requires work study to be continuous as well. The savings can be realized only in the long run and therefore it is no use work study practitioners doing a good job and then sitting back and congratulating themselves, or being transferred shortly afterwards by management to something else. The savings achieved on individual jobs, although sometimes large in them, are generally small when compared with the activity of the company as a whole. The full effect is felt in an organization only when work study is applied everywhere, and when everyone becomes imbued with the attitude of mind which is the basis of successful work study: **intolerance of waste in any form, whether material, time, effort or human ability;** and the refusal to accept without questioning that things must be done in a certain way "because that is the way they have always been done".

3.2 TECHNIQUES

The term "work study" embraces several techniques, but in particular method study and work measurement. What are these two techniques and what is their relationship to one another?

- Method study is the systematic recording and critical examination of ways of doing things in order to make improvements.
- Work measurement is the application of techniques designed to establish the time for a qualified worker to carry out a task at a defined rate of working.

Method study and work measurement are, therefore, closely linked. Method study is concerned with the reduction of the work content of a job or operation, while work measurement is mostly concerned with the investigation and of any ineffective time associated with it; and with the subsequent establishment of time standards for the operation when carried out in an improved fashion, as determined by method study. The relationship of method study to work measurement is shown in Fig. 3.1. Although method study should precede the use of work measurement when time standards for output are being set, it is often necessary to use one of the techniques of work measurement, such as work sampling, in order to determine why ineffective time is occurring and what is its extent, so that the management can take action to reduce it before a method study is begun. Again, time study may be used to compare the effectiveness of alternative methods of work before deciding on the best method to install.

These techniques will be dealt with in detail in the chapters devoted to them. For the present we must consider the basic procedure of work study which applies to **every** study, whatever the operation or process being examined whether in industry, in a service enterprise or in the office. This procedure is fundamental to the whole of work study. **There is no short cut.**

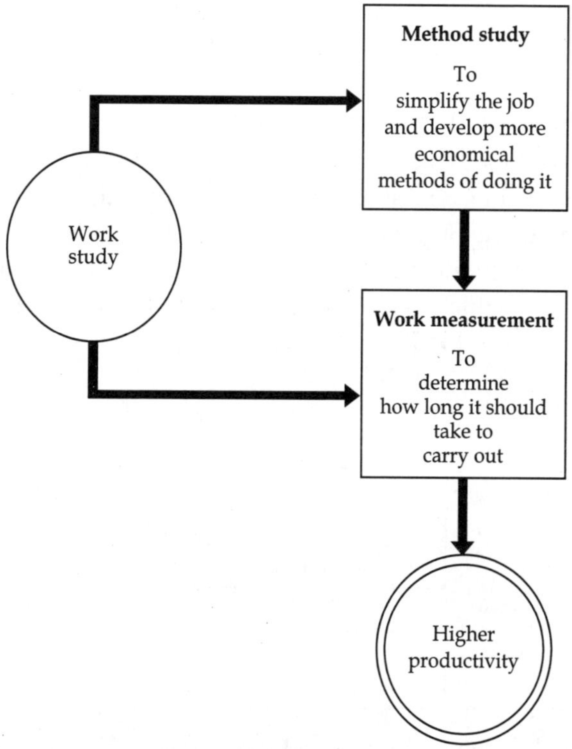

Fig. 3.1: Work study.

3.3 PROCEDURE

There are eight steps in performing a complete work study. They are:

(1) **Select** the job or process to be studied.

(2) **Record** or collect all relevant data about the job or process, using the most suitable data collection techniques (explained in Part Two), so that the data will be in the most convenient form to be analysed.

(3) **Examine** the recorded facts critically and challenge everything that is done, considering in turn: the purpose of the activity; the place where it is performed; the sequence in which it is done; the person who is doing it; and the means by which it is done.

(4) **Develop** the most economical method, taking into account all the circumstances and drawing appropriate various production management techniques (explained in Part Three), as well as on the contributions of managers, supervisors, workers and other specialists with whom new approaches should be explored and discussed.

(5) **Evaluate** the results attained by the improved method compared with the quantity of work involved and calculate a standard time for it.

(6) **Define** the new method and the related time and present it to all those concerned, either verbally or in writing, using demonstrations.

(7) **Install** the new method, training those involved, as an agreed practice with the allotted time of operation.

(8) **Maintain** the new standard practice by monitoring the results and comparing them with the original targets.

Steps 1, 2 and 3 occur in every study, whether the technique being used is a method study or work measurement. Step 4 is part of method study practice, while step 5 calls for the use of work measurement. It is possible that after a certain time the new method requires modification, in which case it would be reexamined using the above sequence. These eight steps are depicted in Fig. 3.2.

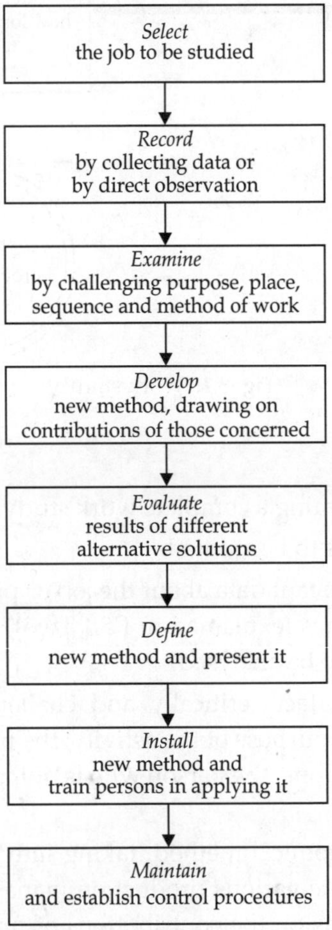

Fig. 3.2

3.4 WORK STUDY AND PRODUCTION MANAGEMENT

When work study emerged in the early part of this century as a technique aimed at rationalizing and measuring work, the emphasis was on economy, motion and movement. Because of that it was called time and motion study. Later on, it began to encompass other aspects of observing and analyzing work, and the earlier term was abandoned in favour of "work study".

Simultaneously, in the late 1940s and later on in the 1960s, other disciplines were developed, namely industrial engineering and production management respectively. These disciplines differed from work study in the sense that they were devoted to increasing the efficiency of a production operation as a whole, not just the methods of work. Thus, modern production management looks at various aspects of production such as product design, quality control, layout and materials handling, production planning and control, maintenance management and invariably work study. These techniques may be applied, singly or in combination, in the enterprise. Furthermore, with time many of them began to rely increasingly on sophisticated quantitative methods such as operations research to solve even more complicated operational problems. Advances in the fields of computers and information systems helped to boost production management techniques to the level attained at present. While work study has continued to be a relatively simple and cheap method of rationalizing methods of work, it has also continued to develop. Thus, many work study trained specialists realize that several of the existing production management techniques can also be used advantageously by them to help develop improved methods of work. In a sense they provide an array of techniques that cannot and need not be ignored. It can also be seen that the career of a work study practitioner can now evolve in two directions: first, a more professional path where he or she can continue to develop knowledge and skills in these new operational fields to become a production management specialist or, second, a managerial path where he or she can acquire a high-level position by virtue of specialized training.

4
Human Factor and Work Study

4.1 HUMAN FACTOR IN ENTERPRISE OPERATIONS

The utilization of resources in any enterprise can be controlled by the management through its people. It is the people that influence the sale of a product and services in an organization. Therefore, human factor is one of the most crucial elements in the effective functioning of any enterprise. To give the best of their ability, employees must be motivated to do so. Managers must be able to provide a motive or a reason for doing something, or make people want to do it. It is of little use for the management to prepare elaborate plans or give instructions for carrying out various activities if the people who are supposed to carry out the plans do not wish to do so – even though they may have to. The result would be half-hearted effort and sloppy workmanship. Coercion is no substitute for action that is taken voluntarily and willingly. Therefore, there must always be an environment where employees at all the levels of the enterprise can have a sense of belonging to the enterprise. The environment must be conducive enough so that the employees always feel secure. Further, the environment should be rich and healthy. Such a working environment will increase the productivity of the employees. Employees will feel free to provide suggestions for improvement in productivity of the enterprise. Further, they can assist by themselves the work study manager in order to develop improved methods of work. One of the greatest difficulties in obtaining the active cooperation of workers is the fear that raising productivity will lead to unemployment. Workers are afraid that they will work themselves out of their jobs. This anxiety is greatest when unemployment is already high and a worker who loses his or her job will find it hard to find another. Even in industrialized countries where the levels of unemployment are relatively lower than developing countries, this fear is very real to those who have already experienced unemployment. Since this is so, unless workers are assured of adequate assistance in facing their problems, they may resist any steps which they fear, rightly or wrongly, will make them redundant, even temporarily. Even with written guarantees, steps taken to raise productivity can meet with resistance. This resistance can generally be reduced to a minimum if everybody concerned understands the nature of and the reason for, each step taken and is involved in its implementation. Workers' representatives should be trained in the techniques of increasing productivity so that they will be able both to explain them to their fellow workers and to use their knowledge to ensure that no steps are taken which are harmful to them. Many of these safeguards can best be implemented through joint productivity committees and works councils. If work study is to contribute seriously to the improvement of productivity, relations between the management and workers must be reasonably good before any attempt is made to introduce it, and the workers must have confidence in the sincerity of the management towards them; otherwise they will regard it as a way of getting more work out of them without any benefit to themselves. Therefore, efforts must be made to conduct jointly by the manager, supervisor and the workforce. This will lead to a work culture that will ultimately lead to increase in productivity of the enterprise.

4.2 WORK STUDY AND MANAGEMENT

As has been said in the previous chapter, that work study is a penetrating tool to increase the productivity of any enterprise. Further, the systematic nature of work study exposes the adverse factors and thereby modifies these to obtain the desired efficiency of the enterprise. It clearly points out the areas where the effort and time is wasted and thus improvising these areas will ultimately lead to increased productivity. The systematic approach clearly reflects on the causes because of which the effort and time are wasted. Some of the prominent causes obtained from the work study may be bad organization, bad planning, and lack of proper training or insufficient control. The causes clearly expose the failure on the part of the management and the supervisory staff as they are the ones performing different functions in the organization. Work study once started in a particular area or department of the organization tends to spread like a chain reaction, i.e., it will spread in all the directions throughout the organization. It seeks to improvise the work method in each and every department of the organization such as plant engineer's department, the design office, the accounts department and the sales office. Because of the new methodology suggested through systematic work study, the skilled and trained workers will feel like novice and will have to do away with their long practised methods. They would feel as though their methods were just wasteful of effort and time. On the other hand, the novice and newly trained workers will surpass them in output and quality. There may arise a feeling of insecurity amongst the workers. Further, their self confidence will decrease which will ultimately affect their efficiency. One can say that the investigation from work study be unfair. In order to do away with the feeling of insecurity and animosity, the work study managers must have support at all levels from the management. The work study managers are honest and hard working people who would work for the betterment of the organization and would not put any obstacle to the point where the task is made almost impossible. They have got years of experience and specialization at par with any of the work study specialists. Their duties must be made clear at all the levels of the organization. If the management at the top doesn't understand that what work study managers are doing is for the betterment of the enterprise then there may even arise a situation of truce between the two. If the work study managers do not have enough backing from the top management then they may fail in their duties and even all the other employees of the organization will feel that the work study managers are just obstructing their way of working. There may be circumstances when the work study managers would lose their case however good it may be. It must always be kept in mind that people lower down tend to take their attitudes from the person at the top. Therefore, the people at the top which includes the managing director or managing agent, the head of the different departments and the assistant heads below them, should be among the first to be explained about the purpose and techniques of the work study. Generally, before applying the work study recommendations, short appreciation courses must be run for the top management. There are some institutions such as the management development institutes, technical colleges, work study schools and other organizations that train the people sent by the organization in this field. However, running of these short courses is not at all easy. It is always recommended for the trainers to seek advice and assistance from the experts in these fields. The work study training staff should always know their subject best. Further, they should always try to persuade the people from top management to involve themselves in the course. Even efforts should be made to ask the top management to inaugurate such proceedings. This will help draw other employees in the organization to attend the course if they know that their boss is going to be there. In this way the advantages of the course can be spread to all parts of the organization.

4.3 WORK STUDY AND THE SUPERVISOR

Arising of confidence in the supervisors by the work study managers is one of the most difficult tasks. Instilling self-confidence is very important to obtain good results and to prevent any hostility from popping up, since hostility may prevent the supervisors to adopt the new work methodology. For the workers at the shop floors, supervisors represent the management. If the supervisor feels that adoption of new work methodology is just wastage of time and effort so will the workers at the shop floor would feel. This will, in turn, affect the productivity of work manager. Further, the workers will have less respect for the work study managers. Therefore, it is the responsibility of the work study manager to carefully explain the work study practitioner about the procedures involved. This is necessary for the efficient working of work study practitioner.

However, there are reasons as to why the work study practitioner will feel the new work methodology to be obstructive. Some of the reasons are discussed below:

- Supervisors may feel that their prestige is being lowered in the eyes of their superiors by challenging their methodology adopted for decades. They may also feel that their reputation in front of the shop floor workers will get reduced. So it is necessary for the work study manager to make it clear to the work study practitioner is that whatever they are suggesting is for the betterment of the enterprise.
- In certain firms and enterprises, supervisors look after some of the important responsibilities such as planning programmes of work, making up time sheets,

developing methods for jobs, hiring and firing of workers. In such a scenario, if the firm hires a work study manager then it is possible that the supervisor may be stripped off with some or all of his duties. The supervisor may feel to have lost his or her ground since no one likes to think that he or she has lost the status that was once enjoyed.

- In circumstances of dispute, it will be the supervisors who will be called upon to clear up the matter. It will be very difficult on the part of the supervisor to do so if he or she fails to understand the problem in hand.

The sources from which supervisors are recruited differ widely in different parts of the world. In some countries, supervisors are frequently selected on the basis of seniority from among the best-skilled persons in the enterprise. This means that they are often middle-aged and may be set in their ways. Because most supervisors have practised their occupation or skills for many years, they find it difficult to believe that they have anything to learn from someone who has not spent a very long time in the same occupation. Supervisors may therefore resent the introduction of work study specialists into their departments unless they have had some training to prepare them for it. The work study courses should be of relatively longer durations in comparison to that for the top management. This is because a supervisor much more intimately connects to the practical side of the job. The duration of courses should not be less than one week. Further, the courses should be full time. The courses will help supervisors to assist the work manager in selection of jobs to be studied. They should be able to segregate the factors involved. This will be only possible if they are fully acquainted with the principal techniques and the method of measurements involved in work study. Further, they should have knowledge of methods to be applied in a particular problem. The aim of the work study course will be fulfilled if the supervisors are also allowed to have some hands-on experience of method studies and the manner of measuring the time. The value to the work study person of a supervisor who understands and is enthusiastic about what he or she is trying to do cannot be overemphasized. He or she is a powerful ally. The work study manager should maintain a friendly relation with the supervisor so that supervisor can adopt the new suggested methods without having the feeling of lost ground or lost face. Further, the supervisor will be confident that no one is trying to usurp his or her power. Some of the rules that a work study manager must observe are discussed below:

- Work study manager should never give any instructions directly to a worker. All the instructions should be given first to the concerned supervisor. Only in certain circumstances where the supervisor has directed his or her workers to carry out the instructions directly from the work study manager, the instructions can be given directly to the workers at shop floor by the work study manager.
- Work study manager should make it clear to the workers at the shop floor about the technical purview in which the work study manager should be referred. For decisions pertaining to outside of the technical purview, supervisor should be referred.

- Care must be taken by the work study manager to never give opinions to workers which may be interpreted as critical of the supervisor. There will be trouble and further deterioration of the relationship between the supervisor and the work study manager if the worker later says to the supervisor: "...but Mr/Ms...said..."
- Work study manager should never kneel down to the requests of the workers through which there may be dispute between the supervisor and the work study manager. In some situations, workers may try to get the instructions given to them by the supervisor altered which they consider harsh.
- The work study manager should always carry out the work in tandem with the supervisor. He should always seek an opinion with the supervisor on the selection of jobs to be studied. Further, technical expertise must be sought from the supervisor even if the work study manager has a great deal of technical knowhow.

The above list is just merely common sense and good manners. Workers should always feel that the supervisor is only their boss. They should try their heart out to uphold the authority of their boss. However, once an understanding has been made between the three then some relaxation can be given. However, this is just the matter of judgment and any relaxation should come directly from the supervisor.

A great deal of space has been given to the relationship between the work study practitioner and the supervisor because it is the most difficult of all the relationships, and it must be good. One of the best methods of ensuring that this is so is to provide both parties with the proper training.

4.4 WORK STUDY AND THE WORKER

When the first conscious attempts at work study were made at the turn of the century, little was known about the way people behaved at work. As a result, workers often resisted or were hostile to work study. During the past 40 years, however, a great deal of research has been carried out to discover more about the way people behave – the aim being not only to explain that behavior but, if possible, also to predict how people will react to a new situation. For a work study specialist this is an important consideration, since through his or her interventions he or she is invariably and continuously creating new situations.

There are certain needs of an individual that should be satisfied. The desire to satisfy the needs motivates the individual to act in a certain way. Abraham Maslow postulated one of the most widely accepted notions about needs. According to him the needs of an individual are arranged in a hierarchical pattern. He further argued that the proceeding need in the hierarchy will start exerting a motivating influence only when the needs above the order have been satisfied. Physiological needs are at the bottom of the hierarchy which is necessary for the sustenance of one's life. Only when the physiological needs have been satisfied, the individual will be concerned of other issues. Once the physiological needs have been satisfied security is the next need that starts exerting its motivating influence. Any individual needs security against physical and psychological harms. Further, one also needs security of employment. Fulfilling the physiological and security needs, affiliation is the next motivating factor. One needs to have satisfaction of belonging to a group or an organization. Need to be recognized followed by the need of fulfilment are the other needs in the hierarchy. The need of fulfilment gives workers an opportunity to show their particular talents.

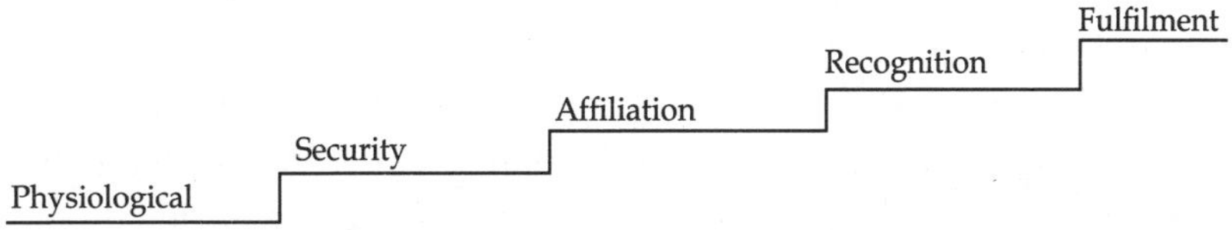

Fig. 4.1: Maslow's hierarchy of needs.

In practice, most people satisfy some of these needs in part and are left with some that are unsatisfied. In developing countries people are probably preoccupied more with their basic needs. In developed countries, on the other hand, where physiological and security needs are normally met in large part, people would seem to be motivated more by needs at the upper end of the hierarchy.

One of the interesting results of the research carried out in this area, and which should be of concern to us here, is the discovery that, in order to satisfy affiliation needs, workers associate with each other to form various types of informal groups. Thus, a worker is usually a member of a task group that is a group composed of workers performing a common task. He or she may also be a member of various other groups, such as a friendship group composed of fellow workers with whom he or she has something in common or with whom he or she would like to associate.

This means that every organization has a formal and an informal structure. The formal structure is defined by the management in terms of authority relationships. Similarly, there also exists an informal organization composed of a great number of informal groups which have their own goals and activities and which bear the sentiments of their members. Each group, it was found, expects its members to conform to a certain standard of behaviour, since otherwise the group cannot achieve its goal, whether this be accomplishing a task or providing a means for friendly interaction. It was found, for example, that a task group tends to establish among its members a certain quota for production which may or may not be in line with what a supervisor or a manager wants. In a typical situation, a worker will produce more or less according to this informally accepted quota. Those who are very high or very low producers, and who thus deviate substantially from that norm, will be subjected to pressure from the group to conform to the norm.

Disregarding or ignoring such basic and elementary notions of behaviour has often created resentment and outright hostility. It is now easy to understand that a work study person, who makes a unilateral decision to eliminate an operation, resulting in the loss of a job for a worker or a number of workers, is in fact undermining the basic need for security;

a negative reaction can therefore be expected. Similarly, the imposition of an output quota on a worker or a group of workers without prior consultation or winning their cooperation can yield resentment and breed resistance. There are some useful hints that a work study manager must follow to ensure proper approach towards obtaining improvised work study methodology. These hints are as follows:

1. There should be a balanced approach towards increasing productivity. There should not be much emphasis on increasing the output performance of the labour force without even looking for the space of increasing productivity through plant machinery and operation. A work study manager should not lay much emphasis of work study on labour force. The emphasis should be proportionate towards plant machinery, operations and space. The workers should not feel that they alone are being targeted, overlooking the efficiency of the management. This can result in resentment amongst the workers. There should be a condition where the work study suggests just halving the productivity time of the workers without even looking for the availability of the material and checking machinery to prevent breakdown.
2. A work study manager should not hide findings of work studies. A work study manager must be honest in dispelling truth when questioned. This will build an increased level of confidence amongst the workers.
3. There should be induction training programmes for the supervisors looking after the work at the floor shop. This will help the work study manager to make the supervisor fully understand the outcome of work study which then can be implemented in a proper manner. Similarly, involving the workers in the development of an improved method of operation can win them over to the new method and can sometimes produce unexpected results. Thus, by asking workers the right questions and by inviting those to come forward with explanations or proposals several work study specialists have been rewarded by clues or ideas that had never occurred to them. After all, a worker has an intimate knowledge of his or her own job and of details that can escape a work study person. One tried and tested practice is to invite the workers in a section to be studied to nominate one of their members to join the work study specialist and, together with the supervisor, to form a team that can review the work to be done, discuss the results achieved and agree on steps for implementation.
4. Although asking for a worker's suggestions and ideas implicitly serves to satisfy his or her need for recognition, this can be achieved in a more direct way by giving proper credit where it is due. In many instances a supervisor, a worker or a staff specialist contributes useful ideas that assists the work study person to develop an improved method of work. This should be acknowledged readily, and the work study person should resist the temptation of accumulating all the glory.
5. The work study person must make it clear that it is the work, and not the worker, that is being studied. This becomes much easier if the workers have had a proper

introductory course explaining the principles and outlining the techniques of work study.

6. In some circumstances it is possible to involve the workforce in work study investigations even more directly (for example, by training them in some of the basic techniques and allowing them to contribute to discussions through the establishment of a "productivity circle", set up for the duration of a project or on a long-term basis). Through such a process the workers can see more clearly that the techniques are used to study the work and not the workers themselves.
7. It is important that the work study person should remember that the objective is not merely to increase productivity but also to improve job satisfaction, and that he or she should devote enough attention to this latter issue by looking for ways to minimize fatigue and to make the job more interesting and more satisfying. In recent years several enterprises have developed new concepts and ideas to organize work to this end and to attempt to meet the workers' need for fulfilment.

4.5 WORK STUDY PRACTITIONER

We have talked a great deal in the preceding sections about what is required from the work study practitioner, suggesting by our requirements a human being who is almost too good to be true. The ideal person for the job is likely to be found rarely, and if he or she is a successful work study specialist, can easily be promoted to higher posts. Nevertheless, there are certain qualifications and qualities which are essential for success.

Education The very minimum standard of education for anyone who is to take charge of work study application in an enterprise is a good secondary education with matriculation or the equivalent school-leaving examination, or better still a university education, preferably in the engineering or business fields.

Practical experience It is desirable that candidates for posts as work study specialists should have practical experience in the industries in which they will be working. This experience should include a period of actual work at one or more of the processes of the industry. This will enable them to understand what it means to do a day's work under the conditions in which the ordinary workers with whom they will be dealing have to work. Practical experience will also command respect from supervisors and workers, and an engineering background enables one to adapt oneself to most other industries.

Personal qualities The person who undertakes the responsibility of work study should have an inventive mind. He or she should have the capability to design the mechanisms and devices that when implemented will save a great amount of time and effort. Further, the methods suggested should have the support of the engineers and the technicians. It is seen often that the person taking the responsibility do not have good human relations and therefore in large companies the measurement section and the measurement section are under different chiefs, i.e., they are different departments. Some of the essential qualities are discussed below:

- **Sincerity and honesty:** These are the two important qualities that a work study person must have. A person will gain confidence and respect of the people with whom he or she will be working if he or she is honest and sincere.
- **Enthusiasm:** A person undertaking the work study should be enthusiastic about what he or she is doing. One should believe in oneself of the work that is being done. Further, he or she must be really keen on the job. The people will follow the suit and thus will produce better results.
- **Interest in and sympathy with people:** It's necessary for the person to be interested in people at all levels of the organization. Doing this will help in understanding the people, to properly understand their viewpoints and hence their motives behind their behaviour.
- **Tact:** The work study person should not use harsh words that can hurt the people around them. Utmost care must be taken not to hurt the feelings of the people around them. Tact will help the work study person to get very far.
- **Good appearance:** A neat and tidy appearance will make the person look efficient which will help him or her gain confidence among the people whom he or she has to work.
- **Self-confidence:** This can only come with good training and experience of applying work study successfully. The work study practitioner must be able to stand up to the top management, supervisors, trade union officials or workers in defence of his or her opinions and findings, and to do so in such a way that will win respect and not give offence.

These personal qualities, particularly the ability to deal with people, can all be further developed with the right training. Far too often this aspect of the training of work study specialists is neglected, the assumption being that, if the right person is selected in the first place, that is all that needs to be done. In most work study courses more time should be given to the human side of applying work study.

It will be seen from these requirements that the results of work study, however "scientifically" arrived at, must be applied with "art", just like any other management technique. In fact, the qualities which go to make a good work study person are the same qualities as go to make a good manager. Work study is an excellent training for young men and women destined for higher management. People with these qualities are not easy to find, but careful selection of persons for training as work study specialists will repay itself in the results obtained, in terms both of increased productivity and of improved human relations in the workplace.

SECTION III
METHOD STUDY

5
Method Study

5.1 APPROACH TO METHOD STUDY

The critical examination and systematic recording of the ways in which the job is done is method study. Therefore, method study leads to improvement in the ways in which a job is done. There are eight steps to method study. These are discussed below:

- **Select:** A work study manager should select an appropriate work for studying. The boundaries of the work selected must be defined properly.
- **Record:** Direct observations must be made to collect the relevant facts and also appropriate data sources must be used to collect the appropriate data.
- **Examine:** The work study manager should critically examine the present way of doing the job. This can be done by challenging the purpose of the job and further the place, sequence and method of performance of the job.
- **Develop:** After critical examination of the job, a new method should be proposed which should be practical, economical and effective.
- **Evaluate:** Different alternatives for developing a new method must be evaluated by comparing the cost-effectiveness of the selected new method with the current method.
- **Define:** The proposed method should be clearly expressed so that those concerned such as the management, supervisors and workers, could be confident to implement the same.
- **Install:** The new proposed method should be implemented and proper training must be imparted to those performing it.
- **Maintain:** Control procedures must be set in place to avoid drifting back to the previous method.

These eight steps constitute the logical procedure that a work study specialist could normally apply. In practice, however, the procedure is not as straightforward as it is presented here. For example, when measuring the results achieved by the new method one may find that the resulting cost effectiveness may be negligible and does not warrant the added investment in time and effort to develop the perceived method. In this case the work study person may have to go back to the drawing-board to examine the job once more and try to develop another improved method. In other circumstances experience with a new improved method may bring new problems to the surface, in which case the process of examination, development and subsequent steps have to be repeated again. In the following chapters we will deal with each of the steps involved in studying the methods of work. The remaining part of this chapter will be devoted to the first step, namely selection of the work to be studied.

5.2 SELECTING THE WORK TO BE STUDIED

One can argue that almost any operation in a work setting can be a candidate for an investigation with a view to improving the way it is carried out. Such an argument would present the work study specialist with an endless workload, some of which may not be productive. However, by focusing on certain key operations, a work study specialist can achieve far-reaching results in a relatively short span of time. The three important considerations that must be borne in mind while selecting a job are: Economic consideration, Technical consideration and the Human consideration.

- **Economic considerations:** The economic viability to investigate a job must be considered by the work study specialist. If the job is of small economic importance, then it will be a waste of time to undertake its investigation. Further, it is not economically viable to study a job if it is not expected to run for long. A work study specialist should ask questions as to whether studying the job will yield profit or the profit from the job is yielded by further continuing the investigation on the job. Some of the obvious choices for study are:
    - The operations that are costly or the ones that produce a great deal of profit. Further, the operations with the largest scrap/waste rates should be among the obvious choices.
    - Lengthy operations that consume a great deal of time that holds other production operations.
    - Operations that demand a great deal of labour and are repetitive in nature. Further, these are required to be run for a long time.
    - Operations that involve the material handling over long distances between workstations. Relatively large proportion of labour is involved in the movement of material over long distances.

Pareto analysis is one of the techniques that can address the operations of the kind mentioned in section 1.1. It is also referred to as "the 76 ABC analysis of value analysis." The technique is named after an Italian economist according to whom, there is some proportion of range of products that yields the maximum profit. The same observation can be used to identify the operations in a plant that yields maximum amount of waste or scrap. Further, the operations with maximum cost or profit can also be identified. Pareto analysis can be well understood using the following illustrative example of an enterprise producing 20 different products. The products with their annual production and per unit profit contribution have been tabulated in the table below:

Table 5.1: Pareto analysis, Step 1: Profit contribution of products.

Product number	Annual production	Profit per unit (Rs)	Total profit generated (Rs)
1.	7000	0.60	4200
2.	1200	4.00	4800
3.	1600	3.00	4800
4.	800	40.00	32000
5.	3200	0.50	1600
6.	7200	0.50	3600
7.	4000	0.25	1000
8.	2400	1.00	2400
9.	1400	20.00	28000
10.	4000	0.90	3600
11.	1800	6.00	10800
12.	2000	3.00	6000
13.	6000	0.60	3600
14.	1600	8.00	12800
15.	1600	3.00	4800
16.	5000	0.80	4000
17.	1200	50.00	60000
18.	8000	0.50	4000
19.	1200	5.00	6000
20.	5000	0.40	2000

The products are then arranged on the basis of descending order of profit generated. The result is shown in the table below:

Table 5.2: Pareto analysis, Step 2: Products arranged in descending order of their profit contribution.

Product number	Total profit	Pareto or ABC analysis
17	60000	"**A**" items that contribute for 60% of the total profit generated.
4	32000	
9	2800	
14	12800	"**B**" items that contribute for 25% of the profit.
11	10800	
12	6000	
19	6000	
2	4800	
3	4800	
15	4800	

Contd...

1	4200	"C" items that contribute for 15% of the profit.
16	4000	
18	4000	
6	3600	
10	3600	
13	3600	

One can clearly see that there are a total of three products which have been classified as "A" items that contribute for around 60% of the total profit generated. Thus, clearly these particular products would yield high profit and will be priority for the study. Then next on the list are the products classified as "B" items that contribute for around 25% of the profit and then the "C" classified items contributing 15% of the total profit generated being given the least priority for the study. Similar analysis can be extended for the products that yield maximum waste or scrap, or the ones that entail large operational costs.

- **Technical or technological considerations:** One of the important considerations is the desire by the management to acquire more advanced technology, whether in equipment or in processes. Thus, the management may want to computerize its office paperwork or its inventory system, or to introduce automation in the production operations. Before such steps are taken, a method study can point out the most important needs of the enterprise in this respect. For example, if paperwork leaves much to be desired and a good deal of unnecessary or unwarranted information or processes exist, computerizing the same method of work will do nothing much to improve the efficiency of the office. A common term used by information systems specialists in this case is "useless material in yields useless material out". The only thing that changes in this case as a result of computerization is that the same unneeded information will be produced at a higher rate. If, on the other hand, computerization is preceded by a method study, the process is then simplified a priori. The type of information needed is determined more clearly and even decisions on the choice of hardware and software are made more rationally. Method study then acts as a scouting operation prior to the introduction of more advanced technology. The introduction of new technology should therefore constitute an important factor in the choice of methods of work to be investigated.
- **Human considerations:** Certain operations are often a cause of dissatisfaction by workers. They may induce fatigue or monotony or may be unsafe or clumsy to operate. The level of satisfaction should point to a need for method study. Thus, an operation which may be perceived as effective by the management may, on the other hand, generate a great deal of resentment by the workforce. If such operations are addressed by work study specialists as part of an overall work study programme, the benefits of work study can become more apparent to the workforce. In a similar vein, a choice of a particular job for study may lead to unrest or ill-feeling. The advice

given here is **to leave it alone,** however promising it may be from the economic point of view. If other jobs are tackled successfully and the study can be seen to benefit the people working on them, opinions will change and it is possible in time to revert to the original choice.

5.3 LIMITING THE SCOPE OF THE WORK TO BE STUDIED

One of the first decisions a work study specialist has to make is to define exactly the type of work to be studied, set up boundaries around it and decide what exactly it will encompass. To take an example, in the preceding section we used the Pareto analysis to select products or processes that are most profitable or most costly, or yield the most waste. The next logical question is to decide on the scope of our investigation with respect to each product or process. Do we wish to examine the whole sequence of operation that goes into producing that product, or only certain parts of it and in this case which part? Would it be more opportune, for example, to concentrate only on the movement of material or operators, or for that matter the handling of material?

To assist in making such decisions, it is important to understand thoroughly the problem at hand or the present situation before looking for solutions or improvements. Having a feel for the situation either from experience or by talking to the various people involved will provide the work study specialist with the clue to the limits of his or her investigation, at least in the initial stage. Once this is decided it should be adhered to. Further work may tempt the specialist to go into greater detail. This should be resisted, although these indications should be noted and tackled separately. In other words, the work study practitioner should not go first for a small one-operative job which may entail detailed study of the worker's movements and yield a saving of a few seconds per operation, unless the job is one that is repetitive. It is of little value to play around with split seconds and centimetres of movements when a great waste of time and effort is taking place as a result of poor layout or inappropriate handling of heavy materials.

As will become evident in the next chapters, defining the nature of the job to be selected for study and identifying its scope will predetermine the type of work study technique that will be used to study it. Thus certain types of charts may be used to record the sequence of work which could be different from those used to record the movement of a worker, say in an assembly operation.

5.4 RECORD, EXAMINE AND DEVELOP

5.4.1 Record the Facts

The next step in the basic procedure, after selecting the work to be studied, is to **record all the facts** relating to the existing method. The success of the whole procedure depends on the accuracy with which the facts are recorded, because they will provide the basis of both the critical examination and the development of the improved method. It is therefore essential that the record be clear and concise.

Recording serves essentially as a basis for subsequent analysis and examination. It is not an end in itself. Recording may be carried out in two phases: first, a rough sketch or charting of the job being studied to establish whether the recorded information is of use; and, second, a more formal and accurate chart or diagram to include in a report or presentation.

The usual way of recording facts is to write them down. Unfortunately, this method is not suited to recording the complicated processes which are so common in modern industry. This is particularly so when an exact record is required of every minute detail of a process or operation. To describe exactly everything that is done in even a very simple job which takes perhaps only a few minutes to perform would probably result in several pages of closely written script, which would require careful study before anyone reading it could be quite sure that he or she had grasped all the details.

To overcome this difficulty other techniques or "tools" of recording have been developed, so that detailed information may be recorded precisely and at the same time in standard form, in order that it may be readily understood by all method study persons, in whatever factory or country they may be working.

The most commonly used of these recording techniques are **charts** and **diagrams.** There are several types of standard charts available, each with its own special purposes. They will be described in subsequent chapters. For the present it is sufficient to note that the charts available fall into two groups:

- those which are used to record a **process sequence,** i.e., a series of events or happenings in the order in which they occur, but which do not depict the events to scale; and
- those which record **events,** also in sequence, but **on a time scale,** so that the interaction of related events may be more easily studied. The names of the various charts are shown in Table 5.3, which lists them in the two groups given above and also lists the types of diagram commonly used.

Table 5.3: The most commonly used method study charts and diagrams.

CHARTS	Indicating process SEQUENCE Outline process chart Flow process chart – Worker type Flow process chart – Material type Flow process chart – Equipment type Two-handed process chart Procedure flowchart
CHARTS	Using a TIME SCALE Multiple activity chart Simo chart
DIAGRAMS	Indicating MOVEMENT Flow diagram String diagram Cyclegraph Chronocyclegraph Travel chart

Diagrams are used to indicate movement and/or interrelationships of movements more clearly than charts can do. They usually do not show all the information recorded on charts, which they supplement rather than replace.

Process chart symbols The recording of the facts about a job or operation on a process chart is made much easier by the use of a set of five standard symbols, which together serve to represent all the different types of activities or events likely to be encountered in any factory or office. They thus serve as a very convenient, widely understood type of shorthand, saving a lot of writing and helping to show clearly just what is happening in the sequence being recorded. The two principal activities in a process are **operation** and **inspection.** These are represented by the following symbols.

○ *Operation*

The main steps in a process, procedure or method are indicated by **operation.** During the operation a part, product or the material related to a process is modified or changed. Operation is the process of receiving and giving the information. Further, an operation is said to take place when planning or calculating takes place.

□ *Inspection*

It indicates inspecting a process for quality or inspection for quantity.

The distinction between these two activities is quite clear: material, component or service is processed towards completion by an **operation.** This can be accomplished by several means. In case of a machined part, it can be the modification in its shape. For a chemical process, it can be accomplished by altering the chemical composition. Addition or subtraction of a material can make an assembly complete. Further, the preparation for any activity to bring it near its completion stage is also operation.

On the other hand, an **inspection** merely verifies if a particular process is carried out when it is intended to. It corrects any activity in terms of quantity or quality. Hence, an inspection does not lead any process towards its completion.

Three more symbols are used to obtain a detailed picture. These symbols are discussed below:

⇨ *Transport*

A **transport** is the movement of material, workers or equipment from one place to another in any operating layout. However, this doesn't include the movements which are part of operations or are caused by the operative at the workstations.

D *Temporary Storage or Delay*

Temporary storage or delay indicates a delay that is caused because of the nature of sequence of events. The delay may be due to a work waiting between consecutive operations or may be due to the work kept aside on the floor without any record. Some of the examples of temporary storage or delay are that of work waiting to be checked against the delivery node, cases stacked one on the other, letter to be signed, parts waiting for the truck to be carried to the storage bins.

△ *Permanent Storage*

Any material is required to be issued from a store or received in a store through some form of authorization. This controlled storage indicates the permanent storage. An item may be retained in the store for some reference purpose. Therefore, when an object is kept or protected against any unauthorized removal it is said to be in permanent storage. While for the temporary storage no kind of authorization is required, the permanent storage demands some form of requisition or authorization. Thus, the difference between the two types of storage is clearly reflected in terms of authorization for a part to be taken out.

◘ *Combined Activities*

The symbols for the activities are combined when they are carried out at the same time or when a particular operative performs the activities at the workstation. For example, the symbol for combined operation and inspection is represented by a circle within a square. Figure 5.1 gives an example of the use of these symbols.

The outline process chart

An outline process chart can be used to obtain a bird's-eye view of a whole process or activity before embarking on a detailed study. The main operations and inspections are recorded in sequence through the outline process chart to obtain the overall picture. Thus, an outline process chart is a valuable tool that can aid in detailed study. The operations of principal nature and their inspection to ensure their effectiveness are only recorded by the outline process chart, irrespective of the person performing the task and the place where it is being carried out. The symbols that are required for the outline process chart are that of operation and inspection only.

A brief note of each operation or inspection is made beside the symbol. Further, the time allowed for it is also added. Figure 5.2 provides an example of an outline process chart. Figure 5.3 shows the assembly represented on the chart. The details of the operations given in the chart have also been discussed.

Example of an outline process chart: Assembling a switch rotor

The rotor for a slow make-and-break switch is shown by the assembly drawing in Fig. 5.2. It consists of three important parts: (1) spindle; (2) a moulding plastic and (3) a stop pin. It is often convenient to start with the operations and inspections undergone by the principal unit or component which in this example is a spindle. The process should start by drawing a vertical line on the right hand side of the page which will be more convenient in drawing an outline process chart. The time required for each piece is shown to the left of each operation. However, since the inspectors are on time work, no specification of the time is shown.

Activity	Example		
Operation ○ A large circle indicates an operation, such as	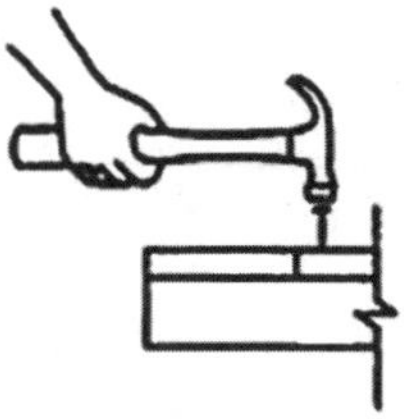 Drive nail	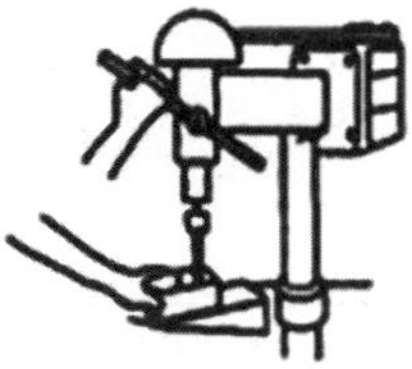 Drill hole	 Type letter
Transport ⇨ An arrow indicates transport, such as,	 Move material by truck	 Move material by hoist or elevator	 Move material by carrying (messenger)
Inspection □ A square indicates inspection, such as	 Examine material for quality or quantity	 Read steam gauge on boiler	 Examine printed form for information
Delay D The letter D indicates a delay, such as	 Material in truck or on floor at bench waiting to be processed	 Employee waiting for elevator	 Papers waiting to be filed
Storage ▽ A triangle indicates storage, such as	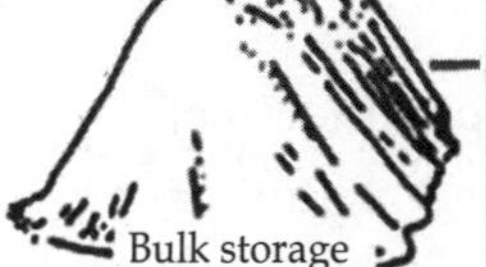 Bulk storage of raw material	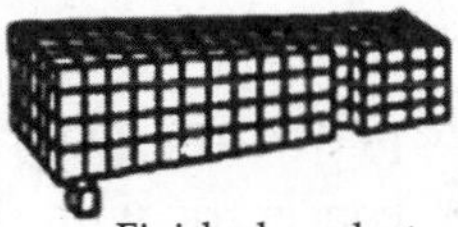 Finished product in warehouse	 Documents and records in storage vault

Fig. 5.1: Method study symbols.

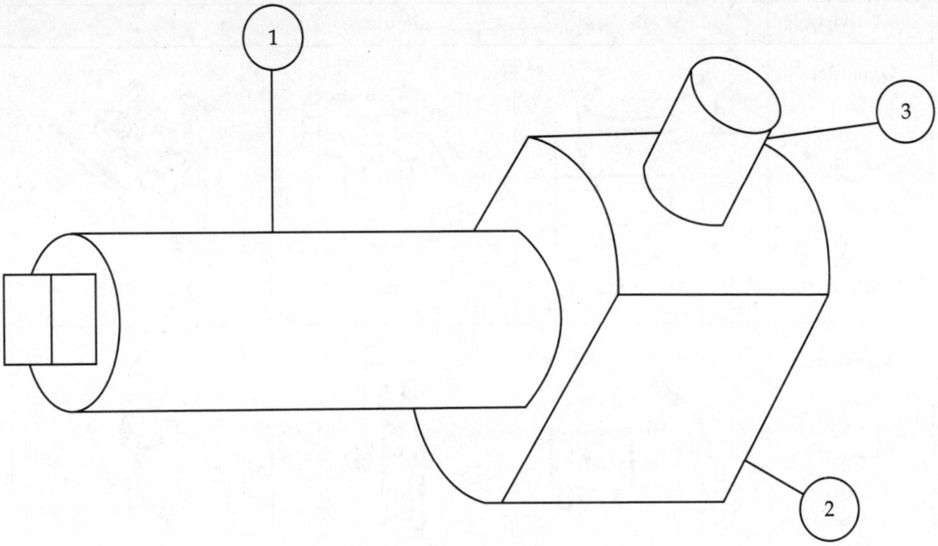

Fig 5.2: Switch rotor assembly.

The description of the operation that are shown alongside the symbols have not been shown in the figure. This has been done to avoid congestion in the figure. The spindle is made from 10 mm steel diameter rod. The different operations and inspections on the spindle are discussed next:

Operation 1: Capstan lathe is used to perform facing, turning, undercutting and parting off operations (0.025 hours).

Operation 2: Same machine is used for facing the opposite end (0.010 hours). The work is then sent to the inspection department.

Inspection 1: The part is inspected to ensure the correctness for dimensions and finish (no specified time). The part is then sent to the milling section.

Operation 3: Straddle-mill is performed to produce four flats on end using a horizontal miller (0.070 hours).

Operation 4: Burrs are removed at the burring bench (0.020 hours). The work is then returned to the inspection department.

Inspection 2: Machine is inspected finally (no time). The part then goes to the plating shop.

Operation 5: Degreasing is performed in the plating shop (0.0015 hours).

Operation 6: Degreasing is followed by cadmium plating (0.008 hours). The work then goes to the inspection department.

Inspection 3: Final checks are performed on the part (no time).

Operation 7: A hole is bored concentric with the longitudinal axis. This is done for the plastic moulding. Facing operation is performed on both sides of the plastic moulding. Capstan lathe is then used to perform the reaming operation (0.080 hours).

Operation 8: Two-spindle drill press is used to drill a cross hole for the stop pin (0.022 hours).

Inspection 4: After the drilling operation finishes, the part is inspected for checking the dimensions (no time). The part is then stored in the storage house, waiting for the withdrawal.

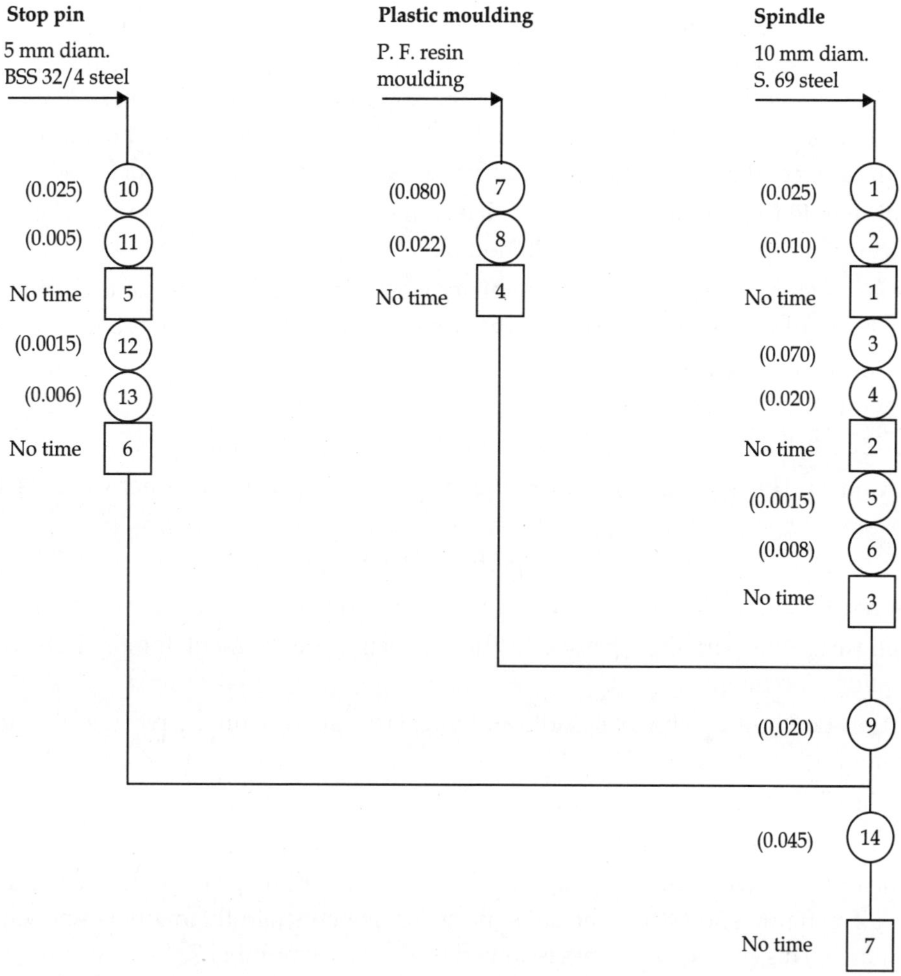

Fig. 5.3: Outline process chart: Switch rotor assembly.

Since plastic moulding is the first component that is to be assembled on the spindle, the operations and inspection process on it are shown by the vertical line next to the spindle. This can be seen clearly in the chart above. Likewise, for showing operation and inspection operation on the stop-pin, a vertical line is drawn next to that of the plastic moulding. If there were more components in the assembly, further left space would have been used. Thus, the sequence follows from right to left in the chart.

One should clearly observe the way in which the operation and inspection process have been numbered. Both the operations and inspections initialize from 1. The numbering continues as one moves from one component to another. The numbering is then continued for the second component till the point of its assembly with the first component. For example, the numbering of operation for the plastic moulding starts from 7 for depicting the operation. The numbering then ends at 9 showing the point of assembly operation of the plastic moulding with the spindle. Likewise the numbering continues for other components. Assembly of any component is shown by a horizontal line. The horizontal line starts from the vertical line of a minor component and continues till it terminates at the vertical line of the major component. It is possible that any minor component is also made up of a number of different components. Then the assembly line is constructed accordingly.

Operation 9: Plastic moulding is assembled to the small end of the spindle. The hole for the stop-pin is drilled through it (0.020 hours).

The stop-pin is made from 5 mm diameter steel rod. The assembly of the spindle and the plastic moulding is ready to receive the stop-pin, once operation 9 has been completed.

Operation 10: Capstan lathe is used to turn 2 mm diameter shank. Chamfering and parting off operations is then performed on the shank (0.025 hours).

Operation 11: The finisher is made free from the "pip" (0.005 hours).

Inspection 5: The part then goes to the inspection department where checks on its dimensions are performed (no time).

Operation 12: Degreasing operation is performed in the plating department (0.0015 hours).

Operation 13: Cadmium plating is provided on the part (0.006 hours).

Inspection 6: The part then passes to the inspection department for final checks and verifications (no time).

Operation 14: The assembly of spindle and the plastic spindle finally receives the stop pin (0.045 hours).

Inspection 7: The completed assembly is finally inspected (no time).

The assembly is then returned to the finished-parts store.

Some of the conventions that are used for drawing outline process chart are shown in Fig. 5.4. The figure shows that the subsidiary components join the main component after inspection 3. This assembly process is shown by operation number 7. Two more operations 8 and 9 are performed iteratively. Thus, the assembly undergoes a total of 4 operations in all.

Since an outline process chart clearly depicts the activities involved, it would be wise to go into detail greater than the outline process chart. In the subsequent sections, flow process charts have been discussed.

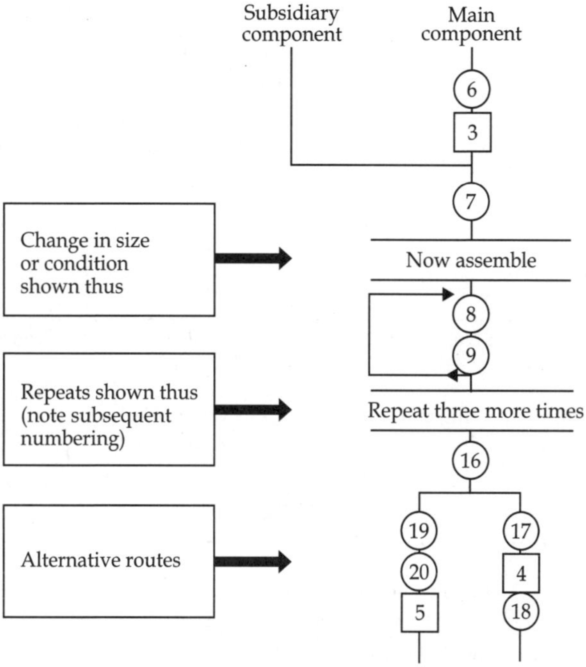

Fig. 5.4: Some charting conventions.

Flow process charts

After having a bird's-eye view of a process, it becomes easier to go into the details of the process. The construction of flow process chart would be the first step in this regard. A flow process chart gives details of the sequence of the flow of a product or process with the aid of appropriate process chart symbols. It records all the events undergone by a product or a process. A flow process chart may be of one of the types:

- Flow process chart – Worker type: A flow process chart of this type records the sequence of events performed by an operator.
- Flow process chart – Material type: It records the way in which any material is handled or treated.
- Flow process chart – Equipment type: A flow process chart of this type records the way in which the equipment are used.

The process of constructing a flow process chart is similar to that of constructing the outline process chart. However, the difference lies in the use of additional symbols in addition to the symbols used for "operation" and "inspection". The additional symbols used are that of "delay", "transport", "storage".

Similar symbols will be used for constructing different types of flow process charts. However, it is customary to use active voice of verbs for worker type flow process chart and passive voice verbs for material type and equipment type flowcharts. Usually, one print form is sufficient for different types of flowchart. The print form bears the heading "Worker/material/equipment type".

Since a flow process chart provides for a great deal of detail when compared to an outline process chart, it is difficult to depict the flow of any process or product on a single sheet. Different sheets of paper are used for each major component of an assembly. This helps in making a proper study of the amount of handling, delays and storages undergone by each of the major components or assembly. This means that the flow process chart is usually a single line.

Figure 5.5 shows a flow process chart of a bus engine. The chart shows in detail the processes undergone by an engine when it is stripped, degreased and cleaned for inspection.

Chart No. 1	Sheet No. of 1	Method:	Original
Product:	Bus engines	Operative(s):	
		Location:	Degreasing shop
Process:	Stripping, degreasing and cleaning used in engines	Charted by:	
		Approved by:	Date

Distance (m)	Symbol	Activity	Type of activity
	▽ 1	In old-engine stores	
	1 ⇨	Picked up engine by crane (electric)	Non-productive
24	2 ⇨	Transported to next crane	"
	3 ⇨	Unloaded to floor	"
	4 ⇨	Picked up by second crane (electric)	"
30	5 ⇨	Transported to stripping bay	"
	6 ⇨	Unloaded to floor	"
	○ 1	Engine stripped	Productive
	○ 2	Main components cleaned and laid out	"
	□ 1	Components inspected for wear; inspection report written.	Non-productive
3	7 ⇨	Parts carried to degreasing basket	"
	8 ⇨	Loaded for degreasing by hand-operated crane	"
1.5	9 ⇨	Transported to degreaser	"
	10 ⇨	Unloaded into degreaser	"
	○ 3	Degreased	Productive
	11 ⇨	Lifted out of degreaser by crane	Non-productive
6	12 ⇨	Transported away from degreaser	"
	13 ⇨	Unloaded to ground	"
	D 1	To cool	"
12	14 ⇨	Transported to cleaning benches	"
	○ 4	All parts completely cleaned	Productive
9	15 ⇨	All cleaned parts placed in one box	Non-productive
	D 2	Awaiting transport	"
	16 ⇨	All parts except cylinder block and heads loaded on trolley	"
76	17 ⇨	Transported to engine inspection section	"
	18 ⇨	Parts unloaded and arranged on inspection table	"
	19 ⇨	Cylinder block and head loaded on trolley	"
76	20 ⇨	Transported to engine inspection section	"
	21 ⇨	Unloaded on ground	"
237.5	D 3	Stored temporarily awaiting inspection	"

Fig. 5.5: Flow process chart: Engine stripping, cleaning and degreasing.

Printed forms as shown Fig. 5.6 are used to provide detailing of flow of different processes and product. This ensures that the method study manager does not omit any essential information.

There are certain important points that one should consider while preparing a flow process chart. The importance of process flowchart in the field of method improvement makes it worth considering the points to be kept while preparing it. These important points are discussed here:

- A complete picture of what is being done and how it is being done is provided by the flow process chart. This helps in understanding the relationship of different events and the facts pertaining to them.
- A flow process chart clearly illustrates to everyone concerned the way the job is carried out. Even the workers and the supervisors who may not be trained can clearly understand the chart and hence identify the inefficiencies in the process. This is clearly reflected in the chart through the delay or transport symbols.
- Direct observations must be given due importance in recording events on a flow process chart. The events recorded will act as a future reference for explaining the situations to others. The chart must not be based on memory. The events how trivial they seem to be must be recorded as and when they are observed. The details of the recorded events must be confirmed with the supervisor. Doing this will serve a twofold purpose. Firstly, it ensures the correctness in the recorded information and secondly it leads to strengthening of bond and relationship between the method study manager and the supervisor. Supervisor would feel as if his/her opinion is valuable during the entire process of the study.
- The charting process should be neat and clean. This is because the chart will be used for suggesting any improvements in the present method of working or for standardizing a method. If the chart is untidy, then it will not only have errors but will also create a bad impression.
- All charts must carry an appropriate heading to give the following information:
    - The drawing numbers or code should accompany the name of the material, equipment or the product.
    - The starting and end point of the process should be clearly stated along with the information regarding the job or process being carried out. Clear mention of whether the process is presented or proposed, should be stated.
    - Location where the operation is taking place must be mentioned clearly.
    - The sheet number, its reference number and the total number of sheets must be mentioned clearly.
    - The name of the observer and in some cases the name of the person approving the chart must be given.

Flow process chart	Worker/Material/Equipment type			
Chart No. 1 Sheet No. 1 of 1	Summary			
Subject charted: Used bus engines	Activity	Present	Proposed	Saving
	Operation ○	4		
	Transport ⇨	21		
Activity: Stripping, cleaning and degreasing prior to inspection	Delay D	3		
	Inspection □	1		
	Storage ▽	1		
Method: Present	Distance (m)	237.5		
Location: Degreasing shop	Time (work-min.)	–	–	–
Operative(s): Clock Nos. 1234, 571	Cost	–		
	Labour	–		
Charted by: Date:	Material	–		
Approved by: Date:	Total	–	–	–

Description	Qty.	Distance (m)	Time (min.)	○	⇨	D	□	▽	Remarks
Stored in old-engine store								•	
Engine picked up					•				Electric crane
Transported to next crane		24			•				Electric crane
Unloaded to floor					•				
Picked up					•				Electric crane
Transported to stripping bay		30			•				Electric crane
Unloaded to floor					•				
Engine stripped				•					
Main components cleaned and laid out				•					
Components inspected for wear; inspection report written							•		
Parts carried to degreasing basket		3			•				
Loaded for degreasing					•				
Transported to degreaser		1.5			•				Hand crane
Unloaded into degreaser					•				
Degreased				•					
Lifted out of degreaser					•				Hand crane
Transported away from degreaser		6			•				Hand crane
Unloaded to ground					•				
To cool						•			
Transported to cleaning benches		12			•				By hand
All parts cleaned completely				•					
All cleaned parts placed in one box		9			•				By hand
Awaiting transport						•			
All parts except cylinder block and heads loaded on trolley					•				
Transported to engine inspection section		76			•				Trolley
Parts unloaded and arranged on inspection table					•				
Cylinder block and head loaded on trolley					•				
Transported to engine inspection section		76			•				Trolley
Unloaded to ground					•				
Stored temporarily awaiting inspection						•			
Total		237.5		4	21	3	1	1	

Fig. 5.6: Flow process chart – Material type: Engine stripping, cleaning and degreasing (original method).

  - The date of the study should be mentioned.
  - The chart should carry a key to the symbols used. The key can be used as a reference by anyone who may study the chart at a later stage and may be accustomed to using different symbols.
  - For comparing the old method with the new method, mention relating to the distance, time and cost of labour and material must be made.
- Following points must be checked before leaving the chart:
  - The correctness of the facts being recorded.
  - Check pertaining to the over-simplifying assumptions must be made.
  - Checks on whether all the factors have been considered should also be taken into account.

So far we have been concerned only with the "record" stage. We must now consider the steps necessary to **examine critically** the data recorded.

5.4.2 Examine Critically: The Questioning Technique

Critical examination of events recorded for each process or a product is carried out using the questioning technique. Each event recorded is subjected to a series of systematic set of questioning. One can categorize the five sets of activities into two main broad classes:

- The activities in which the material or workpiece under consideration works upon the activities. The activities lead to the movement and examination of the material or workpiece under consideration.
- Activities that don't touch the material, whether it being in storage or at a standstill owing to a delay.

Activities in the first category may be subdivided into three groups:

- **Make ready activities:** These activities prepare a workpiece to be worked upon. The MAKE READY activities set the workpiece in position to be worked upon. Figure 5.5 shows these activities. These are clearly reflected by the transporting of the engine to the degreasing shop, loading it to be transported to the cleaning benches, etc.
- **DO operations:** These lead to change in shape, physical condition or chemical composition of the product under consideration. The example in Fig. 5.5 shows this in the form of dismantling, cleaning and degreasing operation. The DO operations may be further classified into key operations. For example, deburring is a DO activity but not a "key" operation. This is because deburring can't be carried out if no machining has been performed.
- **Put away activities:** These activities move the workpiece under consideration away from the machine or the workplace.

Transport symbols and the inspection symbols may be used to represent MAKE READY activities and PUT AWAY activities. However, only operation symbols can be used for representing DO operations. It is the DO operations that will cause the product move forward in its progress. Therefore, the main aim must be to have a very high proportion of DO activities. ("DO" operations in non-manufacturing industries are those operations which actually carry out the activity for which the organization exists, for example, the act of selling in a shop or the act of typing in an office.) These are "productive" activities; all others, however necessary, may be considered "non-productive", including storages and delays which represent tied-up capital that could have been used to further the business. An alternative approach is to first examine the necessity of "key" operations. If these can be removed, associated "do" (but non-"key") and non-productive operations will automatically be removed.

The primary questions: The questioning sequence used follows a well established pattern which examines:

The PURPOSE	for which	the activities are undertaken
The PLACE	at which	
The SEQUENCE	in which	
The PERSON	by whom	
The MEANS	by which	

ELIMINATING COMBINING REARRANGING or SIMPLIFYING	the activities are undertaken

In the first stage of the questioning technique, the purpose, place, sequence, person and means of every activity recorded are systematically queried, and a reason for each reply is sought.

PURPOSE:	**What** **Why**	is actually done? is the activity necessary at all?	ELIMINATE unnecessary parts of the job
PLACE:	**Where**	is it being done? **Why** is it done at that particular place?	COMBINE wherever possible or REARRANGE the sequence of operations for more effective results
SEQUENCE:	**When**	is it done? **Why** is it done at that particular time?	
PERSON:	**Who**	is doing it? **Why** is it done by that particular person?	
MEANS:	**How**	is it being done? **Why** is it being done in that particular way?	SIMPLIFY the operation

Fig. 5.7: Primary questions.

The secondary questions: The secondary questions cover the second stage of the questioning technique, during which the answers to the primary questions are subjected to further query to determine whether possible alternatives of place, sequence, persons and/or means are practicable and preferable as a means of improvement upon the existing method. Thus, during this second stage of questioning (having asked already, about every activity recorded, what is done and why is it done), the method study person goes on to inquire: What **else** might be done? And, hence: What **should** be done? In the same way, the answers already obtained on place, sequence, person and means are subjected to further inquiry.

Combining the two primary questions with the two secondary questions under each of the headings "purpose, place", etc., yields the following list, which sets out the questioning technique in full swing:

Purpose: **What** is done?
Why is it done?
What **else** might be done?
What **should** be done?

Place: **Where** is it done?
Why is it done **there?**
Where **else** might it be done?
Where **should** it be done?

Sequence: **When** is it done?
Why is it done **then?**
When **might** it be done?
When **should** it be done?

Person: **Who** does it?
Why does **that** person do it?
Who **else** might do it?
Who **should** do it?

Means: **How** is it done?
Why is it done **that** way?
How **else** might it be done?
How **should** it be done?

These questions, in the above sequence, must be asked systematically every time a method study is undertaken. They are the basis of successful method study.

Example: Engine stripping, cleaning and degreasing Let us now consider how the method study people who prepared the flow process chart in Fig. 5.5 set about examining the record of facts which they had obtained in order to develop an improved method. Before doing so, we shall transfer the same record to a standard flow process chart form (Fig. 5.6) with the necessary information on the operation, location, and so on, duly filled in. To help the reader to visualize the operation, a flow diagram showing the layout of the degreasing shop and the path taken by the engine in its journey from the old-engine stores to the engine-inspection section is given in Fig. 5.8. It is evident from this that the engine and its parts follow an unnecessarily complicated path. Examination of the flow process chart shows a very high proportion of "non-productive" activities. There are in fact only four operations and one inspection, while there are 21 transports and three delays. Out of 29 activities, excluding the original storage, only five can be considered "productive".

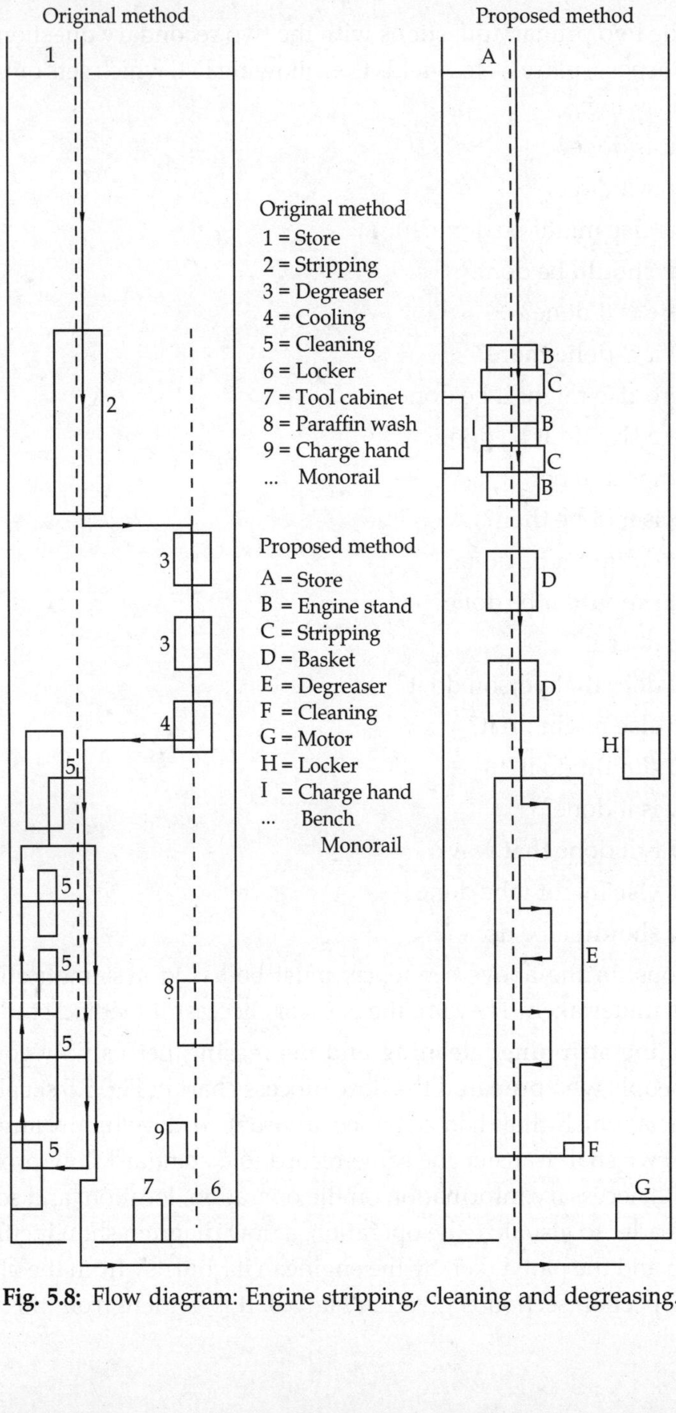

Fig. 5.8: Flow diagram: Engine stripping, cleaning and degreasing.

Method study critically and systematically examines the flowchart. While doing so, a number of questions may arise that need to be addressed to improve the way of carrying out this job. For the example above, we will apply the technique of questioning first to the transport mechanism.

Q1. What is done?

A. The engine is carried to the stripping bay.

Q2. How is this being done?

A. An electric crane is employed to carry the engine to the stripping bay. The electric crane places the engine on the ground which is then picked up by another electric crane. The engine is now transported to the stripping bay from the ground.

Q3. Why is this done?

A. A monorail that runs through the stores and degreasing shop cannot be employed to directly pick up the engine because of the storage nature of the engine.

Q4. What **else** might be done?

A. Monorail must be used to transfer the engine directly to the stripping bay. The engine should be directly accessible to the monorail in the store.

Q5. What **should** be done?

A. The above suggestion should be adopted. The suggestions in the present case were adopted resulting in elimination of three "transports". This can be seen directly in Fig. 5.8. The questioning technique is continued further.

Q6. Why are the engine components cleaned **before** going to be degreased since they are again cleaned after the grease is removed?

A. The reason for this practice has been forgotten. This answer is usually given in the questioning technique.

Q7. Why are they inspected at this stage? It is difficult to inspect greasy parts in a proper way. Further the inspection section is meant for the sole purpose of inspecting the engine.

A. The reason for this practice has been forgotten. There are some activities that are carried out because of the reasons that are important at the time. These activities are then allowed to be carried for long even after the need to continue them has passed. However, if there is no satisfactory reasoning then these activities must be discontinued and hence must be eliminated thereafter.

Further questions can be for the degreaser section. The engine is required to be transported through a distance of 3 metres to put it into the degreaser basket.

There can be a question as to **why** the degreaser basket cannot be kept near the part to be greased. **Why** the provisions cannot be made for the parts to be put straight into the degreaser basket?

Flow process chart		**Material type**			
Chart No. 2 Sheet No. 1 of 1		Summary			
Subject charted: Used bus engines	Activity		Present	Proposed	Saving
	Operation	○	4	3	1
	Transport	⇨	21	15	6
Activity Stripping, cleaning and degreasing prior to inspection	Delay	D	3	2	1
	Inspection	□	1	–	1
	Storage	▽	1	1	1
Method: Proposed	Distance (m)		237.5	150.0	87.5
Location: Degreasing shop	Time (work-min.)		–	–	–
Operative(s): Clock Nos. 1234 571	Cost		–		
	Labour		–		
Charted by: Date:	Material		–		
Approved by: Date:	Total		–	–	–

Description	Qty.	Distance (m)	Time (min.)	○	⇨	D	□	▽	Remarks
Stored in old-engine store		–	–					•	
Engine picked up					•				Electric
Transported to stripping bay		55			•				hoist on
Unloaded on to engine stand					•				monorail
Engine stripped				•					
Transported to degreaser basket		1			•				By hand
Loaded into basket					•				Hoist
Transported to degreaser		1.5			•				Hoist
Unloaded into degreaser					•				Hoist
Degreased				•					
Unloaded from degreaser					•				Hoist
Transported from degreaser		4.5			•				Hoist
Unloaded to ground					•				
Allowed to cool						•			
Transported to cleaning benches		6			•				Hoist
All parts cleaned				•					
All parts collected in special trays		6			•				
Awaiting transport						•			
Trays and cylinder block loaded on trolley					•				
Transported to engine inspection section		76			•				Trolley
Trays slid on to inspection benches and blocks on to platform					•				
Total		150		3	15	2	-	1	

Fig. 5.9: Flow process chart – Material type: Engine stripping, cleaning and degreasing (improved method).

The above example clearly illustrates the way the questioning technique is being adopted by the method study manager. The questioning may seem to be childish in nature but for an experienced investigator it is very rapid. The sequence adopted in the questioning is very rigid and this further ensures in any point being overlooked. Further, adopting of the initial questions in the form of **what** is done and **why** is it necessary, ensures saving of time by eradicating some of the constituents of the method in use or some other ways in which the constituting elements of the method could be improved thereby improvising the overall method. As can be seen from Fig. 5.8, that there has been a improvised method with reduction in number of non-productive activities. By eliminating the unnecessary cleaning and inspection activities, the number of operations has been reduced. The number has come down to three. Further in case of "Transports", the number has come down to 15 from 21 and the distance has been cut short by 87.5 metres, i.e., 150 metres. This amounts to saving of about 37 per cent in the distance travelled by the engine. In order to avoid complexity in the discussed problem, the time relating to different activities has not been mentioned. However, if a two-flow process chart is adopted, then it could be seen that a great saving in time of operation per engine can be achieved.

An illustrative example to show how the time recording can be introduced in a flow process chart has been discussed here. The flow process chart in this case is combined with the flow diagram. It is just a sample to explain the question technique. However in practice, it is a tedious task to arrive at the right answer straightaway. Generally, a number of alternatives will be thought before arriving at the new improvised version of the method study for a job.

Example of the use of a flow diagram with a flow process chart: Receiving and inspecting aircraft parts

The initial layout of the receiving department of the aircraft factory is shown in Fig. 5.10. The broad line indicates the path of movement for the goods from the point of delivery to the storage bins. The symbols for different activities have been inserted at proper places to aid in proper imagination of the various activities that the goods are subjected.

- **Record:** The cases containing aircraft parts are unloaded from the truck. The cases are packed in a carton. The unloading is followed by checking, inspection and marking the cases. These are then put into the stores. An inclined plane is used on which the cases slide one after the other. The cases then slide across the floor to the unpacking space where they are stacked one over the other. In the unpacking space, the cases await their opening. The delivery notes are taken out on unpacking a case. The case with the lid removed is loaded on the hand truck. The hand truck takes the case to a receiving bench. After a short delay, each piece is taken out of the carton and is checked against the delivery note. The case is then placed in its carton and is moved to the side of the receiving bench. Here these wait for transportation to the inspection bench. The case waits on the floor before the inspector takes one for inspection. The parts are unpacked, inspected and replaced as before. The case is then transported to the marking bench. This transportation takes place after a short delay. The parts are then numbered at the marking station and replaced to be transported to the store by the hand truck. The parts are placed in the bins where they await issue order from the assembly shop. The complete sequence of activities is shown in Fig. 5.11.

- **Examine:** Figure 5.10 clearly shows the roundabout path taken by the case on their journey to the bins. The path taken is very long. The flow process chart is not alone sufficient by itself to show this path.

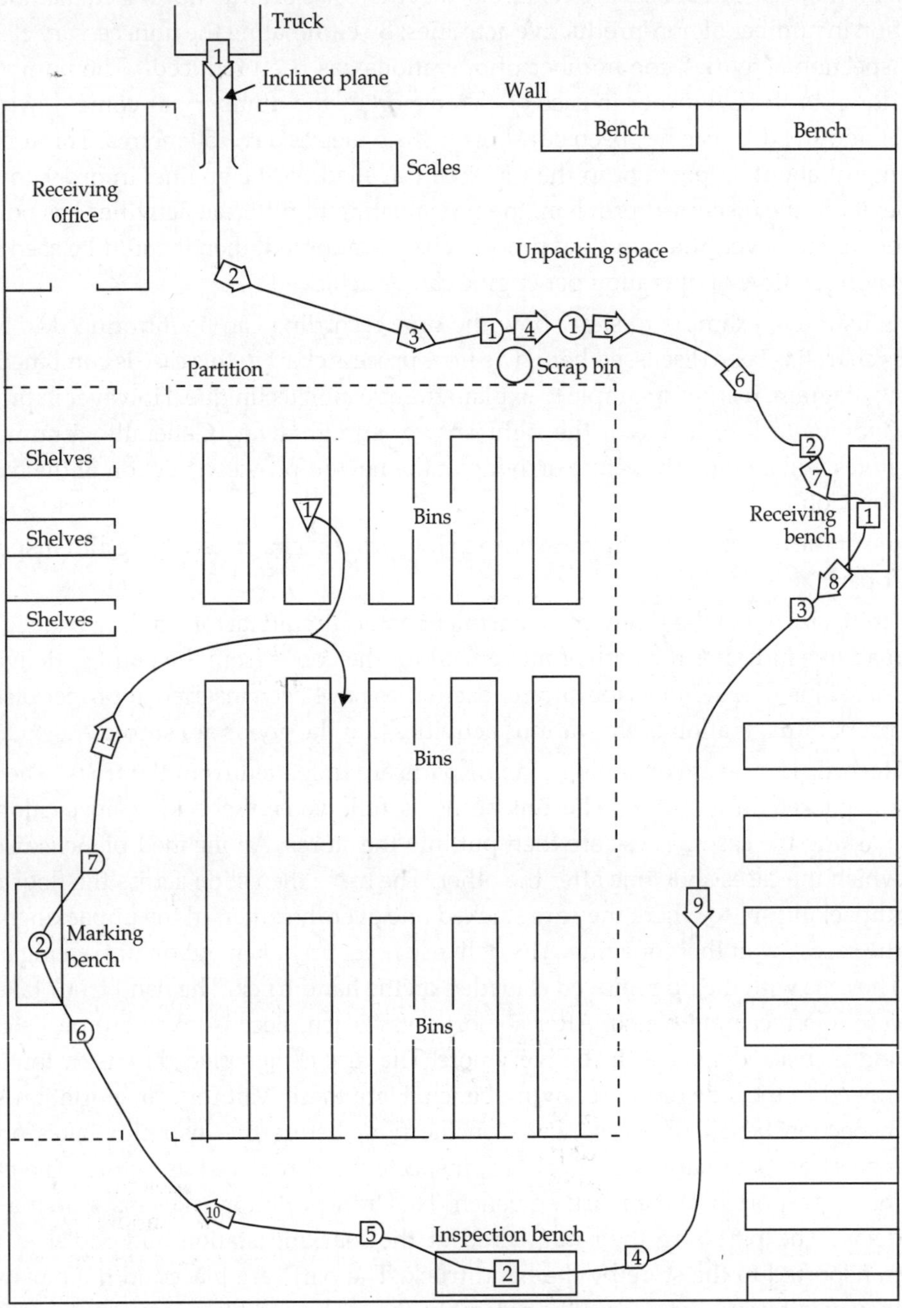

Fig. 5.10: Flow diagram: Inspecting and marking incoming parts (original method).

The questioning technique once applied after the critical examination of the two raises questions such as:

Q. When the cases are to be unstacked in 10 minutes, then **why** are the cases stacked to await opening?

A. The speed at which the work is cleared is relatively slow in comparison to the speed of unloading the truck.

Q. What **else** could be done?

A. (a) The work could be cleared faster.

(b) Enough space must be provided to allow the cases to leave unstacked.

Q. Why there is so much distance between the reception, inspection and marking points?

A. Because they happen to have been put there.

Q. What can then be done?

A. The points of inspection, marking and reception should be made close to each other.

Q. Where **should** they be?

A. Together at the present reception point.

Q. Why does the case have to take the long roundabout path to reach the stores?

A. The location of doors of the stores is just at the opposite end to the delivery point.

After a careful examination of both the flow diagram and the flow process chart, one can have a number of questions to ask. Thus, it is evident that there is much scope for improvement in the present methodology of doing a job. Therefore, one can clearly notice the amount of wasted time and effort if a series of activities is started without proper planning.

- **Develop:** The improved method arrived at after a careful examination by the method study manager is shown clearly in Figs. 5.12 and 5.13. The questions asked have been addressed to propose a new improvised method. With the improved methodology, the cases slide down the inclined plane from delivery truck to hand truck directly. The cases are transported to the unpacking space. While the cases are still on the hand truck, delivery note is taken out. The cases are then transported to the receiving bench, where after a short delay, the parts are taken out. The parts are checked against the delivery notes. The parts are then inspected and numbered on the inspection and numbering benches which have been placed by the side of the receiving bench. They are finally replaced in their cartons and repacked in the case, which is still on the truck.

For the question of the roundabout movement of the cases, there was no satisfactory answer. The team decided to make a new doorway into the stores opposite to the benches. From the summary on the process flowchart, one can see that the inspections have been reduced from two to one, transports to 6 from 11 and delays from 7 to 2. Further, the distance has been reduced by almost 24 metres, i.e., from 56.2 metres to 32.2 metres. Number of work-minutes is used to denote the number of work-hours involved. This is calculated by multiplying the time taken for each item of activity by the number of workers involved. For example, for an activity involving the transfer of case by the truck to the receiving bench involves two labourers and total of five minutes. Hence the time involved is ten work-minutes. Delays are not included as they are caused by operatives being otherwise occupied.

Flow process chart	**Material type**			
Chart No. 3 Sheet No. 1 of 1	Summary			
Subject charted: Case of BX 487 tee-pieces (10 per case in cartons)	Activity	Present	Proposed	Saving
	Operation ○	2		
	Transport ⇨	11		
Activity Receive, check, inspect and number tee-pieces and other store in case	Delay D	7		
	Inspection □	2		
	Storage ▽	1		
Method: Present	Distance (m)	56.2		
Location: Receiving Dept.	Time (work-h)	1.96		
Operative(s): Clock No. See remarks column	Cost Labour	$ 10.19		
Charted by: Date:	Material	–		
Approved by: Date:	Total	$ 10.19	–	–

Description	Qty. 1 case	Distance (m)	Time (min.)	Symbol ○	⇨	D	□	▽	Remarks
Lifted from truck: placed on inclined plane		1.2	–		•				2 labourers
Slid on inclined plane		6	10		•				2 labourers
Slid to storage and stacked		6			•				2 labourers
Await unpacking		–	30			•			
Case unstacked		–			•				
Lid removed: delivery note taken out		–	5	•					2 labourers
Placed on hand truck		1			•				
Trucked to reception bench		9	5		•				2 labourers
Await discharge from truck		–	10			•			
Case placed on bench		1	2		•				2 labourers
Cartons taken from case: opened; checked replaced contents		–	-15				•		Storekeeper
Case loaded on hand truck		1	2		•				2 labourers
Delay awaiting transport		–	5			•			
Trucked to inspection bench		16.5	10		•				1 labourer
Await inspection		–	10			•			Case on truck
Tee-pieces removed from case and cartons: inspected to drawing: replaced		1	20				•		Inspector
Await transport labourer		–	5			•			Case on truck
Trucked to numbering bench		9	5		•				1 labourer
Await numbering		–	15			•			Case on truck
Tee-pieces withdrawn form case and cartons: numbered on bench and replaced		–	15	•					Stores labourer
Await transport labourer		–	5			•			Case on truck
Transported to distribution point		4.5	5		•				1 labourer
Stored								•	
Total		56.2	174	2	11	7	2	1	

Fig. 5.11: Flow process chart: Inspecting and marking incoming parts (original method).

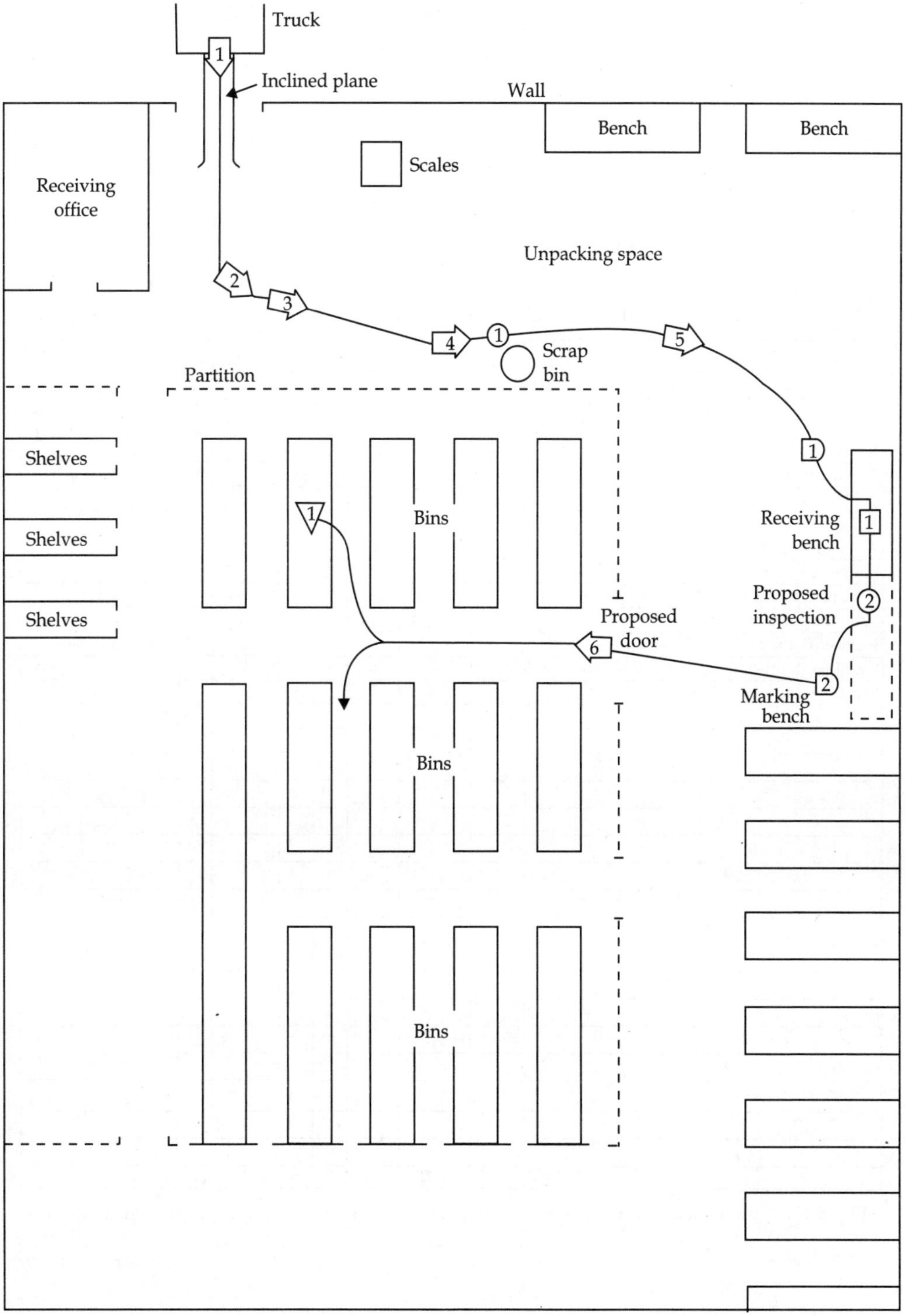

Fig. 5.12: Flow diagram: Inspecting and marking incoming parts (improved method).

Flow process chart	**Material type**			
Chart No. 4 Sheet No. 1 of 1	Summary			
Subject charted: Case of BX 487 tee-pieces (10 per case in cartons)	Activity	Present	Proposed	Saving
	Operation ○	2	2	–
	Transport ⇨	11	6	5
Activity Receive, check, inspect and number tee-pieces and store in case	Delay D	7	2	5
	Inspection □	2	1	1
	Storage ▽	1	1	–
Method: Proposed	Distance (m)	56.2	32.2	24
Location: Receiving Dept.	Time (work-h.)	1.96	1.16	0.80
Operative(s): Clock No. See remarks column	Cost			
	Labour	$10.19	$6.03	$4.16
Charted by: Date:	Material	–	–	–
Approved by: Date:	Total	$10.19	$6.03	$4.16

Description	Qty. 1 case	Distance (m)	Time (min.)	Symbol ○	⇨	D	□	▽	Remarks
Crate lifted from truck: placed on inclined plane		1.2			•				2 labourers
Slid on inclined plane		6	5		•				2 labourers
Placed on hand truck		1			•				2 labourers
Trucked to unpacking space		6	5		•				1 labourer
Lid taken off case		–	5	•					1 labourer
Trucked to receiving bench		9	5		•				1 labourer
Await unloading		–	5			•			
Cartons taken from case: opened and tee-pieces placed on bench: counted and inspected to drawing		–	20				•		Inspector
Numbered and replaced in case				•					Stores labourer
Await transport labourer		–	5			•			
Trucked to distribution point		9	5		•				1 labourer
Stored		–	–					•	
Total		32.2	55	2	6	2	1	1	

Fig. 5.13: Flow process chart: Inspecting and marking incoming parts (improved method).

5.4.3 Develop the Improved Method

There is an old saying that to ask the right question is to be halfway towards finding the right answer. The shortcomings of the present method can be overcome using the following questioning sequence.

What should be done?

Where should it be done?

When should it be done?

Who should do it?

How should it be done?

Once the shortcomings are addressed, the possibility of emergence of new method starts to emerge. One should not directly rush into the solution before investigating other areas. Therefore, further investigations must be carried out to develop a method that will lead to increased efficiency of the operation unit. For example, a simplification in the design of the product or proper use of raw material can save considerably on times of operations. Other issues related to proper layout or to materials handling can also produce the same effect. It is for this reason that work study specialists should be aware of the range of techniques that are available to them in developing a new improved method.

Eventually, and with practice in using the questioning technique, the work study person develops an inquisitive attitude which is constantly pursuing efficiency. Once the step of developing a new method is accomplished, it is recorded on a corresponding chart. In our two previous examples this would be a flow process chart, so that it can be compared with the original method and checked to make sure that no point has been overlooked. This will enable entries to be made in the "summary" of the total number of activities taking place under both methods, the savings in distance and time which may be expected to accrue from the change and the possible cost savings which will result.

6
Movement at Workplace

6.1 MOVEMENT OF WORKERS AND MATERIAL

There are many types of activities in which workers move at irregular intervals between a number of points in the working area, with or without material. This situation occurs very often in industry and commerce, and even in homes. In manufacturing concerns, it occurs when:

- Bulk material is being fed to or removed from continuous process, and is stored around the process.
- An operative is looking after two or more machines;
- Laborers are delivering materials to or removing work from a series of machines or workplaces.

Outside manufacturing operations, examples of its occurrence are:

- In stores and shops where a variety of materials are being removed from or put away into racks or bins.
- In restaurant and canteen kitchens during the preparation of meals.
- In control laboratories where routine tests are carried out at frequent intervals.

6.2 THE STRING DIAGRAM

One of the most useful and simplest of the method study techniques is the string diagram. The string diagram makes use of threads to trace the movements of the workers, materials or equipment during the sequence of operations or activities performed. The thread measures the total movement during different movements. Figure 6.1 shows an example of string diagram. It is a special form of flow diagram.

The main difference between a string diagram and the ordinary flow diagram is in the accuracy to which the scale model has been constructed. The methodology adopted by a string diagram is similar to that of all the other method studies. Direct observations are used to record all the activities. A string diagram supplements a flow process chart to give a clear picture of what is being done. A flow process chart eliminates the unnecessary activities before developing a new method, the string diagram on the other hand is used to analyze critically the distances moved or travelled. The movements of a worker are recorded by the work study manager as the worker moves from one point to another point in doing a job. The work study person analyses the journeys that take more than the stipulated time duration. The manager codes the various machines, stores and other points of the working area which saves a great deal of writing.

Figure 6.2 shows a form of study sheet. The sheets that are used in continuation should only give columns 1, 2, 3, 4 and 5. The work study manager studies the job until a representative picture of the worker's movement has been achieved. The duration may be a few hours, a day, few weeks, or months. He or she ensures that all the movements performed by the worker have been recorded. The movements have been observed with sufficient number of frequency. A misleading picture could be produced if the movements are not recorded correctly. A string diagram can be constructed only if the work study person ensures that he or she has the true picture of the movements and activities. To ensure this, the consultation with the workers concerned should be done. A scale plan of the working area similar to that required for a flow diagram must be made (the same plan may be used so long as it has been accurately drawn). Machines, benches, stores and all points at which calls are made should be drawn to scale, together with such doorways, pillars and partitions as are likely to affect paths of movements. The completed plan should be attached to a softwood or composition board, and pins driven into it firmly at every stopping point, the heads being allowed to stand well clear of the surface (by about 1 cm). Pins should also be driven in at all the turning points on the route. A measured length of thread is then taken and tied around the pin at the starting-point of the movements.

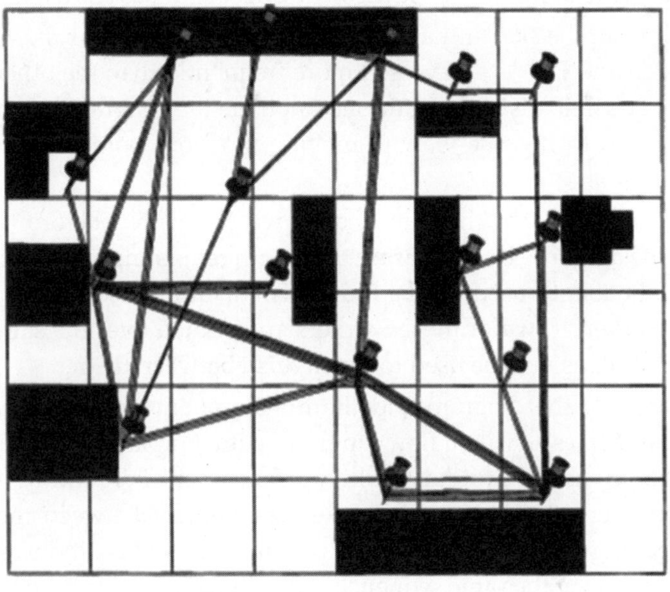

Fig. 6.1: A string diagram.

Movement study sheet				
Chart No. 1 Sheet No. 1 of 2			Operative(s):	
Operation: Transport biscuit tiles from inspection to storage bins and unload into bins			Charted by: Date:	
Location: Biscuit warehouse			Cross-reference: String diagrams 1 and 2	
1 Time dep.	2 Time arr.	3 Time elapsed	4 Move to	5 Notes
			Inspection bench (*l*)	
			to Bin 4	
			l 13	
			l 5	
			l 32	
			l 18	

Fig. 6.2: A simple movement study sheet.

It is then led around the pins at the other points of call in the order noted on the study sheet until all the movements have been dealt with. The result is an overall picture of the paths of movement of the operative, those which are most frequently traversed being covered with the greatest number of strings, the effect being as shown in Fig. 6.1.

It will be seen from the sketch that certain paths – in particular those between A and D, A and H, and D and L – are traversed more frequently than the others. Since most of these points are at a fair distance from one another, the diagram suggests that critical examination is called for, with a view to moving the work points which they represent closer together.

It will be remembered that the thread used was measured before the study person started to make the diagram. By measuring the length remaining and subtracting this from the total length, the length used can be found. This will represent, to scale, the distance covered by the worker. If two or more workers are studied over the same working area, different colored threads may be used to distinguish between them.

The **examination** of the diagram and the **development** of the new layout can now proceed on the same lines as with a flow diagram, with templates being used and the pins and templates being moved around until an arrangement is found by which the same operations can be performed with a minimum movement between them. This can be ascertained by leading the thread around the pins in their new positions, starting from the same point and following the same sequence. When the thread has been led around all the points covered by the study, the length left over can again be measured. The difference in length between this and the thread left over from the original study will represent the reduction in distance travelled as a result of the improved layout. The process may have to be repeated several times until the best possible layout (i.e., the layout with which the minimum length of thread is used) is achieved.

The string diagram is a useful aid in explaining proposed changes to the management, supervisors and workers. If two diagrams are made, one showing the original layout and one the improved layout, the contrast is often so vivid – particularly if brightly colored thread is used – that the change will not be difficult to "sell". Workers especially are interested in seeing the results of such studies and discovering how far they have to walk. The idea of reducing one's personal effort appeals to almost everyone!

The following example shows this technique as applied to the movements of 112 labourers storing tiles after inspection.

Example of a string diagram: Storing tiles after inspection

- **Record:** The biscuit tiles, i.e., the tiles after firing and before glazing, are studied. The tiles are unloaded from the truck onto a bench. The inspection process is carried out on the bench, where the tiles are inspected. The tiles are then arranged on the basis of types and size and are kept on the platform. The loaded platform is then taken to the concrete bins by a hand-lift truck where they are stored until glazing operation is required to be performed. The original layout is shown in Fig. 6.3.

  The present layout is studied using string diagram to find out whether the layout has least amount of transport. The dimension of tiles on each kiln truck varied, although the 10 cm × 10 cm and 15 cm × 15 cm formed the largest part of each load. Therefore, in order to carry out the study, a representative number of truck kiln loads is used. The information is recorded on a form shown in Fig. 6.2. A form of the type shown in Fig. 6.2 was used for recording the information. Since the nature of record is obvious, Fig. 6.2 shows only the part of the form. The bin numbers have been shown in Fig. 6.3. Recording of time was not given due importance. However, for transport involving long distances, time is recorded. One such example for long distance transport is the movement between different departments of the factory. Figure 6.3 shows the obtained string diagram. The number of threads between two points is reflected by the width of the shaded bands. Further, the width also reflects on the relative amount of movement between the two points.
- **Examine critically:** A critical examination of the string diagram shows the majority of movement in 10 cm × 10 cm and 15 cm × 15 cm rows of bins. The occupancy of a particular bin decides the unloading of the tiles. A bin may be empty or full depending on the rate at which the tiles are withdrawn for glazing. Therefore depending upon the occupancy of the bin, the movement can be up or down the rows concerned. Further examination shows that movements are rare in the special feature tiles which are used for decorative purpose. The inspector puts these special purpose tiles in the truck which then carries and unloads in the concerned bins at once. There is even distribution of other types of tiles.

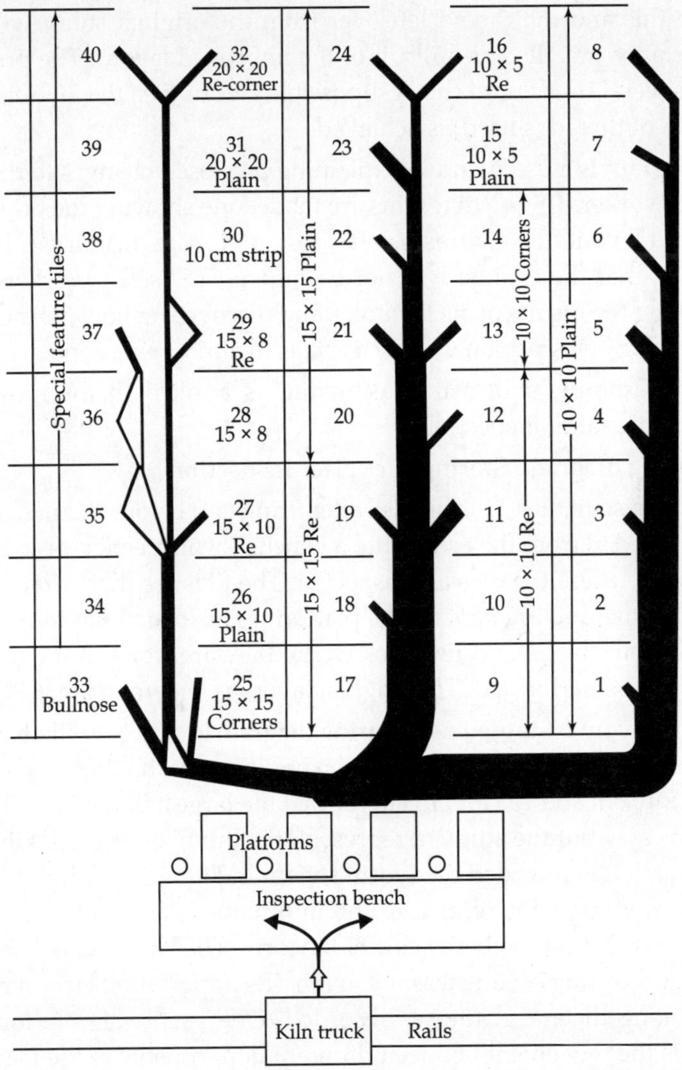

Fig. 6.3: String diagram: Storing tiles (original method).

- **Develop the new layout:** In the new layout to be developed, efforts should be made to locate the bins handling most number of tiles as close as possible to the inspection bench while arranging for bins handling special purpose tiles as far as possible. The new proposed layout will make it difficult to find the appropriate types of tiles. However, cards with contents marked on them can be used for the bins with concrete partitions as high as 1 metre. The new sequence of bins can then be easily memorized by the workers. After a number of alternative layouts adopted, one finds the layout shown in Fig. 6.4 to be the most suitable with the least transport distances.

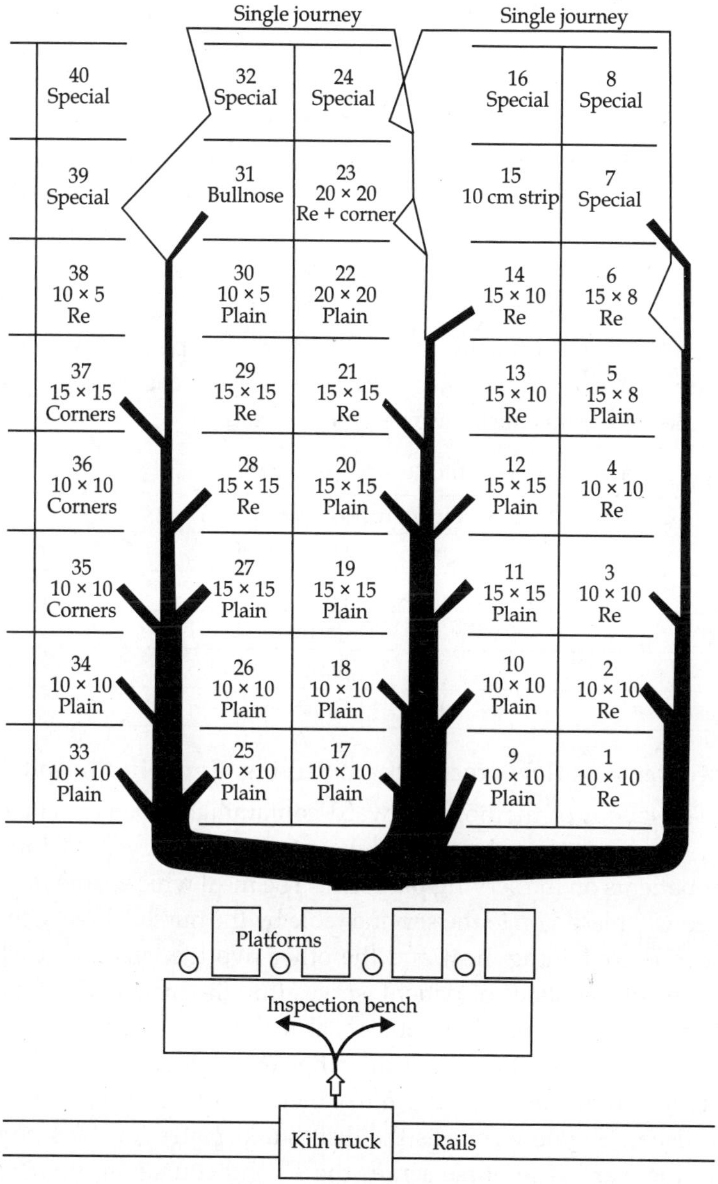

Fig. 6.4: String diagram: Storing tiles (improved method).

6.3 THE WORKER-TYPE FLOW PROCESS CHART

The activities of a worker are recorded by a worker-type flow process chart. The movements of a person can be recorded in the same manner as has been done to follow the movements and operations of the material. The jobs that are highly repetitive in nature and standardized can be studied using the worker-type flow process chart. Laboratory procedures, service and maintenance work and major proportion of the work performed by the supervisor and executives can be recorded using chart of this type. The standard flow process charts can be used to record an individual or group performing the same activities in sequence. The observations relating to the path followed by a worker while performing a certain operation is recorded in the form of a sketch and attached to the worker type flow process chart.

The charting procedure that is used in compiling the worker-type flow process chart is replicated in the same manner as has been done while compiling the same for the material type flow process chart. However, there is difference between the charting conventions that distinguishes a material type flow process chart from the worker type flow process chart.

Mainly active voice is used for the charting of worker-type flow process chart since it addresses the question of what a worker does. However, for charting of material type and equipment type flow process chart, passive voice is used.

Table 6.1: Example of conventions used for flow process chart.

Flow process charts	
Worker type	Material type
Drills casting	Casting drilled
Carries to bench	Carried to bench
Picks up bolt	(Bolt) Picked up
Inspects for finish	Finish inspected

Example of a worker-type flow process chart: Serving dinner in a hospital ward

- **Record:** The layout of the hospital ward containing 17 beds is shown in Fig. 6.5. Following the original method the nurse places out a large tray together with the plates for patients on the serving platform. The meal which is the first course is also simultaneously placed on to the serving table by the nurse. Three dishes are used by the nurse, one containing meat and the other two the vegetables. The nurse then takes out one of the plates of patient, serves first the meat and vegetable. She then carries the plate to bed 1 and then comes back to the serving table. The same procedure is adopted by the nurse for each of the other 16 patients. Full lines in Fig. 6.5 show the path followed by the nurse. The nurse then returns to the kitchen with the empty tray and dishes. She now collects the dishes and plates for the second course and returns to the ward. The nurse serves the second course on the new plates at the serving table. She then goes to every bed, replacing the empty plate with the new ones. The empty plates are stacked one over the other by the nurse on the serving table. Finally, the nurse makes a tour of the ward, collects the empty plates for the second course and then returns back the empty plates to the serving table. She then carries everything back to the kitchen. The final collection of plates is however not shown in the figure in order to avoid confusion. Figure 6.6 shows a part of the form on which the activity has been recorded. It could be seen clearly that the form is similar to that used for material type flow process chart, the latter however being used for the material.

- **Examine critically:** One can find a room for improvement in the original method after making a critical examination of the flow process chart. Many questions can come to mind. The first being why the nurse carries only one plate to the bed at a time. This stems out another question of how many plates can she carry. Certainly the distance travelled by the nurse would be halved if she carries two plates at a time. Other key questions can pertain to the serving table. Why the serving table is in the middle and why is it still.

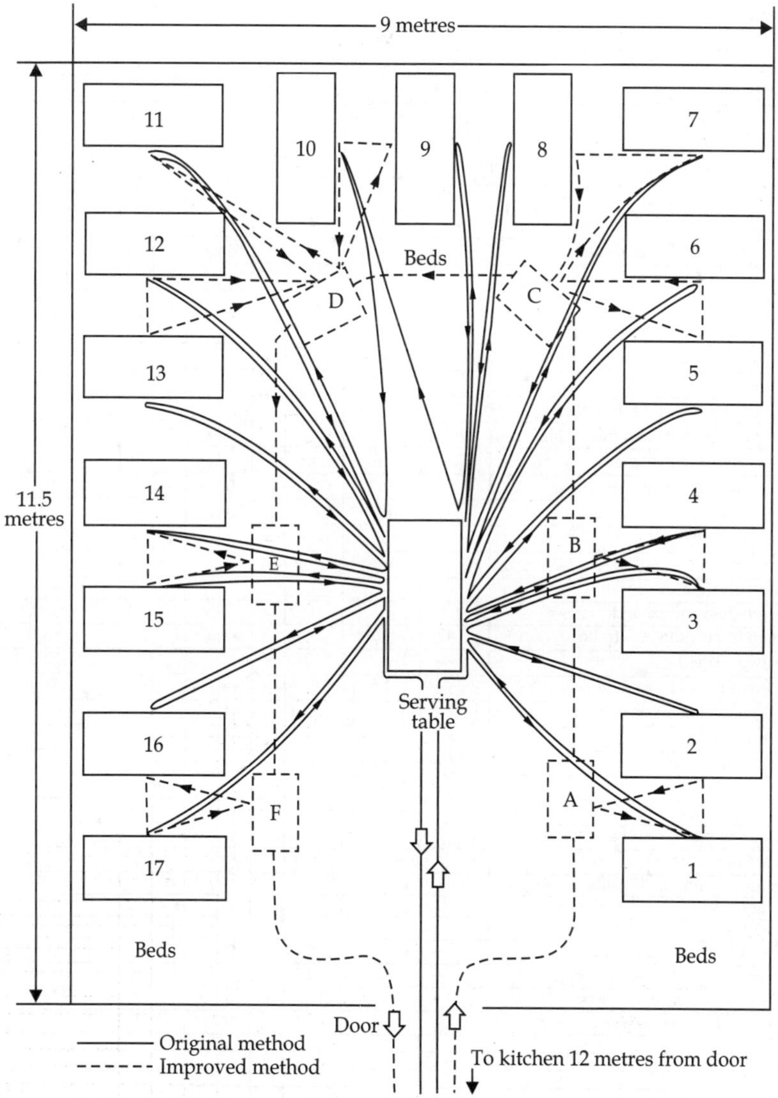

Fig. 6.5: Flow diagram: Serving dinner in a hospital ward.

Certainly trolley is an alternative to the still serving table. The key questioning leads straight to the development of a new method.

Flow process chart		**Worker type**			
Chart No. 7 Sheet No. 1 of 1		Summary			
Subject charted: Hospital		Activity	Present	Proposed	Saving
		Operation ○	34	18	16
		Transport ⇨	60	72	(-12)
Activity: Serve dinners to 17 patients		Delay D	–	–	–
		Inspection □	–	–	–
		Storage ▽	–	–	–
Method: Present/Proposed		Distance (m)	436	197	239
Location: Ward L		Time (work-min.)	39	28	11
Operative(s):	Clock No.	Cost	–	–	–
		Labour	–	–	–
Charted by:	Date:	Material (Trolley)	–	$24	–
Approved by:	Date:	Total (Capital)		$24	

Description	Qty. (plates)	Distance (m)	Time (min.)	○	⇨	D	□	▽	Remarks
Original method									
Transports first course and plates– kitchen to serving table on trey	17	16	.50						Awkward load
Places dishes and plates on table	17	–	.30						
Serves from three dishes to plate	–	–	.25						
Carries plate to bed 1 and returns	1	7.3	.25						
Serves	–	–	.25						
Carries plate to bed 2 and returns	1	6	.23						
Serves	–	–	.25						
(Continues until all 17 beds are served. See figure 37 for distances)									
Service completed, places dishes on try and returns to kitchen	–	16	.50						
Total distance and time, first cycle		192	10.71	17	20	–	–	–	
Repeats cycle for second course		192	10.71	17	20	–	–	–	
Collects empty second course plates		52	2.0	–	20	–	–	–	
Total		436	23.42	34	60				
Improved method									
Transports first course and plates– kitchen to position A – trolley	17	16	.50						Serving trolley
Serves two plates	–	–	40						
Carries two plates to be 1: leaves one; carries one plate from bed 1 to bed 2; return to position A	2	1.5 0.6 1.5	.25						
Pushed trolley to position B	–	3.0	.12						
Serves two plates	–	–	.40						
Carries two plates to bed 3; leaves one; carries one plate from bed 3 to bed 4; returns to position B	2	1.5 0.6 1.5	.26						
(Continues until all 17 beds are served. See figure 37 and note variation at bed 11)									
Returns to kitchen with trolley	–	16	.50						
Total distances and time, first cycle	–	72.5	7.49	9	26				
Repeats cycle for second course	–	72.5	7.49	9	26				
Collects empty second course plates	–	52	2.00	–	20				
Total	–	197	16.98	18	72				

Fig. 6.6: Flow process chart – Worker type: Serving dinners in a hospital ward.

- **Develop the new method:** The nurse in the proposed new method carries two plates at a time. The movements in the flow process chart are represented by the broken lines. This leads to a reduction of over 54% in the total distance which is reflected in the chart. The new proposed method however doesn't lead to much reduction in cost but the method is important because it reduces the fatigue of the nurse which results from the distance travelled during the entire process of serving the two courses.

6.4 THE MULTIPLE ACTIVITY CHART

When relation is to be shown of activities of one subject to another, multiple activity charts are useful. A common time scale is used to record the activity of more than one subject, i.e., may be for a worker, machine or item of equipment. This can be used to show their interrelationship. For each subject, a separate vertical bar or a column is used to indicate the activities on a common time scale. It becomes easier to analyze the period of idleness from the chart during the process on the part of each subject. The ineffective time then can be reduced by carefully studying the chart and therefore rearranging the activities. Teams of operatives can be organized on mass productive work with the aid of multiple activity charts. Further, for an expensive plant which cannot remain idle, the operatives can be organized for maintenance work. A multiple activity chart is also helpful in deciding the number of machines to be looked after by an operative.

The activities of different operatives or the machines are recorded in terms of idle time and working time. Depending on whether for an activity, minutes or seconds are critical, different instruments for recording its time can be used. Some examples of such instruments are wristwatch, stopwatch or electronic timing. Whatever be the instrument used, the time recorded data must be accurate to make the chart an effective tool. Figure 6.7 shows the manner in which the time recorded is plotted in their respective column. An illustrative example will make the use of multiple activity chart clear.

Example of a multiple activity chart applied to team work: Inspection of catalyst in a converter

- **Record:** The example illustrates that method study is not only confined to activities of production or repetitive operations. It is necessary to make frequent checks on a new catalytic convertor of a chemical plant during the running-in period. The condition of the catalyst is required to be monitored frequently. The job is mainly studied to ensure a required amount of idle time for the catalytic converter and therefore to further ensure that the converter is not out of service than the stipulated time. In the original method, until and unless the heaters are removed the top of the vessel is not started. Further, the replacement of the heater is not started until and unless the top is fixed completely. Figure 6.7 shows the working time of different workers on a common time scale.
- **Examine critically:** A critical examination shows that the fitters could only remove the top of the vessel when the electrician has removed the heater. This means that

the fitter has to wait until the heater is removed by the electrician. Similarly, the heater can only be replaced by the electrician when the top of the vessel has been secured by the fitter. Therefore, in this case it was the electrician who had to wait. The examination led to the fact that it is not necessary to wait for the electrician to remove the heater to allow the fitter to be removed from the top of the vessel.

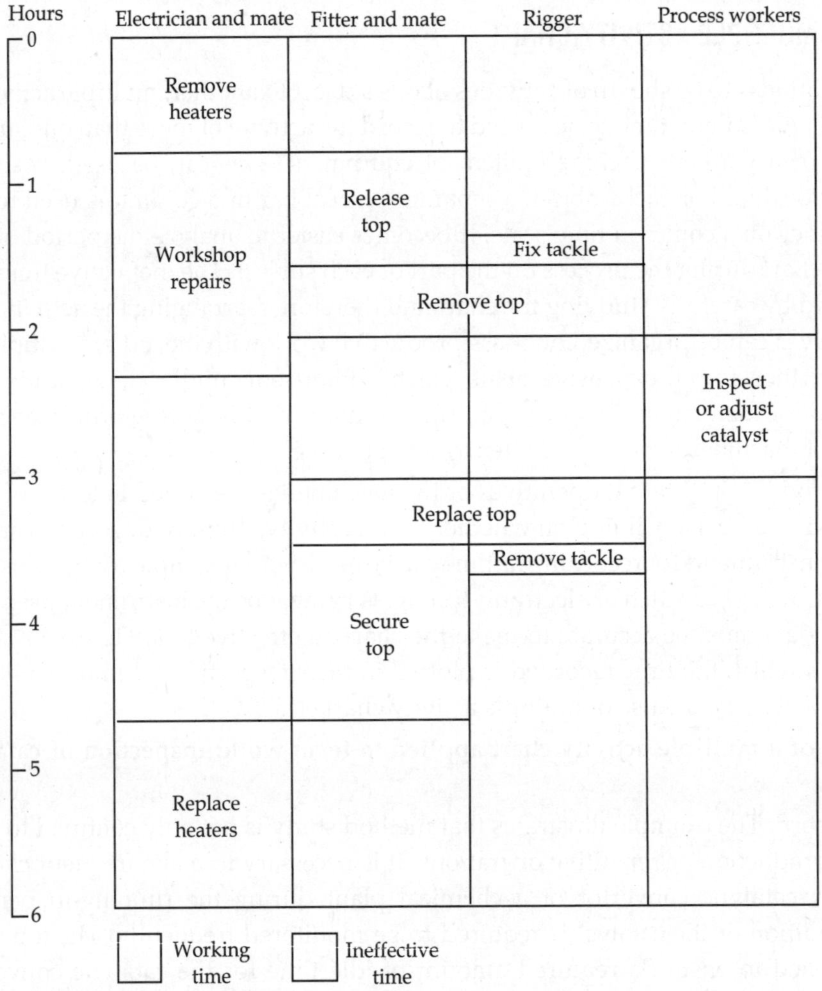

Fig. 6.7: Multiple activity chart: Inspection of catalyst in a converter (original method).

- **Develop the new method:** A new method is proposed in which it is possible to remove the top of the vessel by the fitter before waiting for the electrician to remove the heater. Further, it also became possible to replace the heaters before the top is secured. Figure 6.8 shows the new proposed method. It can be seen in the new proposed method that there has been reduction in the idle time of the fitter and the electrician. However, the idle time for the rigger remains the same. The total saving time amounts to about 32% of the total time of operation. For a simple activity, the chart can be drawn on a simple piece of paper but for a larger and complex system, a printed form must be used. Figures 6.9, 6.10 and 6.12 show multiple activity charts drawn on printed forms.

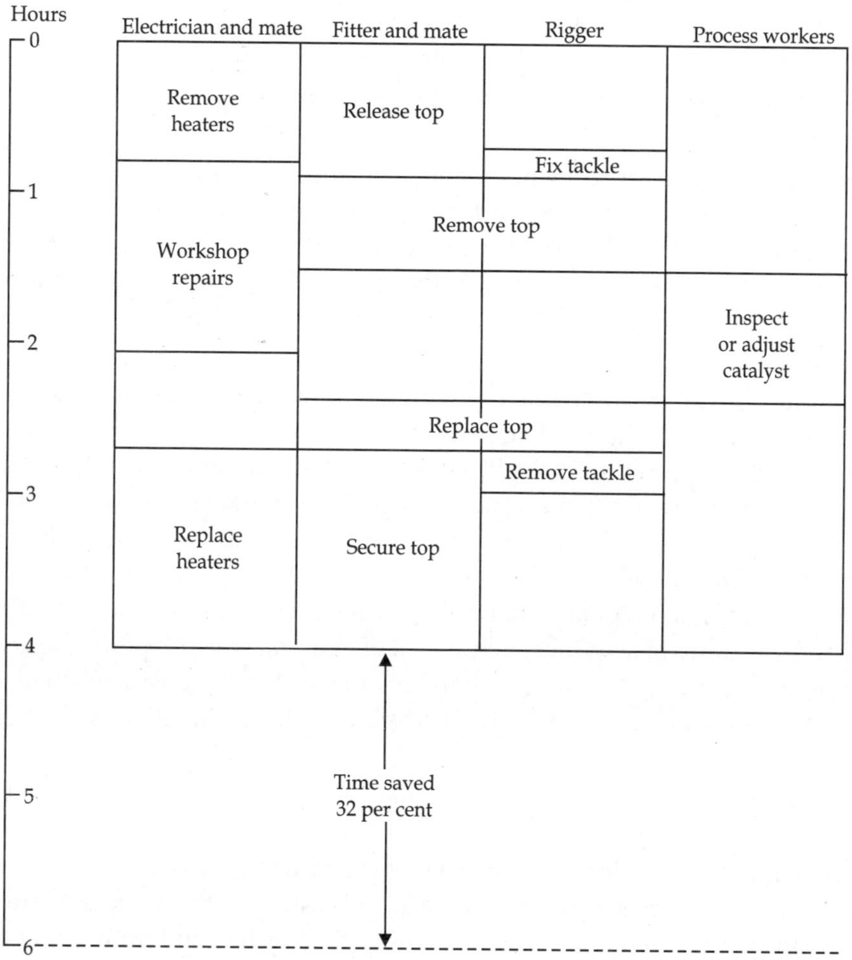

Fig. 6.8: Multiple activity chart: Inspection of catalyst in a converter (improved method).

The operation performed by a worker and a machine can be shown simultaneously on a common time scale using the multiple activity chart. The chart is shown in Fig. 6.9. The vertical bars are drawn close to each other down the middle of the sheet. The bars clearly indicate the start and end of each activity both for the worker and the machine. The duration of each activity either for a worker or a machine can be visualized clearly. Therefore, the relationship between the activities performed by a worker and the machine can be well established. A careful study then can lead to the new method where the improvement in the idle time of the worker as well as that of the machine can be made. This can be done by analyzing whether the idle time of the worker operating on a machine can be used to make the worker to perform on another machine, or whether the increase in ineffective time of the two machines will offset any gain to be obtained from employing the worker's time more fully. An illustrative example is used to clarify the situation of recording an activity of a worker and machine.

Example of a multiple activity chart recording worker and machine: Finish mill casting on a vertical miller

- **Record:** A common form of worker-and–machine multiple activity chart is shown in Fig. 6.9. The form is used to record the operation of a vertical milling machine. The vertical milling machine is used to mill an end of the cast iron casting the opposite end of which is used for locating it in the fixture. The usual standard information is recorded in the heading of the chart. Any time scale can be represented by the graduated scale on the edge of the chart.
- **Examine critically:** The critical examination of the current method shows that the machine on which the worker performs the operation is idle for almost three-quarters of the operation cycle. It is observed that most of the activities performed by the worker with the machine stopped. The worker remains idle when the machine is running. For making a careful study one can divide the activities performed by the worker in two categories: first the group of activities such as removal and location of jobs that are performed when the machine is not running, second the group of activities such as that of gauging which is performed when the machine is running. It is obvious that the utilization will increase when most of the job is performed when the machine is operative which will reduce the overall cycle time.
- **Develop the new method:** A new method is developed which is shown in Fig. 6.10. It is seen from the figure that operations like gauging, using a file to break the edges of the machined face, placing of the casting in the desired box containing the finished work, placing of the un-machined casting on the work table are all done while the machine is running. The boxes of the finished and un-machined casting are placed side by side to each other. This also leads to improvement in the time. Further, the cleaning operation for the part is not taken until the sharp edges of the casting have been removed. The new developed method has led to a saving of around 0.64 minute, i.e., a gain of nearly 32 per cent in the productivity of a milling machine and the operator. The next example is one of a multiple activity chart recording the 126 activities of a team of workers and a machine.

Multiple activity chart

Chart No. 8	Sheet No. 1	of 1
Product B. 239 casting		
	Drawing No. B. 239/1	
Process: Finish mill second face		
Machine(s): Cincinnati No. 4 vertical miller	Speed 80 r.p.m.	Feed 15 in./min.
Operative:	Clock No. 1234	
Charted by:	Date:	

Summary	Present	Proposed	Saving
Cycle time	(min.)		
Worker	2.0		
Machine	2.0		
Working			
Worker	1.2		
Machine	0.8		
Idle			
Worker	0.8		
Machine	1.2		
Utilization			
Worker	60%		
Machine	40%		

Time (min.)	Worker	Machine	Time (min.)
0.2	Removes finished casting: cleans with compressed air	Idle	0.2
0.4	Gauges depth on surface plate		0.4
0.6	Breaks sharp edge with file: cleans with compressed air		0.6
0.8	Places in box: obtains new casting		0.8
1.0	Cleans machine with compressed air		1.0
1.2	Locates casting in fixture: starts machine and auto feed		1.2
1.4		Working Finished mill second face	1.4
1.6			1.6
1.8			1.8
2.0			2.0
2.2			2.2
2.4			2.4
2.6			2.6
2.8			2.8
3.0			3.0
3.2			3.2
3.4			3.4
3.6			3.6
3.8			3.8

Fig. 6.9: Multiple activity chart – Worker and machine: Finish mill casting (original method).

Multiple activity chart						
Chart No. 9	Sheet No. 1	of 1	Summary			
				Present	Proposed	Saving
Product B. 239 casting			Cycle time	(min.)		
	Drawing No. B. 239/1		Worker	2.0	1.36	0.64
Process: Finish mill second face			Machine	2.0	1.36	0.64
			Working			
			Worker	1.2	1.12	0.08
			Machine	0.8	0.8	–
Machine(s): Cincinnati No. 4 vertical miller	Speed 80 r.p.m.	Feed 15 in./min.	Idle			
			Worker	0.8	0.24	0.56
			Machine	1.2	0.56	0.64
			Utilization			Gain
Operative:	Clock No. 1234		Worker	60%	83%	23%
Charted by:	Date:		Machine	40%	59%	19%

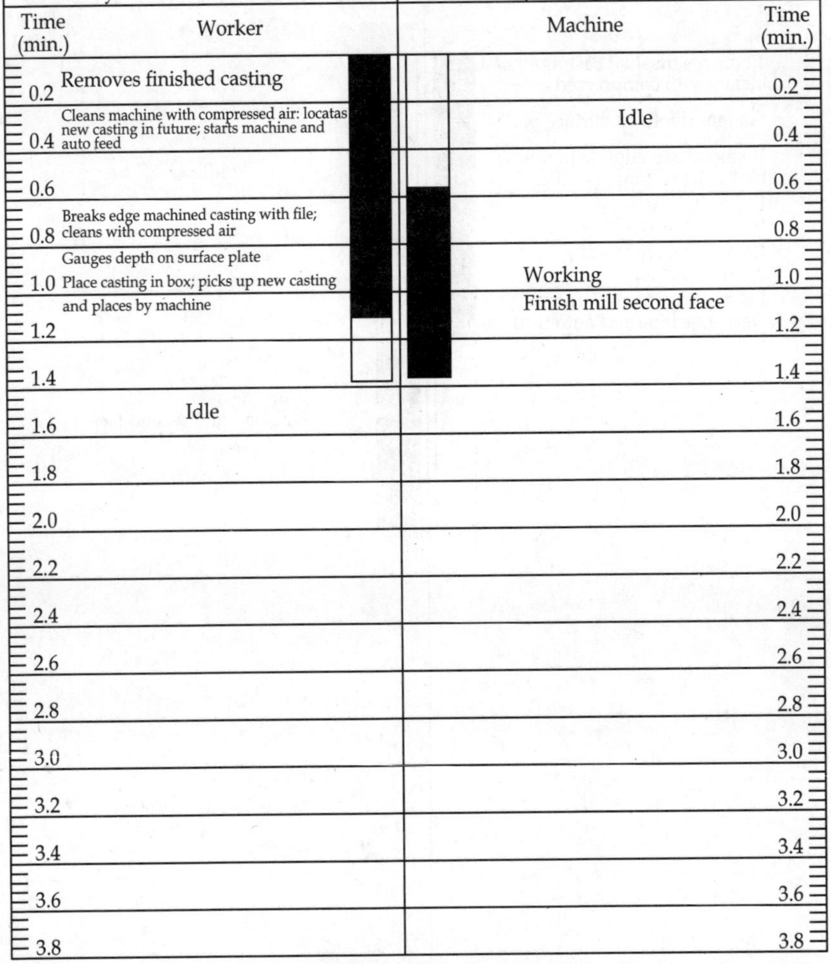

Fig. 6.10: Multiple activity chart – Worker and machine: Finish mill casting (improved method).

Example of multiple activity chart recording the activities of a team of workers and a machine: Feeding bones to a crusher in a glue factory

The example in this section is of a glue factory, where the bones are fed from a storage dump to a crushing machine. This simple example illustrates the recording of activities of both the workers and the machine on a common time scale. Figure 6.11 shows the original layout of the working area. The combined teamwork and machine multiple activity chart is shown in Fig. 6.12. The bones of all sorts were brought by the supplier and stored in the bin labelled "Bones". This bin is located at a distance of 80 metres from the crusher. The bones are then fed to the crusher using a small trolley running on rails.

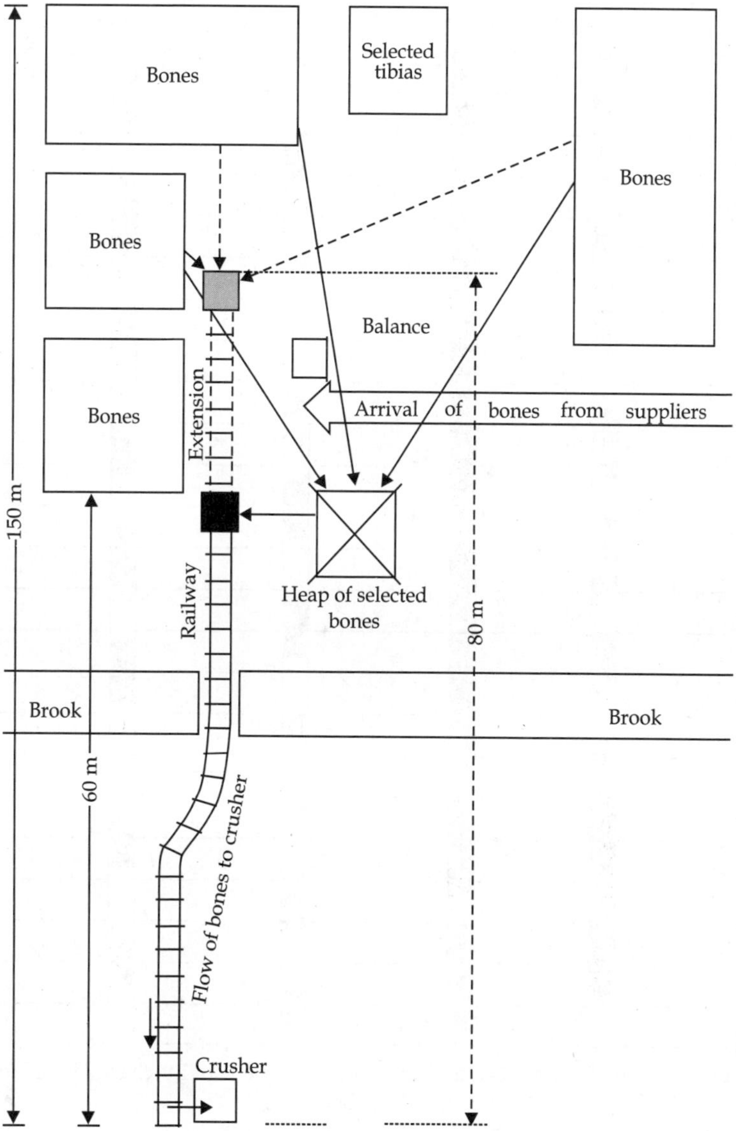

Fig. 6.11: Crushing bones: Layout of working area.

Multiple activity chart				
Chart No. 10 Sheet No. 1 of 1	(1) Machine(s) (2) Labour	% Utilization		
Product/Material: Mixed bones		Present	Proposed	Gain
Operation: Load and transport bones in trolley (250 kg load) from dump to crusher	(1) Crusher Trolley	68 96		
Method: Present/Proposed Location: Bone yard Charted by: Date:	(2) Loaders 2 Trolley operatives 2 • Crusher operatives 4	47.5 47.5 •Not studied		

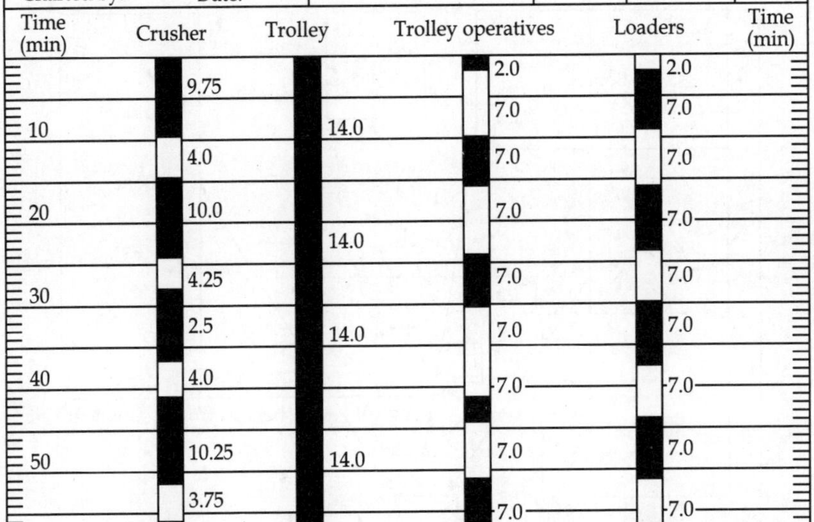

Fig. 6.12: Combined team work and machine multiple activity chart: Crushing bones (original method).

- **Record:** The bones were sorted into "soft" and "hard" by the workers. The selected bones are then carried to a heap where from they are loaded into the trolley by two workers using hands. The trolley was carried to the crusher, emptied into it and brought back by other two workers. Therefore, the first set of workers was idle when the trolley was carried to the crusher. Similarly, when the trolley was loaded, the set of workers carrying the trolley to the crusher were idle. The entire cycle of loading, unloading and crushing takes place eight times and consumes about 117.5 minutes. Loading of trolley takes about 7 minutes, another 7 minutes to carry the load to the crusher, empty the load and then return to the heap. The trolley load transported in one cycle is around 250 kg. Therefore for the entire cycle of operation, the total load comes out to be $8 \times 250 = 2000$ kg. The crusher waiting time amounts to 37.5 minutes.

Figure 6.12 relates the activities of different subjects on a common time scale. It is clearly observed from the chart that for replacing a broken belt, 10 minutes of the crusher waiting time is consumed. However, after the belt is repaired, the crusher runs for 16.5 minutes continuously instead of usual 10 minutes, since the fresh load was ready to be received by it. The net idleness due to broken belt becomes 6 minutes if a normal idle time of 4 minutes is allowed.

- **Examine critically:** After the critical examination of the activities, one can observe that the trolley remains idle for 31.75 minutes out of 111.5 minutes (if 6 minutes breakdown time is included then it amounts to 31.75 out of 117.5 minutes), i.e., nearly for 28.5 per cent of the possible working time. Further observation shows that the two groups of workers were idle for nearly 50 per cent of its available time. The examination leads to an obvious question that why not the same set of workers perform the task of loading the trolley and carrying it to the crusher and feed the crusher. The obvious answer is that if this is done then there will be no rest for the workers and feeding the crusher operating for the same percentage of time. Hence, there would be saving in manpower but no improvement in the productivity of the plant. Also it is worth noticing that the allowance for such heavy loading tasks is normally around 25 per cent of the total time allowed for the job. Therefore, the productivity of the crusher will still be lower if the workers take their relaxation allowances into account.

  A further examination of the layout of the working area shows that the workers have to carry the bones from the bins labelled "Bones" to the heap of selected bones. The trolley is unloaded and then carried back to the bins. This leads to the questioning as to why the workers do not sort the bones at the bins and loads straight into the trolley. This is only possible if the rails for the trolley are extended 20 metres more from the heaps to the bone dumps. However, this leads to reduction in manpower but at the same time leaves the problem of 4 minutes of idle time for the crusher. Since the number of sorters is more than the number of loaders, it would probably take less time to load the trolley and push it with lesser effort provided that the load on the trolley is reduced. Thus, a reduction of load was proposed for the new method. The load in the trolley is reduced to 175 kilograms from 250 kilograms.

- **Develop the improved method:** Figure 6.12 shows the extension of rails to the bone bins. The loaders who were eliminated were sent to the factory. There was a substantial increase in the output of the crusher. The improved method is depicted by the multiple activity chart in Fig. 6.13.

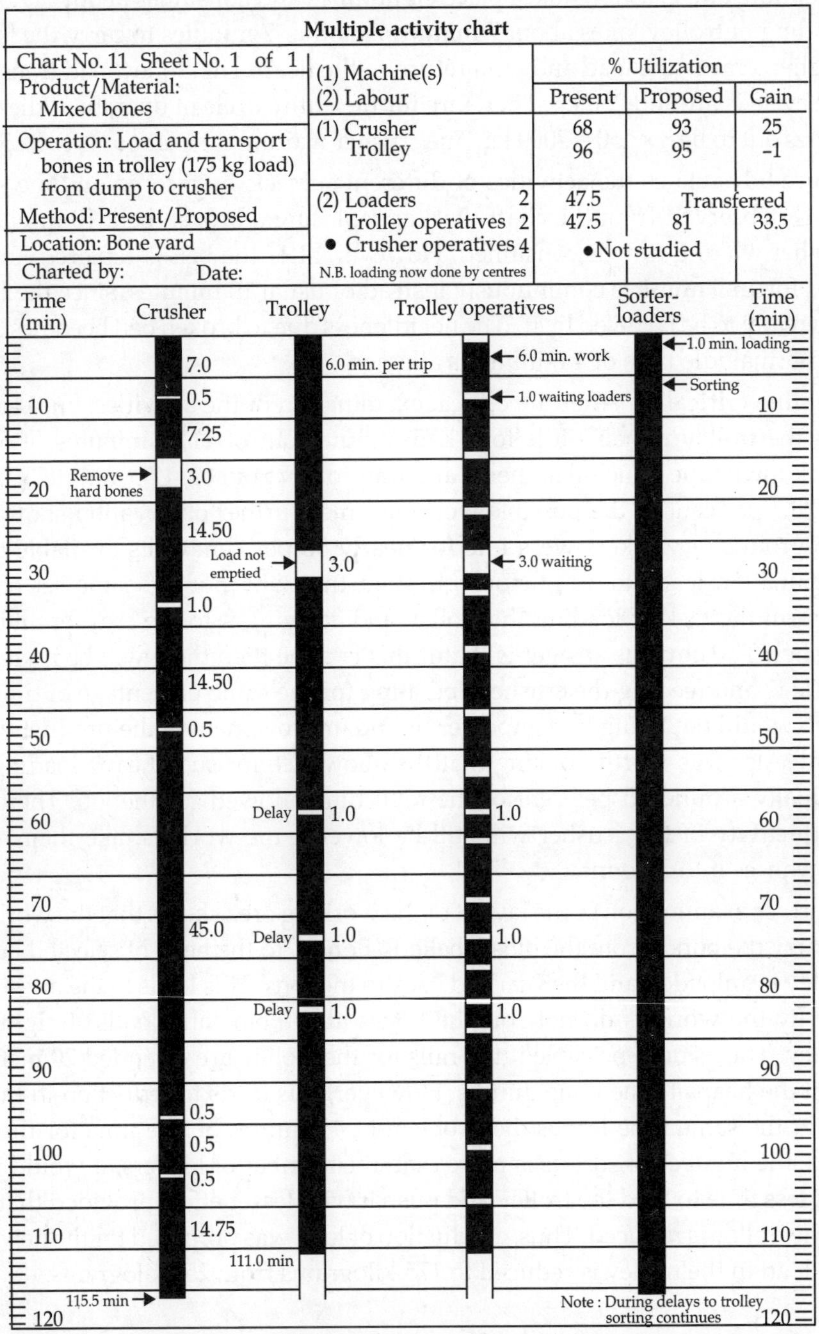

Fig. 6.13: Combined team work and machine multiple activity chart: Crushing bones (improved method).

Thus, just at a cost of extension of railway track to 20 metres, there was improved productivity of land, labour and the plant.

6.5 THE TRAVEL CHART

The movements of the workers in the work area can be presented neatly by a string diagram. It is a very effective tool for recording the movements for critical examination. The proposed change can be easily understood with the help of "before" and "after" models. When the number of movements to be recorded increases, the time taken to construct a string diagram increases too. Further, the diagram may end up looking like a forbidding maze of criss-crossing lines. In the cases of increased number of complex movements, a travel chart is a more manageable recording technique. The movements of workers, materials or equipment are recorded quantitatively on a travel chart. A travel chart is a tabular record for presenting quantitative data about the movements of workers, materials or equipment between any number of places over any given period of time.

A typical travel chart is depicted in Fig. 6.14. The movements of a messenger are recorded by the travel chart. The messenger delivers the papers to the various desks and workstations in an office. A sketch showing the locations of different workstations is shown below the travel chart. A travel chart is in the form of a square, containing smaller squares within it. The workstations are represented by these small squares. Since there are ten workstations, so ten squares numbered from 1 to 10 are made from left to right and from top to bottom. Therefore there are a total of 100 small squares in a travel chart with a problem involving ten workstations. The chart also has a diagonal line drawn from the top left corner of the chart to the bottom right corner of the chart.

The squares at the top which are numbered 1 to 10 from left to right represent the workstations from where the travel takes place. The squares from top to bottom indicate the stations to which the travel has been made. For example, in order to examine the movement of the messenger from workstation 2 to workstation 9, the work study manager enters the chart at the square numbered 2 along the top of the chart. Then the manager travels down all the squares beneath this square until the square just horizontally opposite to the square number 9 marked on the left edge is reached. A mark is then made in this square to show that the recording has been made for the movement from workstation 2 to workstation 9. All the other movements are recorded in a similar manner.

Example of a travel chart: Movement of messenger in an office

- **Record:** A simple study sheet is used initially for recording the movements of the messenger in the office. The study sheet is shown in Fig. 6.15. This is the first stage of the recording process. Recording of the journey will require very little writing once the numbering of the workstations has been done and keyed to a sketch of the workplace. The movements made from and to a particular workstation are recorded using a tick mark on the chart. The sum total of number of ticks of a particular square is entered in the concerned square itself. The summary of the movements are made

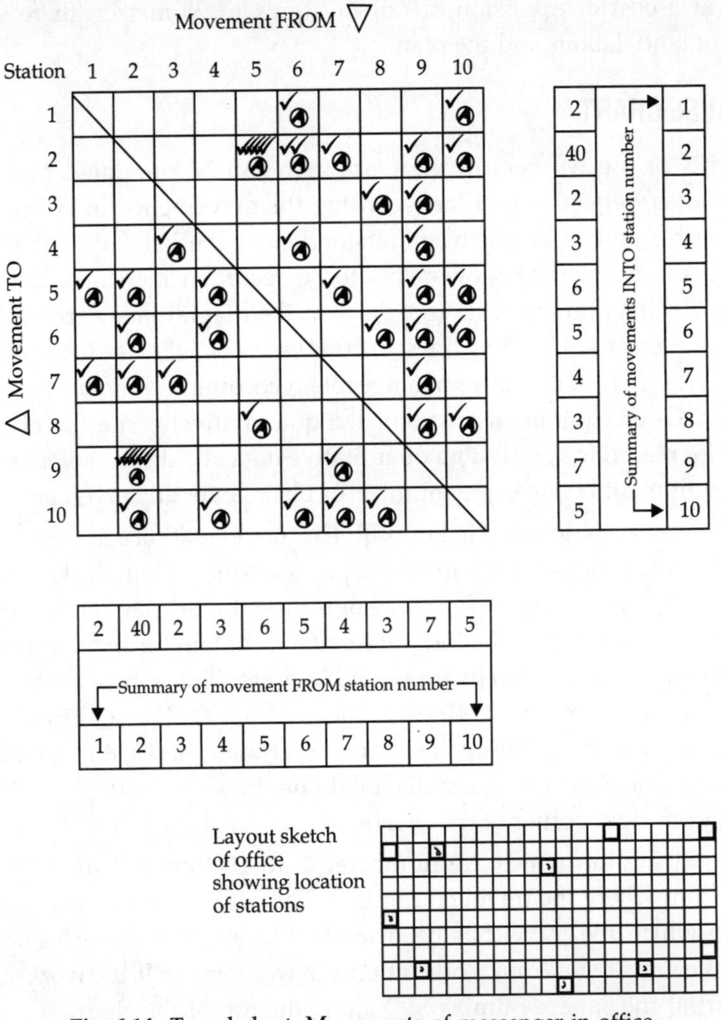

Fig. 6.14: Travel chart: Movements of messenger in office.

in two ways. As can be seen from Fig. 6.14, the summary of the number of movements **into** each station is represented on the right hand side of the chart. This is done by reading from the left edge of the chart against the station for which the summary is to be made. For summarizing the movements for the "**from**" stations, the movements are recorded underneath the relevant square as read from the top of the chart. The summary is made underneath the chart. For example, after looking from Fig. 6.14, one can see that there are a total of two movements into station 1. This can be read by reading horizontally against the station marked 1 on the left end edge of the chart. Similarly, for station 2, one can see that there are a total of ten movements into station 2. Now, for the movements from station 2, it comes to a total of 10 movements as can be read vertically from the top of the chart under station marked 2.

Study sheet		
Department: Mixing	Section ⁄	Study No. 447
Equipment: Lift truck: Pallals		Sheet: ⁄ of 2
Operation: Move 25-like cans of material to mixing machines and then to inspection (stations)		Taken by: CBA Date:

From	2	9	7	4	3	9	6	4	9	6	3	2	9
To	9	7	4	3	9	6	4	9	6	3	2	9	7
No. of cans	40	-	20	40	-	30	40	-	30	40	-	30	-
From	7	4	6	4	9	8	2	5	9	7	2	5	9
To	4	6	4	9	8	2	5	9	7	2	5	9	6
No. of cans	40	20	-	30	40	20	30	40	40	20	40	30	40
From	6	4	9										
To	4	9	6										
No. of cans	-	30	30										

Fig. 6.15: A simple study sheet.

One can make a note that the number of movements for "**into**" stations is same as the number of movements recorded for the "**from**" stations. This indicates that the messenger starts and ends the journey at the same workstation. However, if the messenger would have finished at some other workstation, then there would be one station for which the number of movements "**into**" it would be more than 1 for the number of movements "**from**" it.

- **Examine critically:** On critical examination of the chart one could observe that the busiest stations are stations 2, 5 and 9. These stations have respectively 10, 7 and 6 journeys "**into**" them. Further, the busiest route that was determined was 5-2-9. The analysis suggests that it would have been better to locate these stations as close as possible to each other.

Example of a weighted travel chart: Material handling

Weighted travel chart is a variation of the travel chart. The chart records the movements over a given period of time. The weight or the volume of the material moved is also depicted in addition to the movements made between the stations. The total volume of traffic between each set of stations is entered at the end of the time period.

Movement FROM ▽ (columns); Movement TO ▷ (rows); Summary: No. of trips / INTO / No. of cans

Movement TO \ FROM	1	2	3	4	5	6	7	8	9	No. of trips (INTO)	No. of cans (INTO)
1						✓40 ✓–	✓40			3	20
2			✓–				✓20	✓20		3	40
3				✓40		✓40				2	20
4						✓–	✓20			2	20
5		✓30 ✓40								2	40
6	✓20								✓50 ✓30 ✓20 ✓30	5	450
7									✓– ✓– ✓40	3	40
8									✓40	A	40
9	✓30 ✓–	✓40 ✓30	✓–	✓30	✓40 ✓30					8	470

Summary

FROM	1	2	3	4	5	6	7	8	9
No. of trips	3	4	2	2	2	4	3	4	8
No. of cans	50	80	–	40	70	20	50	20	480

Fig. 6.16: Weighted travel chart: Material handling.

Figure 6.16 shows the weighted travel chart compiled for the material handling study. Eight mixing machines were used to mix materials in different proportions. The final mixture was then taken to the inspection bench. The mixes were contained in the 25-litre cans.

- **Record:** Figure 6.15 shows the movements recorded on a study sheet. The number of cans carried and the movements made for each trip is shown on the sheet. There are a total of nine stations shown in the travel chart in Fig. 6.16. The nine stations consist of eight mixing machines and one inspection bench. The travel chart carries the number of cans carried in addition to the tick marks which shows the movements made between the stations. For instance, for movements between stations 5 and 9, one can count a total of two journeys made one with a can load of 40 and other with 30.
- **Examine critically:** From the study sheet, one is able to get only the information about the trips that were run without any load and the variation of the load size. It

is found that a total of 29 trips were made without any load and the number of cans carried varied from ten to forty. However, detailed information can be obtained using the travel chart. Stations 6 and 9 were identified to be the busy ones. A total of five trips were made to station 6 out of which four were made from station 9. A total of 150 cans were delivered at station 6. Out of these 150 cans, 130 were from station 9. Hence, one can certainly say that majority of trips with majority of cans were between stations 6 and 9. The improved method should be such that, the stations 6 and 9 are located as close as possible. A roller conveyer can be installed between these two stations.

After examination for station 9, it is found that a total of 8 trips were made from stations 1, 2, 4 and 5. There was one empty trip from station 3 to station 9. Thus, it seems that the aforementioned stations feed station 9 from where the cans are delivered to the inspection bench. As such there should be modification in the layout to bring these stations as close as possible to each other.

Further, one can note that there is a difference of one for the trips made into and from station 2. Similar applies for station 6. This is because the trip started from station 2 and terminated at station 6.

7

Methods and Movements at the Workplace

7.1 INTRODUCTION

So far we have studied how through the process of work study, the productivity of an organization can be increased by increasing the productivity of the workers and the machines. Further, it was also studied as to how the sequence of operations can be improved considering the material flow pattern. The movements of workers and their relationship with the machine have also been studied. In the following sections, we will look at analyzing the worker at the workplace. The fatigue undergone by the individual worker and the amount of effort put are the primary factors in increasing the productivity of an individual worker. However, it should be ensured that the work performed by an individual is done at the right place and in the manner it is intended to be done. Questioning techniques must be applied, keeping in mind the following:

- **PURPOSE**: this ensures the necessity to perform the job.
- **PLACE:** this ensures the place of performance of the job.
- **SEQUENCE**: this ensures the proper sequence of performance of the job.
- **PERSON:** this ensures that the job is performed by the person who is intended to perform it.
- **MEANS:** by which the job is being done and to simplify them as much as is economically justified.

The recording techniques are discussed in the later part. Before commencing the journey for the same, we have discussed the principle of motion of economy. This is because it underlines the principles in which the workplace needs to be designed to make the working area convenient for the workers to perform their activities and operations.

7.2 THE PRINCIPLES OF MOTION ECONOMY

There are a number of "principles" concerning the economy of movements which have been developed as a result of experience and which form a good basis for the development of improved methods at the workplace. They may be grouped under three headings:

- Use of the human body

- Arrangement of the workplace
- Design of tools and equipment

They are useful in shop and office alike and, although they cannot always be applied, they do form a very good basis for improving the efficiency and reducing the fatigue of manual work. The ideas expounded by Professor Barnes are described here in a somewhat simplified fashion.

- **Use of the human body**

  When possible:
  - The movements for both the hands should start and finish simultaneously.
  - Except during the periods of rest, the two hands should not be idle.
  - There should be symmetry of motion for both the arms. The motion should be in opposite direction and should be made simultaneously.
  - Lowest classification at which the work can be performed satisfactorily should be maintained for the hands and body motions.
  - For motions involving sudden and sharp changes in the direction, continuous curved movements should be preferred over the straight line motion.
  - The movements with free-swinging nature are faster, easier and should be preferred over restricted or controlled movements.
  - The work should be arranged to permit for the easy and the natural rhythm. This helps in performance of smooth and automatic performance of the repetitive operation.
  - In order to provide a comfortable level for the eyes, the work should be arranged to aid eyes to remain focused on a confined and restricted area.
- **Arrangement of the workplace**
  - The tools and materials should be provided definite and fixed stations. This leads to habit formation.
  - To reduce the searching of tools and materials, pre-positioning should be done.
  - The delivery of materials to the point of use is done using gravity feed, bins and containers. These should be located as close as possible to point of use.
  - Within the maximum work area, different tools, materials and controls should be located.
  - The best sequence of motions should be taken into account while arranging the materials and tools.
  - In order to avoid the use of hands by the worker to dispose of the finished work, ejectors must be used.
  - Adequate lighting in the working area should be arranged. Further, the seats should be designed ergonomically to permit good posture.
  - In order to reduce the eye fatigue the colour of the workplace should be in contrast to that of the work.

- **Design of tools and equipment**
  - o Jig, fixture or foot operated devices relieve the hands of a worker to hold the workpiece. Therefore, wherever possible the use of such devices should be made to relieve the hands of the worker.
  - o Wherever possible, tools should be combined.
  - o The load on the fingers should be distributed on the basis of inherent capacities of the fingers. This will help in smooth functioning of the job involving finger movements such as that of typewriting.
  - o The design of the handles for the cranks and that of the screwdrivers should be designed so that much of the surface of the hand is in contact with the handle. The design is essential in cases involving the use of large magnitude of force.
  - o In order to have a greater mechanical advantage, the arrangement of levers, crossbars and handwheels should be such that there is least body movement in using them.

The normal working area and the storage area is shown in Fig. 7.1. Care must be taken to not store the materials directly in front of a worker. This is because it can lead to fatigue.

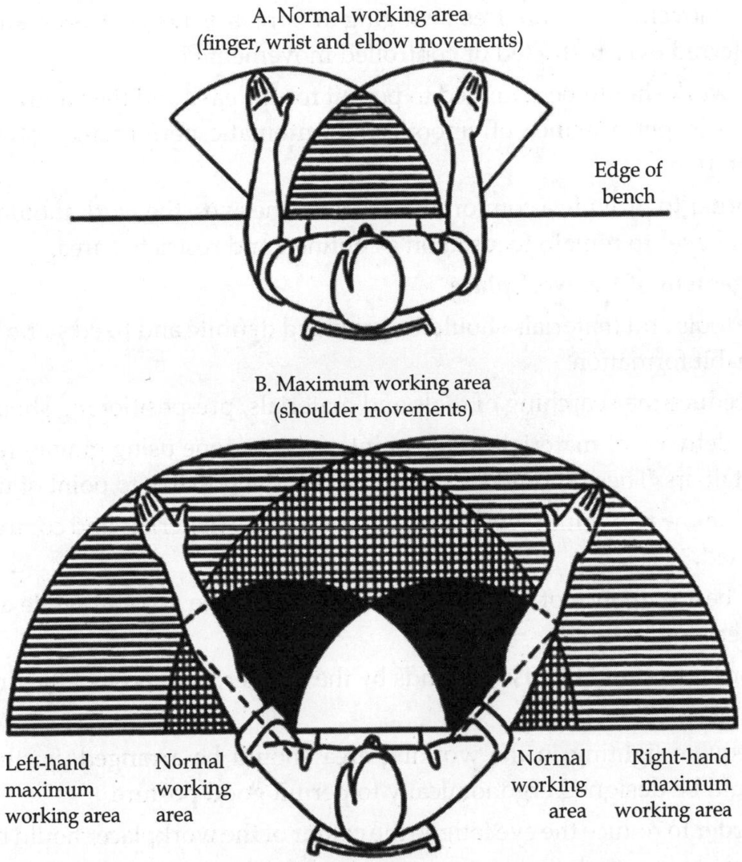

Fig. 7.1: Normal and maximum working areas.

7.3 CLASSIFICATION OF MOVEMENTS

The body movements to be at the lowest classification levels form the fourth rule of motion economy. Table 7.1 shows the classification of movements which is built on the pivots around which the body parts must move.

Table 7.1: Classification of movements.

Class	Pivot	Body part(s) moved
1	Knuckle	Finger
2	Wrist	Hand and fingers
3	Elbow	Forearm, hand and fingers
4	Shoulder	Upper arm, forearm, hand and fingers
5	Trunk	Torso, upper arm, forearm, hand and fingers

7.4 WORKPLACE LAYOUT AND SIMPLIFICATION OF MOVEMENTS

Some of the rules on laying out workplace are as follows:

- There should be supply of separate material for each hand, if similar work is being done by each hand.
- The material should be kept in area where eyes can easily locate the material without turning the head.
- Circular arrangements should be avoided as far as possible. Further, use of semi-circular should be preferred over the circular ones (Fig. 7.2).
- The workplace should be designed on the basis of ergonomic principles (Fig. 7.3).
- The nature and shape of the material influence its position in the layout. Use various bins such as those shown in Fig. 7.4 to accommodate material.
- There should be least possible disturbance to the rhythm and symmetry of movements while picking up a hand tool. As far as possible the operator should be able to pick up or put down a tool as the hand moves from one part of the work to the next, without making a special journey. Natural movements are curved, not straight; tools should be placed on the arc of movements, but clear of the path of movement of any material which has to be slid along the surface of the bench.
- Tools should be easy to pick up and replace; as far as possible they should have an automatic return, or the location of the next piece of material to be moved should allow the tool to be returned as the hand travels to pick it up.
- Finished work should be:
    - o dropped down a hole or a chute;
    - o dropped through a chute when the hand is starting the first motion of the next cycle;
    - o put in a container placed so that hand movements are kept to a minimum;
    - o if the operation is an intermediate one, place in a container in such a way that the next operative can pick it up easily.

- Always look into the possibility of using pedals or knee-operated levers for locking or indexing devices on fixtures or devices for disposing of finished work.

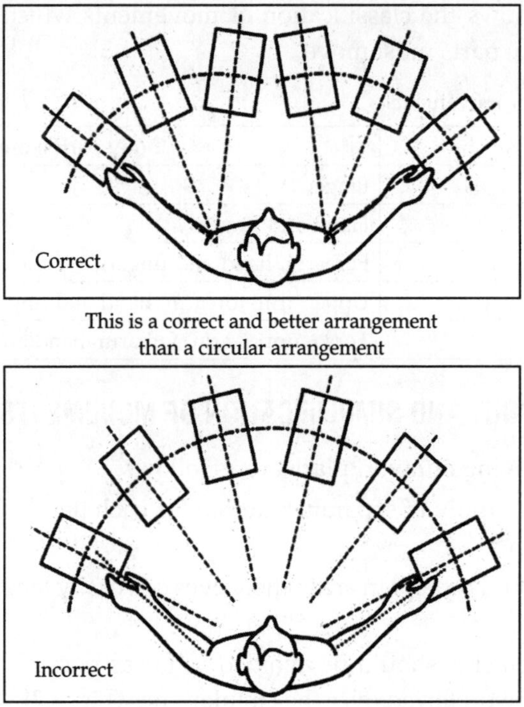

Fig. 7.2: Semicircular and circular working arrangement.

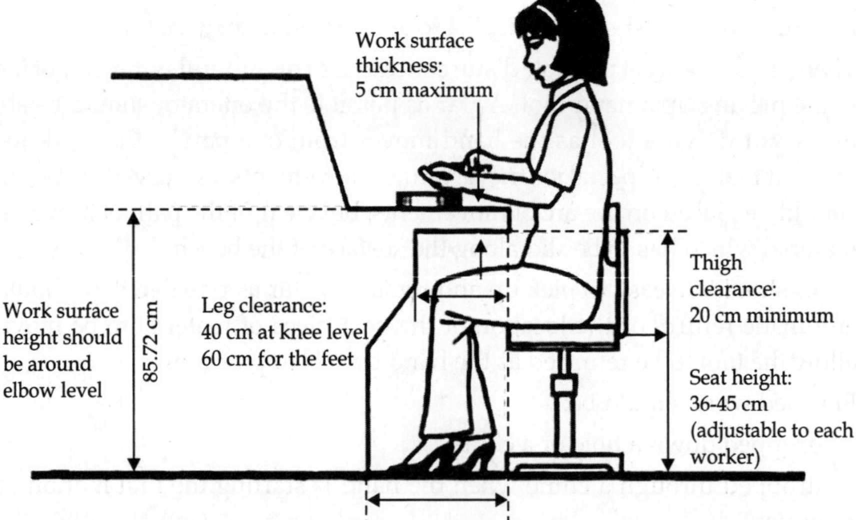

Source: Thuman et al., op. dt., figure 54.

Fig. 7.3: Recommended dimensions for seated tasks.

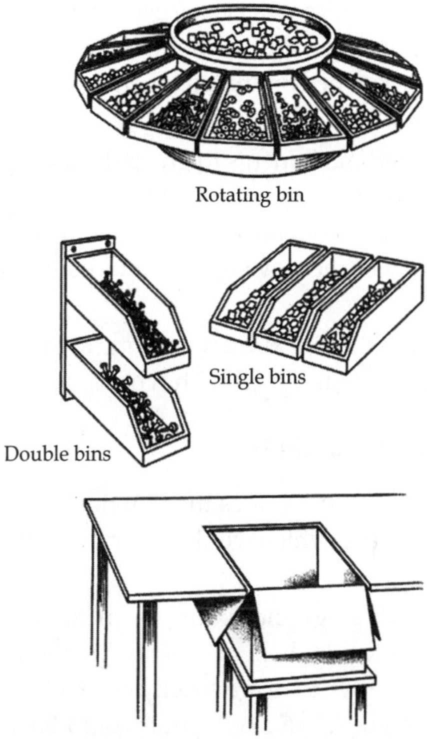

Depression in table to hold flaps of a carton for packaging operation

Fig. 7.4: Various bins and motion-economy devices.

An example of a workstation layout

A typical example of the workstation explaining the principles of motion economy is illustrated in Fig. 7.5. The workstation is for the assembly of electrical equipment. There are some points that can be noted:

Fig. 7.5: An example of workstation layout.

- Both the hands of the operative are free because a fixture has been provided to hold the workpiece. Engaging of one hand for holding the workpiece must always be avoided. Although fixtures can be eliminated when the operations are too short and the use of fixtures is not justified.
- The worker has to make short movements to grasp the tool. This is made possible by the hanging tools. However, there are certain tools such as the wire cutter and the hammer that are on the table but operative can search them without searching. Such tools are placed on one side of the tray so as to avoid any interference with the use of other tools.
- All the small parts are within the "maximum working area". For the easy withdrawal of the parts the trays have been designed with scoops.

7.5 DESIGN OF JIGS, TOOLS AND FIXTURES

A jig holds parts in an exact position and guides the tool that works on them. A fixture is a less accurate device for holding parts which would otherwise have to be held in one hand while the other worked on them.

The designer's object in providing jigs and fixtures is primarily accuracy in machining or assembly. Often, opening and closing them or positioning the workpiece calls for more movements on the part of the operative than are strictly necessary. For example, a spanner may have to be used to tighten a nut when a wing nut would be more suitable; or the top of the jig may have to be lifted off when the part might be slid in.

Cooperation between the work study person and the jig and tool designers, in industries where they are employed (principally the engineering industry), should start in the early stages of designing, and tool designers should be among the first people to take appreciation courses in method study. Some points worth noting are:

- Clamps should be as simple to operate as possible and should not have to be screwed unless this is essential for accuracy of positioning. If two clamps are required, they should be designed for use by the right and left hands at the same time.
- The jig should be designed so that both hands can load parts into it with a minimum of obstruction. There should be no obstruction between the point of entry and the point from which the material is obtained.
- The action of unclamping a jig should at the same time eject the part, so that additional movements are not required to take the part out of the jig.
- Where possible on small assembly work, fixtures for a part which does not require both hands to work on it at once should be made to take two parts, with sufficient space between them to allow both hands to work easily.
- In some cases jigs are made to take several small parts. It will save loading time if several parts can be clamped in position as quickly as one.
- The work study person should not ignore machine jigs and fixtures such as milling jigs. A great deal of time and power is often wasted on milling machines owing to

the fact that parts are milled one at a time, when it may be quite feasible to mill two or more at once.

- If spring-loaded disappearing pins are used to position components, attention should be paid to their strength of construction. Unless the design is robust, such devices tend to function well for a while but then have to be repaired or redesigned.
- In introducing a component into a jig it is important to ensure that the operative should be able to see what he or she is doing at all stages; this should be checked before any design is accepted.

7.6 MACHINE CONTROLS AND DISPLAYS OF DIALS

Machinery and plants of all kinds were designed without considering the convenience of the operative. The workers had to perform awkward movements while performing certain operations on machinery. Changing the speed on a capstan lathe is example of one such awkward movement. However, once the machinery is purchased by the user nothing can be done about these controls but certainly the users can draw attention of the manufacturer to the inconvenient controls that result in the awkward movements. This can help the manufacturer to come out with an improved model of the machinery in the later stage.

With the passage of time, the manufacturers have become conscious of this operative inconvenience. The work study department is now included in early stages of design of the machinery by the plants that manufacture their own machinery and related equipment. The work study department provides their advice and assistance to design machinery that causes less inconvenience to the operatives. Further, the manufacturing units also seek assistance from physiologists and psychologists in making proper arrangements of the dial on the machinery. This helps in minimizing the fatigue to the people who watch the dials. For the processes involving chemical reactions and other related processes, the arrangement of the dials are often made at the works installing them.

The growing consciousness amongst the manufacturers to minimize the inconvenience caused to the operatives has led to the development of entirely a new field of science known as **ergonomics**. Ergonomics can be defined as the study relating to the establishment of relationship between the operative and the environment in which he/she works. Experiments have been carried out by the ergonomists to decide on matters of best machine layout for best controls, the pedal pressure that is convenient to be applied, the dimensions of the seat and the worktops that are ergonomically friendly and so on. These are then incorporated in the design of the machinery and other equipment.

7.7 TWO-HANDED PROCESS CHART

The activities performed by worker's hands are recorded in relationship to one another in the two-handed process chart. The two-handed process chart is a specialized form of a process chart which shows the two hands and in some cases the feet of the operatives. The relationship is shown by using a common time scale. The inclusion of time scale on the chart has an advantage that the symbols that are used to represent the movements of two hands of the operative are brought in opposite to one another.

Repetitive operations of operatives are generally recorded by the two-handed process chart. The operations are recorded in more detail in comparison to the other process charts. The process can be broken down into a number of elemental activities in the case of two-handed process chart. However, the symbols used in the two-handed chart are similar to that of other process charts but the meaning that they carry is different.

○ OPERATION

The activities relating to the grasp, use, release of a tool, component or material are shown by the operation symbol.

⇨ TRANSPORT

The movements of the operative's hand to or from a tool, component or material are shown by the transport symbol.

D DELAY

The delay symbol represents the time during which the hand or limb remains idle.

▽ HOLD

The symbol is used to represent shortage in case of process flowchart, but in case of two-handed process chart the symbol designates the operation of holding a tool, material or a component.

Since the hand movements while inspecting any article may be classified as an operation for the two-handed process chart hence the symbol for **inspection** is not much used. However, to draw the attention towards the examination of a piece the inspection symbol can be used.

The work study specialist can gain an intimate knowledge of the operations and movements performed by the worker from the two-handed chart. Different elements of the job can be studied individually and also in relation to one another. After the careful study of the chart, the ideas for improvements are developed. The ideas arrived at after critical questioning should be recorded on the chart. The charting of information provides a way to compare all the activities and to simplify the work. The work that involves the least amount of movements is the best.

There are numerous areas such as assembly, machining, where the two-handed process chart can be used to optimize the movements of the operative. For example, in the case of assembly, there are certain problems related to the tight fits and award positioning. The positioning in case of close fits should be shown separately. One can use a two-handed process chart to take care of such awkward movements and also reduce the number of positioning. This can lead to major savings.

Notes on compiling two-handed process charts

- The chart should include some space at the top for providing some of the usual information.

- The chart should carry adequate space for sketching of the layout of the workspace. This should be comparable enough to that used for flow diagram in association with the flow process chart.
- The movements of the right and left hands of the worker should be depicted clearly by the chart.
- The chart should provide for summary of movements and the other related analysis.

Some points on compiling charts are worth mentioning:

- The operation should be studied for a few cycles before recording on the chart.
- To avoid any confusion, one hand should be charted at a time.
- Care must be taken to not use more than a few symbols at a time.
- The recording procedure on charting should start with the action of grasping or picking a tool. The hand that is to be first recorded should be decided either on the basis of the first use or on the basis of maximum movements that the hand performs. However, the starting point is not so essential since the complete cycle will eventually come round to it again. The movements performed by the other hand should be added in the next column.
- The actions that occur at the same moment should be only recorded at the same level.
- Different horizontal levels should be used for recording moments that occur in sequence.
- The chart should record each and every element of the activity performed by the worker. One should not combine different operations and transports or positioning.

Example of a two-handed process chart: Cutting glass tubes

The example illustrates the use of two-handed process chart for depicting the process of cutting of glass tubes with the aid of jig. The operations involved are represented on a form shown in Fig. 7.6.

- **Record:** The tube in the original method was pressed against the stop which is located at the end of the jig. The tube is marked with the file and then eased back for notching. The breaking operation was then performed on the tube after taking it out of the jig. The chart records each and every small movement of the hands. The small proportions of time needed for performing each element of the job when added together will represent the larger proportion of time needed to perform the entire job.
- **Examine critically:** The critical examination of the job performed will lead to questioning of the technique used to perform the job. Some of the questions that may arise are:
    - Why the tube needs to be held by the jig?

      The observation leads to the answer that the length that is supported by the jig is smaller in comparison to the total length of the tube.
    - Why notching cannot be performed while the tube is rotating in which case the right hand will not have to wait?

Two-handed process chart	
Chart No. 1 Sheet No. 1 of 1	Workplace layout
Drawing and part: Glass tube 3 mm dia., 1 metre original length	Original method
Operation: Cut to lengths of 1.5 cm	
Location: General shop	
Operative:	
Charted by Date:	

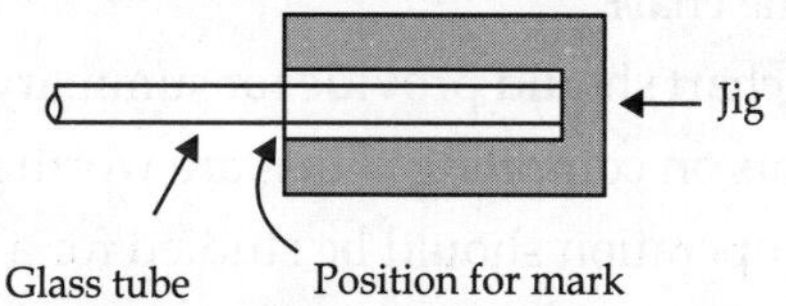

Left-hand description	○ ⇨ D ▽ ○ ⇨ D ▽	Right-hand description
Holds tube		Picks up file
To jig		Holds file
Inserts tube to jig		File to tube
Presses to end		Holds file
Holds tube		Notches tube with file
Withdraws tube slightly		Holds file
Rotates tube 120°/180°		Holds file
Pushes to end jig		Moves file to tube
Holds tube		Notches tube
Withdraws tube		Places file on table
Moves tube to R.H.		Moves to tube
Sends tube to break		Bends tube
Holds tube		Releases cut piece
Changes grasp on tube		To file

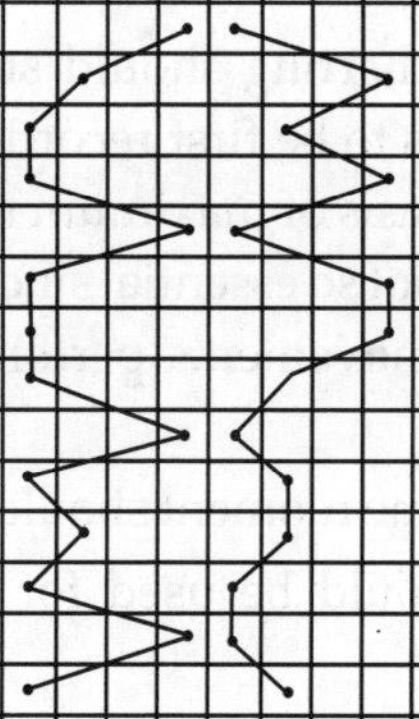

Summary

Method	Present		Proposed	
	L.H.	R.H.	L.H.	R.H.
Operations	8	5		
Transports	2	5		
Delays	–	–		
Holds	4	4		
Inspections	–	–		
Totals	14	14		

Fig. 7.6: Two-handed process chart: Cutting glass tubes (original method).

The examination leads to the answer that there is no reason as to why the notching cannot be performed while the tube is rotating.

- o Why for performing the breaking operation on the tube it needs to be taken out of the jig?

  The short end of the tube will stick to the stop and will have to be taken out. The movement for picking the reaming part will be awkward if only small proportion of the tube sticks to the stop. However, it wouldn't have been necessary to withdraw the tube from the jig if the jig was designed such that the remaining portion of the tube falls automatically out of the jig.
- o Why the file cannot be held instead of putting it down and then picking it up for each cycle of operation?

  Breaking requires the use of both hands.

- **Develop the new method:** The questioning technique makes it easier to find answers to the solution of the problem. One such possible solution is depicted in Fig. 7.7. The study manager has devised the jig in such a way that the short end of the tube will break when given a slight tap. This is made possible by arranging the notch on right hand side of the cutting pieces. The design eliminates the movement to withdraw the tube from the jig. The total number of movements was reduced down to six from the original twenty-eight. This led to the increase in the productivity of about 133 per cent. The new method leads to easier training of the workers. Further, the fatigue involved is also less.

7.8 MICROMOTION STUDY

In certain types of operations, and particularly those with very short cycles which are repeated many times over, it may be worth while going into much greater detail to determine where movements and efforts can be saved and to develop the best possible pattern of movement, thus enabling the operative to perform the operation repeatedly with a minimum of effort and fatigue. The techniques used for this purpose are known collectively as **micromotion study.**

In the earlier periods of work study special types of chart such as the SIMO chart, as well as special micromotion symbols known as therbligs, were used for micromotion study. These have now been replaced by the use of Predetermined Time Standards charts (PTS charts), which will be explained in Part Four of this book, as well as by the use of film and video.

Both film and video cameras can be used to record activities at the workplace. Although film provides greater flexibility in terms of filming and playback speeds, video is generally cheaper and easier to use. With a good quality video playback unit, it is possible to have high-quality slow motion and still-frame facilities.

Two-handed process chart	
Chart No. 2 Sheet No. 1 of 1	Workplace layout
Drawing and part: Glass tube 3 mm dia., 1 metre original length	Improved method
Operation: Cut to lengths of 1.5 cm	
Location: General shop	
Operative:	
Charted by Date:	

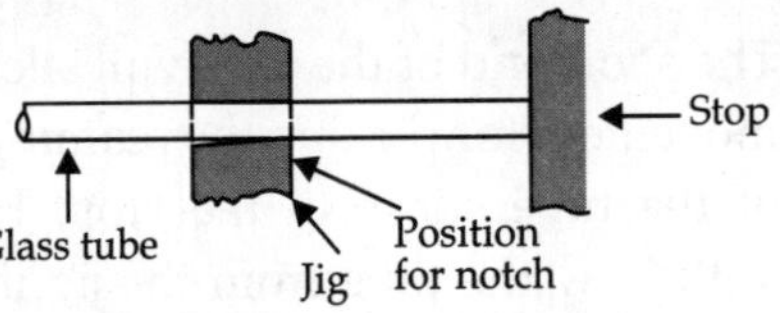

Left-hand description	○	⇨	D	▽	○	⇨	D	▽	Right-hand description
Pushes tube to stop	•							•	Holds file
Rotates tube	•				•				Notches with file
Holds tube				•	•				Taps with file; end drops to box

Summary

Method	Present		Proposed	
	L.H.	R.H.	L.H.	R.H.
Operations	8	5	2	2
Transports	2	5	–	–
Delays	–	–	–	–
Holds	4	4	1	1
Inspections	–	–	–	–
Totals	14	14	3	3

Fig. 7.7: Two-handed process chart: Cutting glass tubes (improved method).

The advantages of film and video over direct observation are that they:

- permit greater detailing than physical observation;
- provide greater accuracy than pencil, paper and watch techniques;
- are more convenient;
- provide a positive record; and
- help in the development of the work study persons themselves.

Use of Films

In micromotion study, films may be used for the following purposes:

- **Memomotion photography:** A cine camera is used to record the activity which is adapted to take pictures at longer intervals than normal. Memomotion photography is a time-lapse based photography. Generally the time interval lies between 0.5 sec and 4 secs.

  A camera is located at a place such that it can record the activities of the whole working area. Pictures are taken by the camera at the rate of two frames per second, whereas the normal camera takes around 24 frames per second. As a result, the activities which are of 10 to 20 minutes duration can be compressed into one minute. The work study manager can examine the general pattern of the movements involved in performing the activities in the working area. After the critical examination, the activities involving larger duration of movements leading to wasted efforts can be identified. Proper steps then can be taken to eliminate these longer duration movements. The method has been developed recently and is economical.
- **Retraining of operatives:** Both for this purpose and for analysis it may be necessary to have slow motion pictures of the process (produced by photographing at high speed); considerable use can be made of loops for this purpose.

Use of Videos

Video is used more and more as a vehicle for analysing motions, though it is difficult to obtain equipment with the capacity for time-lapse recording. Video is also used in a wider sense in method study to record the movements of people and materials in a given workplace, and the type of handling or storage facilities used. A multitude of useful data can then be viewed quickly by the work study specialist in order to assist him or her in drawing up charts, analysing the operation and developing a new method. In addition, video is becoming a very useful tool for training, for presenting to the management, supervisors and workers the existing and the proposed methods of work, and for actively involving those concerned in discussing the nature of the improvements proposed.

7.9 OTHER RECORDING TECHNIQUES

The other techniques of recording are the cyclegraph and the chronocyclegraph. A source of light on a photograph is used to trace the movements and is recorded in the form of **cyclegraph**. The source of light is stereoscopic. For example, the movements of the hand of a worker can be recorded on a photograph if the worker is made to wear a ring carrying a source of light. The path then can be traced on a photograph. In the similar manner if the movement of the worker is to be recorded as and when the task is performed, a source of light can be used on the helmet.

If the path of light is interrupted while tracing any movement then the path traced will appear as a series of pear-shaped dots. This technique of recording leads to another special form of cyclegraph known as the **chronocyclegraph.** The direction of movement is indicated by the pointed end of the dots and the spacing indicates the speed of the movement.

7.10 THE DEVELOPMENT OF IMPROVED METHODS

In the discussion so far, the three stages of **record, examine and develop** were discussed. The first two stages were given more emphasis in comparison to the last stage of development. The last stage of development was only discussed to the extent to draw the attention of the improvements made in the method after making critical examination of the original method. In this section, a discussion of the last stage is made more elaborately. The manner in which the improved methods can be developed is discussed in this section.

Method study often leads to large savings by making very small changes in the original method and making use of inexpensive devices.

A spring loaded table used for removing tiles from the automatic tile-making machine is an example of this. The table is made from plywood. The spring is calibrated such that it compresses to the extent where the tile drops to the level of machine platform. The automatic machine will then be ready to receive the next tile. The simple mechanism will enable the operator of the machine to focus on loading the tile on to a rack ready for firing. The new stock of tiles will be piled up on the table automatically. When a dozen of tiles were piled up, the operator could lift them off the table. This causes the spring to reach again to its normal position preparing the table to receive the next stack of tiles. The simple device will release the worker employed for pressing the tiles to be released to some other important section of the manufacturing unit.

The work study person may also have to go beyond recording the movements of the workers in order to increase the productivity of the manufacturing unit. A work study person should always be prepared for instance to discuss with the designer the availability of alternative materials that could ease the manufacturing of the product. The designers will also take into account the possibilities of the alterative material once they know about the interest of the work study department. Other possibilities on the part of designers which were overlooked previously will also be considered to improvise the original method as a whole.

The development of new improved methods demands for skill and creativity. The sole purpose to increase the productivity will also be successful if the work study person gets acquainted with the industry with which one is associated. Even if they know the technicalities of the method, they must always seek the opinion of the supervisors and the workers. This will lead to the acceptance of new method more readily which will ultimately assure it of the success. The more the ideas that come to the table, the more it becomes easier to develop a new improvised method. Further, a prior training to the operators and the supervisors involved at the floor shop is a must for the successful implementation of the new proposed method. Often organizations use the term quality circles or productivity circles for the departments and its people involved in developing a new method.

8

Evaluate, Define, Install, Maintain

8.1 EVALUATING ALTERNATIVE METHODS

The **Develop** stage of the method study procedure should result in proposed changes to the existing ways of carrying out the work under review. Sometimes the changes to be made are clear-cut and a revised method can be clearly defined. In many instances, however, the method study highlights a number of possible changes and therefore a number of potential new methods. Some of these may be capable of immediate introduction, while others – such as the introduction of new equipment, the building of new jigs or fixtures, operator training and so on – may require further actions to be carried out before they can be implemented. The sponsors of the investigation (normally the managers or supervisors in the area in which it is taking place) must make a decision as to the preferred solution. To make this decision, they need appropriate information on the alternative methods, the likely results of the proposed changes and the costs of implementation. Thus the method study person should prepare a cost-benefit analysis for each of the proposed methods. This is normally done in a number of stages.

A "first pass" is carried out in which very broad costs and benefits are associated with each potential change. This can often be done quickly and gives sufficient information to exclude a number of possible changes and methods from the more detailed evaluation process.

It is important when examining benefits to include not only those that can be easily quantified (such as direct financial savings) but also those that can be expressed only in qualitative terms. Such benefits (for example, improvements in job satisfaction, employee morale or industrial relations) can have significant long-term effects on financial performance and must be included in the evaluation process.

In order to allow the inclusion of qualitative factors alongside quantitative factors as part of the evaluation of alternative methods, use is often made of "pseudo-quantitative" techniques. These express the qualitative benefits in quantitative terms (by translating subjective judgements into numerical scores), allowing the quantitative and qualitative benefits to be combined in an overall evaluation.

A common approach is to use a combination of scoring and weighting. The various factors (normally benefits, but they can include negative benefits or disadvantages) that relate to the potential solutions are listed. This list may include such entries as direct cost savings, improved safety, greater labour flexibility and so on. A relative weighting is assigned to each factor to indicate its relative importance to the organization. This weighting must be achieved by discussion with the managers or supervisors involved in the work area. (One advantage of this method is that it requires those responsible for the decision making process to think carefully about their priorities.)

Each potential method is then "scored" against each factor (normally on a simple 1 to 5 or 1 to 10 scale). This scoring can be based on quantitative data, where this is available, or on subjective judgement.

Finally, the score of each factor is multiplied by the weighting for that factor and the resultant sum gives an overall score for that particular potential method, as shown in the example below.

	Weighting	Score	Factor
Cost reduction	4	1	4
Labour flexibility	2	4	8
Increased output	1	4	4
		Total	16

In the above example, a method that will increase output significantly (scoring 4 out of 5 points on that factor) obtains a low overall score because that particular factor carries a low weighting – since the enterprise is not able to sell any increased output.

The main advantage of such a method is not that it produces a numerical result but that it forces those involved in the evaluation process to consider all factors (even those which are not easily measurable) and makes them think carefully about the relative importance of each one. The final figures are guidelines only.

For some kinds of investigation, it is possible to make use of formal decision-support techniques such as decision matrices and decision trees. As with the simple weighting and scoring method above, such techniques do not make decisions – they provide a framework through which information can be presented and judgemental thinking can be carried out.

When measuring financial costs and benefits which accrue or are expended over time, it is necessary to use such techniques as discounted cash flow to allow the comparison of incomes and expenditure at present-day monetary values.

The nature of the evaluation outlined above depends on the nature of the situation under review and the scope and scale of the proposed changes. Where the change is minor both in terms of any disruption involved and in terms of the implementation costs, the evaluation can be carried out in a matter of minutes and a decision taken by the supervisor; in other cases it may require a significant investigation in its own right to determine and assess the likely costs and benefits.

The findings of this evaluation phase are included in the project report, perhaps with a recommended course of action, submitted to the management of the area under review. The format of this report may be determined by a "house style" within the organization. Where this is not the case, the practitioner should simply follow the simple "*A-B-C* " rule by ensuring that the report is

- ACCURATE
- BRIEF and
- CLEAR

Discussions that have taken place during the method study should ensure that the findings contained within this report are no surprise to the readers – the purpose of the report is to summarize the investigation, to present the findings, to produce evaluation data and to make recommendations supported by the material in the report.

Where the recommendation to proceed with a particular new method is very strong and the resulting decision to proceed is clearly anticipated, the report may include a detailed implementation plan for the changes to be adopted. Where this is not the case, the detailed plan may be left until after the decision has been taken – but an outline plan is constructed so that implementation costs could be included in the valuation of alternative methods.

If the investigation has been carried out in a structured and systematic manner, and the report has been soundly constructed, the manager is best able to make a rational decision, and the practitioner should ensure that his or her reputation is enhanced.

8.2 DEFINING THE IMPROVED METHOD

Once a decision has been taken on the changes in the method to be adopted, it is important that the new method should be strictly defined.

For all jobs other than those performed on standard machine tools or specialized machines where the process and methods are virtually controlled by the machine, it is desirable to prepare a written standard practice, also known as an "operative instruction sheet". This serves several purposes:

- It records the improved method for future reference, in as much detail as may be necessary.
- It can be used to explain the new method to management, supervisors and operatives. It also advises all concerned, including the work of engineers, of any new equipment required or of changes needed in the layout of machines or workplaces.
- It is an aid to training or retraining operatives and can be used by them for reference until they are fully conversant with the new method.
- It forms the basis on which time studies may be taken for setting standards, although the breakdown by element will not necessarily be the same as the breakdown by motion.

The written standard practice outlines in simple terms the methods to be used by the operative. Three sorts of information will normally be required:

- The tools and equipment to be used and the general operating conditions.
- A description of the method. The amount of detail required will depend on the nature of the job and the probable volume of production. For a job which will occupy several operatives for several months, the written standard practice may have to be very detailed, going into finger movements.
- A diagram of the workplace layout and, possibly, sketches of special tools, jigs or fixtures.

A very simple written standard practice for the operation is illustrated in Fig. 8.1. The same principle is followed in more complex cases. In some of these, the description may run into several pages. The workplace layout and other diagrams may have to be put on a separate sheet. With the more widespread use in recent years of standardized printed sheets for process charts, it is becoming common practice to attach a fair copy of the appropriate process chart to the written standard practice, whenever the simple description entered on it does not constitute a complete definition of the method.

8.3 INSTALLING THE IMPROVED METHOD

Perhaps the most difficult stages amongst all are the final stages in the basic procedure. Support from the management and the trade unions are required at this juncture. It is at this point the importance of the ability of a work study person to clearly explain about the things he or she is doing and winning the trust and confidence of others is realized. The installation stage can be divided into five stages as follows:

- Obtaining the acceptance from the management regarding the changes made.
- Obtaining the acceptance regarding the change by the departmental supervision.

Without getting the required acceptance from the respective departments it is not possible to proceed further.

- The acceptance of change sought from the workers and their representatives.
- Preparing to make the changes.
- Controlling the change-over.

The workers' representative should be consulted in situations where the change affects the number of workers employed. There may be existing agreements about the displacement of labour and these, naturally, must be adhered to. Plans must be constructed that minimize the hardship or inconvenience caused to workers. This applies not only to job losses but also to changes in work organization, location and so on. Individuals working within a particular section establish bonds and social relationships which are often very important in determining job satisfaction. Any changes to these established relationships will be resented.

Standard practice sheet

Product: 3 mm dia. glass tube, supplied in 1 metre lengths

Equipment: Jig No. 231, Half-round 15 cm

Operation: File and break to lengths of 1.5 cm

Working conditions: Light good

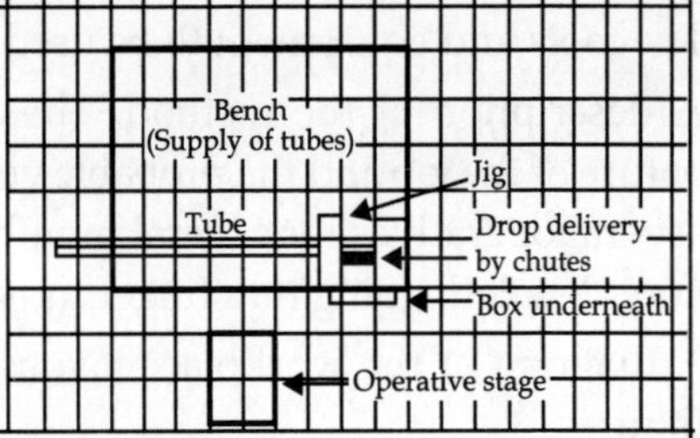

Location: Fitting shop | Ref. studies Nos. 12, 13

Operative: Clock No. 54 | Charted by: Date: | Approved by: Date:

EL	Left-hand	Right-hand	EL
1	Take tube between thumb and first two fingers; push forward to stop	Hold file; wait for L.H.	1
2	Rotate tube between thumb and fingers	Notch tube all round with edge of file hard up against face of jig	2
3	Hold tube	Tap notched end of tube sharply with file so that it falls into chute	3

Fig. 8.1: Standard practice sheet.

In the case of team or group working, the bonds are far stronger; and breaking up such a team may have serious, adverse effects on productivity, in spite of improved methods. Allegiance of group members to their working group is often stronger than their allegiance to the organization. Failure to take this into account may lead the workers to resist changes which they would otherwise accept.

It is in carrying out the first three steps of installation that the importance of preliminary education and training in work study for all those likely to be concerned with it – management, supervisors and workers' representatives – becomes evident. People are much more likely to be receptive to the idea of change if they know and understand what is happening than if they are merely presented with the results of a sort of conjuring trick. Where work groups are involved in the work under review, it is often advantageous to hold discussions with the group, rather than separately with individual members. This allows group views and fears to be expressed and dealt with.

8.4 PREPARING TO MAKE THE CHANGES

The new methods are more likely to be accepted by the workers in the development phase and particularly in the situations where involvement of redundancy or a transfer is least. It is the responsibility of the work study person to tell the workers from the start about what is being done and why is it being done. Further, the means by which it would be done should also be explained to the workers. One of the instruments that portray the activities of the worker is the string diagram. Ideas and suggestions about the improvement in the method should be sought from the workers and wherever possible should be implemented. For eliciting ideas, credit in the form of monetary reward can be given to a worker. The workers should feel as though the new method has been developed by them.

The active cooperation from the unskilled personnel can reduce the wasted time and effort as the ideas from such personnel can be a useful lead to a work study person in improvising the established method and developing the new method. Entrusting confidence and trust will make it possible to seek wholehearted cooperation at any level.

The management should also be convinced of the method and the means adopted by the work study person to improvise the current method. The technicians and supervisors should feel that the work study person is not developing a new developed method to show them up or to displace them, but is at their disposal to help them.

Analysis with regard to savings that would be made by adopting new method should be made where there is more resistance to change. The cost should be justified with regard to the time and trouble that would be involved in implementing the method and retraining of the operatives. It would be more economical to let the older workers continue with the work while training the new workers for the improved method.

Situations may often arise where the workers may straightaway turn to the work study person for gaining an advice or giving the advice with regard to the new method. This is seen when the work study person is trying to entrust confidence in the workers. In such cases the supervisor's role is overlooked. Such situations should not be allowed to stem out. The work study person should clearly explain to the workers that any instructions or advice cannot be given directly to a top executive and that it should come through a proper channel. Hence, all the advice from the workers should come through the supervisor.

Proper planning of the change-over from the existing to the new method must be done. With this comes the identification of different activities that must be undertaken before implementing the new method. Some of these activities include purchasing of new equipment, tools, etc., alteration of layout, training of operators and so on. Different "lead time" can be associated to the different activities and therefore a properly planned out schedule for implementation of each should be constructed.

Training and retraining operatives

The nature of the job will decide the extent to which the workers will require retraining. The jobs that are associated with a higher degree of manual dexterity require more effort into retraining of workers. Films must be used to demonstrate the changes in movements in the old and new methods. Each job will have to be treated on its merits.

Developing habit in workers to do the job in correct ways is an important thing that must be kept in mind while training and retraining the operatives. The need of conscious thought is reduced and thereby aids to increase productivity. Thus habit is a valuable trait to have.

Beginners must be made to understand the reason for every movement. This can be done by either teaching the workers to follow the numbered sequence on a chart or by directly teaching on the machine. Films are usually preferred while retraining. Still pictures with the instruction sheets, slides are also useful. Through the films, the workers will be able to know about their exact movements and once the movements are understood properly, there would be no difficulty to perform the job according to the new method. In order to ensure that the workers do not slip back to the older method, the new method should be completely different from the old method.

Initially, while learning the new movements, the operatives perform the movements with speed and hence the time required to perform the series of movements. However, the consistency reduces with the passage of time. It becomes difficult to perform the activities with consistent fast speed without long practice sessions. Figure 8.2 shows a typical learning curve. The rests between periods of practice must be longer than the periods of practice themselves in order to obtain the best results. The rest periods can be much shorter, when the operator has begun to grasp the new method. A close touch to the job being performed by the operative is essential to ensure that the required speed and skill is being developed by the operative and that there is no unforeseen snag. The process is known as "nursing". Once the work study person is satisfied with the results, the operative can be left independently for a time period.

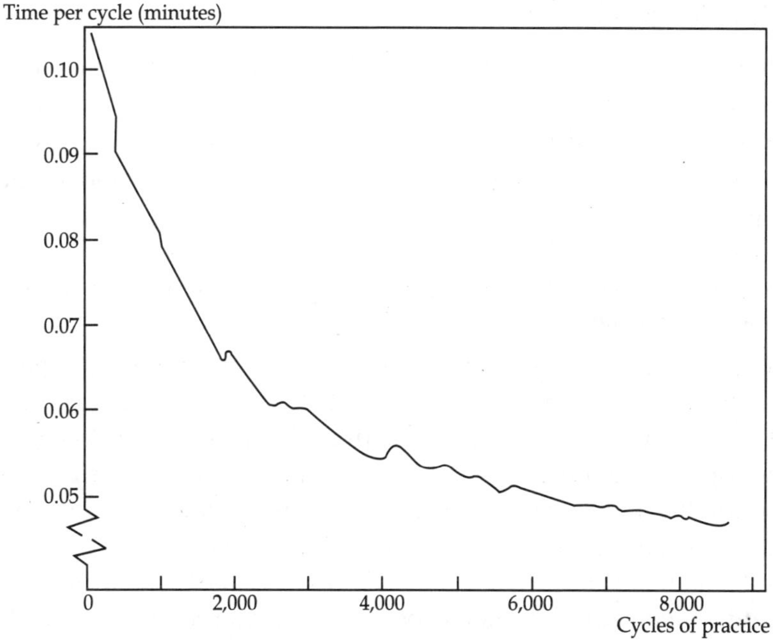

Fig. 8.2: A typical learning curve.

8.5 CONTROLLING THE CHANGEOVER

Changing from one method to another must be planned and controlled. Section 8.4 above has ensured that the work study person has identified, planned and scheduled all the tasks that are prerequisites of the new method. It is now necessary to ensure that these are completed according to schedule and that everyone is ready for the actual changeover.

The first consideration is to decide when the changeover should take place. Even though a new method is more efficient and will ultimately result in greater output, there is often an interim period when output falls, while the workers get up to speed on the new method. Naturally, this should not coincide with a crisis such as the completion of an urgent order, unless additional staff can be used on a temporary basis to keep output levels up. The changeover date should thus be chosen to be as convenient as possible – this is particularly important where radical changes must be made to layout, involving the re-siting of machines and equipment. Management will have to plan for the labour to make such moves, and may want to make such changes over a weekend or other non-working time to cause minimum disruption to normal production.

Having established the date of the changeover, the work study person can work back along the critical path of activities to put a date on each of the other activities. For a simple changeover, the control mechanism for this process may be a simple record of activities in a diary. For complex changes, a formal project planning and control technique, such as network analysis, may be used.

8.6 MAINTAINING THE NEW METHOD

It is important that, when a method is installed, it should be maintained in its specified form, and that workers should not be permitted to slip back into old methods, or introduce elements not allowed for, unless there are good reasons for doing so.

To be maintained, a method must first be very clearly defined and specified. This is especially important where it is to be used for setting time standards for incentive or other purposes. Tools, layout and elements of movement must be specified beyond any risk of misinterpretation. The extent to which it is necessary to go into minute details will be determined by the job itself.

Action by the work study department is necessary to maintain the application of the new method because, human nature being what it is, workers and supervisors or chargehands will tend to allow a drift away from the method laid down, if there is no check. Many disputes over time standards arise because the method being followed is not the one for which the time was specified; foreign elements have crept in. If the method is properly maintained, this cannot happen. If it is found that an improvement can be made in the method (and there are very few methods which cannot be improved in time, often by the operative involved), this should be officially incorporated, a new specification drawn up and new time standards set.

The procedure for maintaining a new method may depend on the nature of the relationship between the work study person and the part of the organization in which the method has been implemented. Some work study specialists are permanently assigned to work in a particular part of the organization and will be able to keep methods constantly under review. Where this is not the case and the work study person moves from location to location, it may be necessary to establish a formal method review or method auditing procedure when all methods introduced within a given time span are subjected to a review examination after the lapse of a specified period. The advantage of this formal review process is that it signals to the workers and their supervisors that the review will be carried out according to the predetermined schedule. They are therefore more likely to be motivated to adhere to the specified method.

9
Method Study in the Office

9.1 THE IMPORTANCE OF METHOD STUDY IN THE OFFICE

Work study in general is traditionally associated with a manufacturing environment. The purpose of work study is to improve the efficiency of the conversion of resources or inputs into outputs, thereby raising the productivity of the organization – this must be applied to every part of the enterprise, and not just to the manufacturing side. Offices use resources, and these resources must be used efficiently. Indeed, the importance of resource utilization within the office becomes even more important as the percentage of workers in offices continues to increase. Administrative and clerical costs are a significant and growing cost for most organizations and must be controlled. The costs associated with office work are often referred to as "overheads"; in that they do not contribute directly to the final product of the organization. At the same time the introduction of advanced technology and the application of production management techniques, as well as work study on the shop-floor, have raised efficiency to a level where many gains are incremental rather than revolutionary. Office workers, on the other hand, have been subjected to very little systematic study and the potential for improvement is greater. There is thus a need for the application of work study in the office.

One common objection raised against the use of work study in an office is the fact that office work is concerned with mental activity or "brain work" and cannot be easily identified, observed, measured or analyzed. However, in most offices, most of the work is routine and any mental activity is at a fairly low level, with decisions being based on firm's precedents. Increasingly, also, the office is furnished with technological aids. Such equipment bear a close parallel with shop-floor machinery. Operating a photocopying machine is like operating any other machine. The argument that office work is in some ways fundamentally different from factory work is fallacious.

Another reason that work study is often not practised within offices is the different statuses of manual and clerical workers. What is perceived as a factory technique is not acceptable to those who think of themselves as having higher status.

This is one of the reasons for the growth of organization and methods (O & M). Properly, O&M is something more than work study in the office, being also concerned with the organizational structures in use; but in practice most O & M is concerned with the "methods" part of the technique and is indistinguishable from work study – if perhaps, because of its different name, more acceptable. The purposes and principles remain the same, wherever work study is applied. Work study in the office still consists of the basic areas of method study and work measurement, and both of these follow the same pattern as we have seen elsewhere throughout this book. What we shall do in this chapter is to highlight minor changes or additions to techniques that have proved particularly effective within an office environment. The point about the perception of difference by office workers has also to be applied to managers of administrative and clerical units. They too are probably not used to "experts" coming in and advising them on how to run their departments and sections. They may be suspicious and wary. The practitioner should expect some resistance and be prepared to deal with it. It is important to gain the confidence of those involved and ensure that by the time any investigation is complete, they are committed to the changes that are necessary.

9.2 THE PROCEDURE FOR IMPROVING METHODS OF WORK IN THE OFFICE

The basic procedure of method study

- *SELECT*
- *RECORD*
- *EXAMINE*
- *DEVELOP*
- *EVALUATE*
- *DEFINE*
- *INSTALL*
- *MAINTAIN*

remains valid for studies carried out in an office environment. We still have to move systematically from selection of the problem or opportunity to be studied for implementation and maintenance of an improved situation.

Office automation and computerization are often seen as the prime means of improving office efficiency. Yet there is now a growing sense of potential unfulfilment among many computer systems. This is because the computerization or automation often simply speeds up existing inefficiencies. Computers and other information handling aids are useful devices but their use should be determined as part of a systematic analysis of the work involved and not instead of it. Method study provides the means by which that systematic analysis can be undertaken.

Select: Selection of the area or activity to be studied follows the same basic principles as for shop-floor work study. Selection consists of two components: finding those areas which represent significant problems or opportunities, and then giving priority to them. In the office we shall be looking for areas or activities that:

- account for a significant proportion of office labour costs (Pareto analysis can be used to good effect here);
- are producing large number of errors or serious errors;
- are creating high levels of dissatisfaction; and
- need to change in response to some external change (e.g., the introduction of new technology such as computerization).

In addition, it may be felt necessary to have some form of regular review of operations. Situations change over time. People also change. Shortcuts will be found in working methods, new techniques will be found, new equipment installed. At the same time, less efficient ways of working may be introduced. Even if no alterations take place, there may be changes in levels of dissatisfaction on the part of either the management or workers as their expectations change. Changes in procedures may take place for the best of reasons and may in fact increase productivity at a local level. However, it is possible that such unplanned or uncoordinated changes may have repercussions elsewhere in a wider system that are unforeseen by those making the change. Increasing throughput of one section, for example, may create a bottleneck in a procedure at a subsequent stage in the overall system. For all these reasons, some form of structured programme of review is advisable. This may take the form of a procedural audit, a departmental review or a system study, as long as it is a regular review of clerical activity to maintain and improve office efficiency.

Another source of projects to be studied is the employees themselves. Projects could arise out of an employee suggestion scheme or out of such structures as quality circles, implemented as part of an organization-wide attempt to improve the way activities are carried out. Often issues raised by such circles require additional work or study before changes can be suggested and/or evaluated; these investigations may be suitable work study projects where the work study practitioner works on behalf of the quality circle.

Record: It is the stage that the most obvious changes are seen when comparing shop-floor with office work study. This is because we are usually recording something that is fundamentally different. On the shop-floor, we record the progress or activity of one of three things — workers, materials or equipment. Materials are normally those that make up the final end product of the activity.

In the office, there is no end product. The important material objects in use are normally forms or documents, and thus there are a number of techniques aimed at recording the content of and progress of documents as they move through clerical systems and procedures.

Most office work can be placed on a hierarchy which includes systems, procedures, activities and methods (Fig. 9.2). The system is the overall scheme that links different departments and sections together in pursuit of a final aim or objective. Procedures are subunits of the system, often relating to one particular document, workstation or individual. Each procedure is made up of a number of activities (some of which may be common to a number of procedures), while the methods are the means of carrying out such activities to fulfil the needs of a particular procedure.

Recording often follows this hierarchy, so that first the observer will record information pertaining to the entire system, before moving on to record specific procedures and then particular activities and working methods. This should be the case even where the particular study is concerned only with one procedure or method – knowledge of the fuller system is important in that it provides a context for the investigation. Where an investigation is carried out by an in-house work study person, the knowledge of the overall system within which a procedure takes place may already exist and recording can start at the procedural level.

Recording follows the same pattern as with shop-floor work study. Normally, a system or procedure is recorded in outline form to allow consideration of larger issues, and gradually the investigation moves down to a more detailed level, using techniques that allow more detail to be recorded.

One useful recording technique is that of the procedural narrative, which is a "shorthand" means of recording basic textual information about who does what within a procedure. It is a very simple record but serves to identify the main steps in a procedure.

- **Accounts clerk** Opens and sorts incoming mail
  Passes invoices to invoice clerk
- **Invoice clerk** Date-stamps incoming invoices
  Matches invoices with filed orders
  Checks order for completeness
  Updates order record
  Enters invoice details to computer invoicing system

Similarly, at this outline recording stage, it is useful to collect together a copy of each form and document used in a particular procedure. These can be mounted on to a backing sheet which, together with possible annotation, is sometimes referred to as a **specimen chart** (Fig. 9.1).

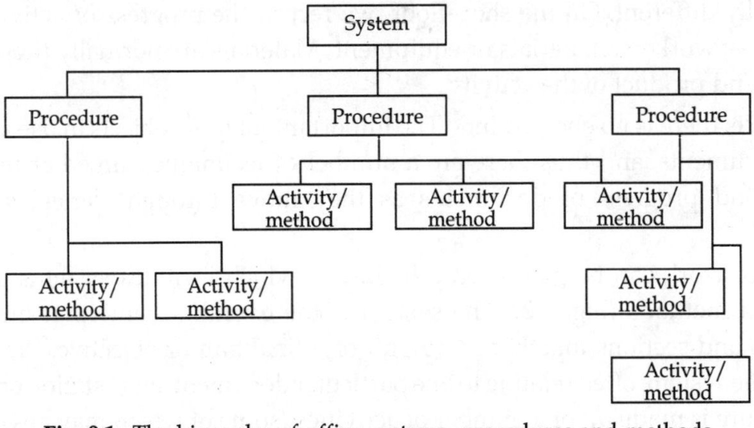

Fig. 9.1: The hierarchy of office systems, procedures and methods.

Such recording devices serve the same purpose as an outline process chart: they record the major details and provide the basis for a first-level examination of the procedure. This first-level examination is aimed at eliminating whole areas of activity before the most crucial areas are recorded and examined more closely. At this level, a more detailed recording method must be employed.

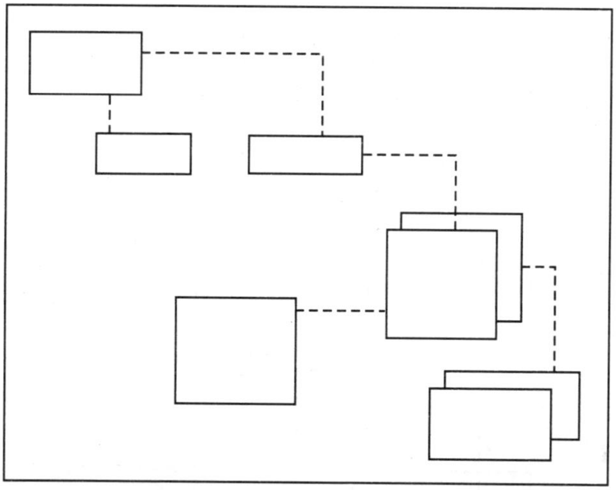

Fig. 9.2: An example of a specimen chart.

Process charts can be used in the office but it is more useful to use a variation of the process chart known as a **procedure flowchart** – this is in effect a document-type flow process chart, since it charts the progress of a document or series of documents through a procedure. Since procedures often involve a number of departments, it is common to use the chart in a columnar form in which each column represents one department or section of the organization (Fig. 9.3). This allows each department to concentrate on its own part of the procedure and for transfers between departments to be easily recognized.

As with all recording techniques, the important point is to concentrate on recording information to a level of detail and in a form that makes it suitable for subsequent examination.

When recording office work, there is often little that can be directly observed. Much of the information comes from interviews or by asking questions to elicit the detail of what is observed. The practitioner thus needs well-developed interpersonal and communication skills.

Examine, develop, evaluate and define: The examination of the recorded data must be systematic and complete; the critical examination process is useful here in providing the structure. All the points made when discussing critical examination are valid here, the purpose of the examination being to eliminate, then simplify or combine activities. As before, one of the difficulties with the *EXAMINE* stage is to stress its importance in spite of the fact that, unlike the *RECORD* stage, there is a limited range of available techniques to support it.

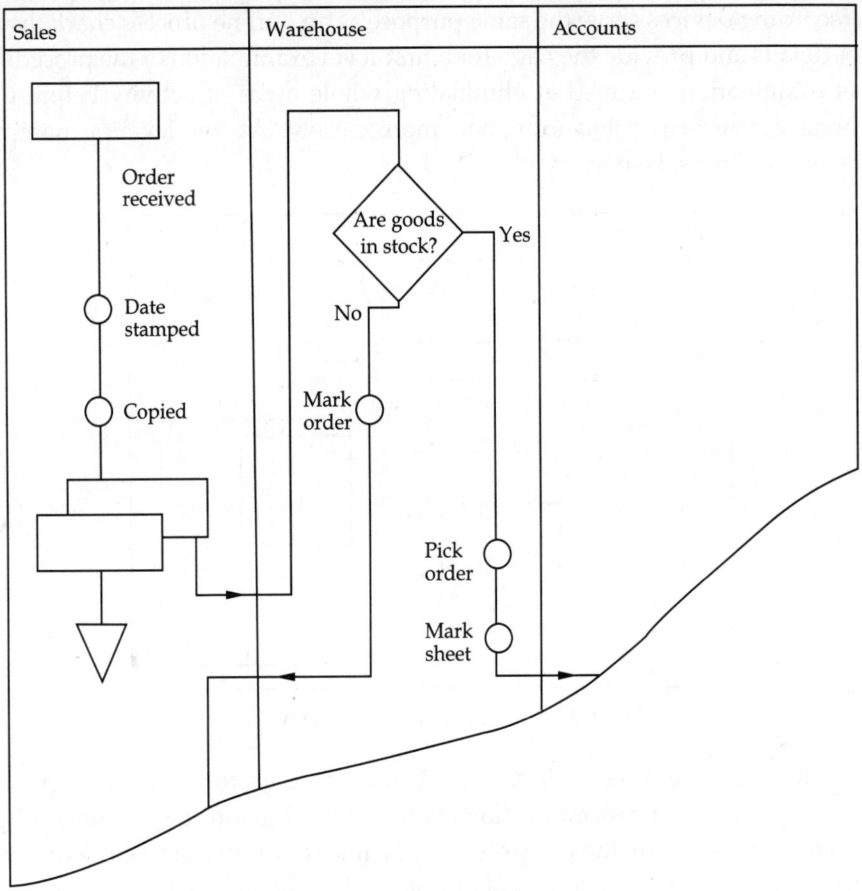

Fig. 9.3: A procedure flowchart

Increasingly, technology is being used in support of office work. Thus, when it comes to developing new and improved methods of working, the work study practitioner needs an up-to-date knowledge of information systems and computerization. There is often a conflict here between the work study practitioner and the computer specialist. One common distinction is that "computer systems" which are part of the mainstream of business activity (such as payroll, stock control, invoicing, etc.) remain the province of the computer professional, while "computer support" (which tends to be based on a micro or personal computer) is part of office work and workstation design, and is hence the province of the work study practitioner. In reality, if all is working well, the two types of staff should work in tandem and cooperatively.

Similarly, in many organizations, the computer department will lay down the overall computerization strategy and will define the types of equipment to be used with due regard to their compatibility, while others (including work study personnel) will be able to design and provide systems to meet local needs as long as they adhere to these overall standards. The use of personal computers is only an extension of the use of such devices as typewriters and calculators; in fact, the two most common applications are word processing (involving the manipulation of text) and spreadsheets (involving the manipulation of numbers) – both essential parts of office work. Since the personal computer is now in the same category, and is available at a price that brings it within most office budgets, it should be treated in the same way – as an office tool, rather than as part of the computer infrastructure. Where offices make use of centralized databases and local area networks, the setting of hardware and software standards is especially important, but there should still be scope for individual offices to solve for themselves specific office problems within the framework of the overall organizational strategy and policy regarding information technology.

Another factor to be considered in evaluating technology is the conflict between cost and ease or convenience of use. For example, although it may be much more "friendly" to place individual photocopying machines in each department of the organization, this may result in much higher reprographic charges than having a centralized copying department which can use high powered, more efficient machinery to produce bulk copies. The same is true of other facilities such as a centralized facsimile (fax) service compared with fax machines around the organization. It may be necessary to establish a company policy with regard to some of these services so that individual departments know the "ground rules".

An important aspect of the development of new methods is to evaluate one potential method and compare it with the existing method or a different potential change. It is important to ensure that any new method meets the aims of the investigation, but it is also important to identify the secondary benefits of any change. Word processing may be introduced, for example, to increase efficiency but it often has secondary benefits such as improved presentation. Such secondary benefits should be included in any cost-benefit analysis.

Install, maintain: Installation of a revised method is always important. If the installation is handled badly, the new method stands little chance of being a success. However, the principles involved in installing and then maintaining a new method within an office environment are exactly the same as for installing changed methods on the shop-floor.

Training and support of those involved in the change are very important. The first task is to ensure that they know exactly what is expected of them. Some organizations have manuals of formal procedures in which all clerical routines are recorded. When a new system or procedure is first implemented, it may be necessary to supplement the formal description with specific training or instruction sheets and/or with training courses. It is useful to construct some kind of changeover sheet so that workers can look up what they did under the old system or procedure and see immediately what their action should be under the new one.

Where procedures manuals exist, it is vital that they are kept up-to-date. There must be some way of ensuring that, whenever a change is made to a system or procedure, all copies of the manuals are updated and all those involved, however remotely or occasionally, are made aware of the change and its implications for them.

Whenever a system or procedure changes, there will be some teething troubles. These may be minor in themselves, but if there are a number of them they may accumulate to present a major problem or to lower confidence in the changes. It is therefore important that the implementation is carefully monitored and that minor modifications, if necessary, can be made before problems become severe.

9.3 DESIGN AND CONTROL OF FORMS

As we have stated above under *RECORD*, documents and forms are common features of all offices, often being the only physical evidence of a procedure. Documents are used as the carriers of information, and the effectiveness of this process is determined by the effectiveness of the document itself – the way in which it holds and transfers information, and the way in which it interrelates with other documents and with the people who use it.

Perhaps we might by now have expected to see the paperless office, but this appears to be a long way off. Information is harder to read from a screen than it is from paper and people therefore tend to take paper copies of information even though it may originate on screen. The electronic form makes transfer of information much faster and the rise of such technologies as electronic data interchange is having some impact on the volume of paper forms being transferred between organizations. The proper design of forms, however, remains an important part of office-based work study. In addition, there tends to be a proliferation of forms in many organizations – ad hoc forms are designed for a specific, perhaps temporary, function but then get absorbed into the mainstream of office life. Over a period of time, many new forms arrive on the scene but very few forms are ever deliberately discontinued. There is thus an equal need for the control of forms.

The objectives of form design are the same as that of method study itself – to eliminate activity, and where this is not possible to combine or simplify. In terms of forms, this can mean eliminating (and then combining or simplifying) whole forms, or eliminating (and then combining or simplifying) particular entries on forms. The design and control of forms is therefore a specialized form of method study rather than an alternative activity.

Design of Forms

Naturally, a document or form should be examined together with the procedure in which it is used. Changing a system or procedure may have automatic implications for forms used. Forms themselves should be examined when the procedure itself has been examined and improved or validated. Examination of a form follows the basic critical examination process, asking:

- **Why** is the form necessary?
- **What** information does it convey?
- **Who** uses it?

- **When** do they use it?
- **Where** is it used?
- **How** is it used? (Is the form produced by a computer; are entries typed on to the form; is it filled in manually, etc.?)

and then examining and evaluating alternatives.

In addition, we need to gather information about the frequency and volume of use, the methods of filing, the length of time that the form is to be kept, and the relation to other forms in this or other procedures.

Once we are clear that a particular form (which may be a combination of two or more existing forms) is necessary, we can start to (re-)design it. When designing forms we are trying to make the form:

- **Compatible with its intended use:** For example, a form that has a long expected length of use or that has to be used in an outdoor environment, and perhaps in adverse weather conditions, needs different quality paper from a form which is used internally or has a short lifespan.
- **Easy to complete:** This means that the form should be clear and unambiguous. Entries should be compatible with the source of the data – if data are copied from another form, they should be in the same sequence – or in some logical sequence. (Transcription errors are very common. They are minimized when the data have a structure and a context which enables errors to be easily identified.) There should be sufficient space for each entry, allowing for the method of entry (printing, typing, etc.). Multiple-choice and abbreviated-entry formats should be used where possible both to save time and to minimize the number of errors.
- **Easy to use:** This refers to the part the form plays in a procedure after it has been completed. Generally, the information it carries must be read and acted upon by another person, and the design must therefore depend on what this action is. It may be that the only action is for the form to be filed, and occasionally retrieved for the information to be accessed. In such a case, the prime requirement is that the reference identity (form number or identifying entry – employee number, department name, or whatever) is clear and positioned as appropriate to the filing method. If the form is to be posted, it should be designed to fit into a standard-sized envelope with the minimum of folding. Further considerations are discussed under "detail design", below.

These criteria may conflict with one another. For example, when considering ease of use, it may be necessary to place the information on a given form in a particular sequence since some of it will later be copied on to another form which already contains the data in a given sequence. This may, however, be different from the sequence of data on the source document. In such a case, it may be necessary to extend the scope of the exercise to take in all the forms that are affected, even if one or two stages are removed. If this is not possible, some form of compromise design must be reached.

If it is necessary to examine a number of forms involved in the same procedure, the X-chart provides a useful means of summarizing the entries on the different forms and highlights overlap between the forms. An X-chart is simply a matrix which shows all the forms against all the entries on each form. An X in a matrix cell indicates that a particular form has a given entry (Fig. 9.4). This chart is useful in helping to identify overlap and duplicate entries so that forms can be combined with one another.

Data item / Document	Customer name	Address	Contact name	Sales record	Sale terms
Order	X	X	X		
Delivery note	X	X			
Invoice	X	X			
Customer card	X	X	X	X	X

Fig. 9.4: An X-chart.

The design of the detail of the form should be based on practical rather than aesthetic considerations, although often the most practical forms are the most aesthetically pleasing. Consideration must be given to:

- Paper size
- Paper weight
- Shape
- Colour
- Maintaining any house style or corporate identity
- Balancing these with the cost involved.

Detail Design

We have also referred to the fact that detail design depends on the way in which the form will be used. Details that affect design are:

- the filing/retrieval process;
- the routing of the form throughout the organization (and the degree to which additional entries are made on the form at subsequent stages); and
- the nature of data entered on the form and the degree to which they can be grouped.

Grouping of data is one of the first considerations when designing a form. Often data can be split into two or more basic categories. A personnel record form, for example, may contain personal data about the member of staff, departmental data about the job to which the person is appointed and its place in the organization, and salary data about rates of pay and conditions of work.

A simple example of such a form is shown in Fig. 9.5. In this form, the name and address have been placed as they would be on an envelope (since they will almost certainly be copied from this form on to envelopes in the future). The employee number is placed at the top right-hand side to fit in with the filing method. The entries for employee number, department, section, salary scale and point on scale are pre-fixed since codes are used for department and section, and boxes have been provided to guide the user to fill in the correct number of characters.

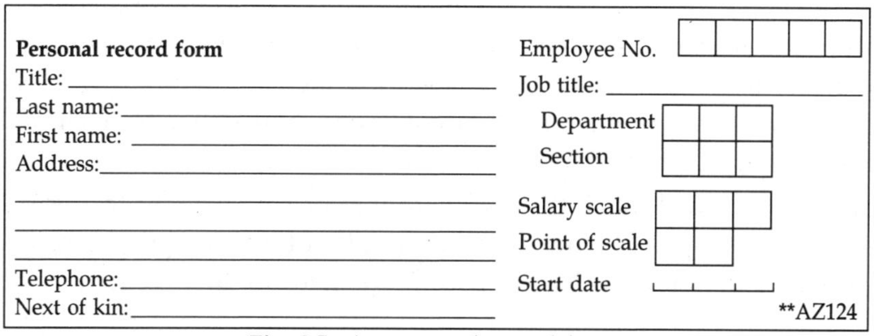

Personal record form
Title:
Last name:
First name:
Address:

Telephone:
Next of kin:
Employee No.
Job title:
Department
Section
Salary scale
Point of scale
Start date
**AZ124

Fig. 9.5: A personnel record form.

Similarly, the start-date box has been included to ensure that the date is entered in the correct format. The form reference number is included at the bottom so that the form can be easily reordered and the name of the form is included clearly at the top so that it can be easily verified that the right form is being used.

Multi-part form sets can be useful in certain circumstances, but this must be balanced by the additional costs of production. When such forms are not used but multiple copies are required, people often revert to photocopying forms. This is expensive, not so much in terms of photocopying costs but in the cost of the staff time involved.

It is always worth producing a "mock-up" of the form and talking through the design with those who are going to have to use it.

Many forms, these days, are produced in-house using special-purpose packages or desktop publishing software for the design of forms. There is a danger, with the proliferation of such software, that form design will be carried out by many people within the organization, many of whom will not have appropriate training, expertise or experience. The danger with desktop publishing is the range of facilities and design options it provides. There is a tendency among the untrained users to make use of too many in any one publication. This is one of the reasons why the control of forms is important.

Control of Forms

The most important part of controlling forms is to undertake regular audits to discover if each form is still necessary to serve a particular business function (in effect, the *MAINTAIN* stage of method study applied to the design and control of forms). This is best served by having a central register of all forms in use, together with a review schedule for each form in the register. Where the purpose of the form is still valid, questions must be asked about the environment in which the form operates and whether changes, for example, in technology or filing methods are required.

Other items to be considered are:

- **The production method:** How is the form produced and are there now better or cheaper ways?
- **Stocks:** How much stock of each form is held, and where is it held? Is this appropriate to the use of the form? (Is the minimum stock dictated by use or by the economics of production? If the latter, is there an alternative production method?) How are supplies to users reordered? How is stock issued to users? How is issued stock tracked? (For example, if a form is discontinued, how do we trace all copies of it so that they can be destroyed?)

The nature of disposal: What is the useful life of information on the form? Are there any legal constraints on disposal? How do we ensure that forms are disposed of, after their useful life is ended (to release valuable space)? Are there security restrictions on disposal.

9.4 OFFICE LAYOUT

Office layout is another specialized form of method study in the office – in effect, it is an extension of plant layout, the principles and the approach remaining the same. All types of layout except layout by fixed position, are valid in an office environment. In addition, there is often a debate about the relative merits of open-plan or cellular offices (see below). In reality, most offices combine the two, the choice often depending as much on such factors as the constraints of existing buildings and the organizational culture as on practical design considerations. Planning office layout should follow the hierarchy of the system. The overall system will dictate the broad layout; the procedural breakdown will determine the detailed layout and the nature of working methods will dictate the workstation design.

The differences then relate to the overall type of layout selected. A layout built around particular procedures will obviously be different from one built around specific office functions.

As with all method study investigations, we need information to base any decisions on the type of layout. The *RECORD* stage of the investigation must provide details of equipment in use, volumes and flows of documents, numbers of staff, communication flows and so on. Such devices as travel charts may be used to supplement the data from procedure flowcharts and provide information on communication and contact between workstations.

The increasing use of office technology means that office layout must pay attention to power and service requirements, to proper lighting and to the avoidance or reduction of noise. Additionally, there is a strong need for the appropriate arrangement of cables – a workstation may have a computer, a printer, an answering machine, a facsimile machine, a telephone and perhaps other devices, all with power and connecting cables. If not handled correctly, these are unsightly and constitute a safety hazard.

Open-Plan Office Layout

The main drive towards open-plan offices is the cost of space. Open-plan offices almost always result in space saving compared to a suite of small, cellular offices. However, in open-plan offices great care must be taken to ensure privacy for those activities which require it and to minimize the effects of noise. The advantages of open-plan working are: the saving of space devoted to walls and partitions; improved communication and contact between different workstations – this should lead to a reduction in the number of internal telephone calls and of internal memoranda; greater flexibility, if the layout needs to be changed in the future to cope with a change in working methods; easier supervision of staff; easier and cheaper cleaning of office space; easier power and service distribution. There is often a reluctance of staff to move from a traditional, cellular office layout to an open-plan one. However, this resistance is often minimized if the change is accompanied by a significant improvement in the quality of office furniture and decor, and if careful landscaping is used to split up a large, open-plan space into smaller, screened areas.

Office Layout Studies

Taking account of the above points, an office layout study should consist of the following steps. This assumes that, as a result of the *SELECT* and *DEFINE* stages of the project, the practitioner is aware of the constraints on the investigation – especially those dictated by existing buildings and by limitations of finance.

- Record details of the major systems in use within the office.
- Record details of the clerical procedures that support those systems.
- Examine the working methods of those procedures and carry out a basic method study of each one. (For most of them this may be a very simple exercise, but some may demand a fuller study before the method is confirmed as the most appropriate.) This stage is important as it is pointless to build a layout around working methods that may change in the near future. In particular, it is important to identify the range of equipment that is currently in use, or is proposed to be in use in the short term.
- Carry out a capacity assessment of each part of the procedure – possibly down to each workstation within the procedure. (This is a work measurement exercise; where there is no formal work measurement system, it may be necessary to obtain the information from estimating, with help from managers and supervisors.)
- Analyze volumes of output and question the senior managers to discover likely future trends.
- Identify communication and contact paths and frequencies.
- Design individual workstations. Make use of ergonomic principles. Some of the workstations may be simple desks, while others may be computer workstations or photocopiers. The workstation should be designed as a complete entity, including

working surfaces, seating and equipment. Where appropriate it should also include space for "personal" filing. At this stage, the design should remain conceptual, consisting only of the details of what is needed and not how they are going to be provided.

- From volume and capacity data, calculate total workstation requirements.
- Decide on basic type of layout.
- Identify any "external" constraints. For example, a department that has a high number of external visitors may need to be located close to the reception area. A department that makes use of heavy machinery may need to be on the ground floor of a multi-level building.
- Use communication and contact data to draw up a schematic layout showing the location of different work areas or work functions relative to one another.
- Investigate available hardware solutions (choice and arrangement of furniture, filing, screening, document transfer technologies, etc.). Consider packaged solutions in which different components are designed to fit with and match each other. Generally, modular solutions are to be preferred since these allow greater flexibility through the interchangeability of units.
- Design a provisional layout, fitting proposed solutions to a scale plan of the work area. This layout should take account of the existing doors, lifts, etc., and should include the provision of power and services.
- Discuss the provisional layout with both the users and the services or building department (where one exists) to discover operational and financial feasibility.
- Modify the layout in accordance with the results of discussions and prepare the proposed layout.

The layout should also include an analysis of lighting, heating and ventilation needs, and the provision of toilet facilities and rest rooms. It should be detailed enough to include such things as waste bins, coat stands or cupboards, filing cabinets, bookshelves and so on (since it is often the small items that have a major effect on overall efficiency). The layout may, in some circumstances, have to take account of additional factors such as security, for example by grouping together sections or departments which have to be within a particularly secure space envelope.

Items such as heating, lighting, ventilation and noise control require specialist knowledge, and advice may be required before such matters can be properly included in a layout. It is important to remember that modern office equipment generates considerable amounts of heat and that air conditioning may be required to maintain a suitable working temperature. Similarly, although noise control is a specialist area, much of it is common sense and many basic preventive measures (such as using sound-deadening material under typewriters and printers, acoustic hoods and screens, furnishings and fittings which are sound absorbent, etc.) can be specified at the office layout design stage.

Since documents are the main "product" of offices, careful thought should be given to filing and retrieval systems. It may be possible at the filing stage to replace the paper document by microfilm or magnetic media to reduce the space consumed by filing. The nature of the medium used for filing will depend on the nature and frequency of subsequent retrieval and on any legal requirements for documents to be maintained. Where large quantities of documents have to be stored (as for example in many financial services organizations), it may be necessary to investigate automated storage systems.

Document transport is another area in which technology is developing. There are now systems by which documents can be routed around buildings, including changes of floor level, on a pre-programmed basis using tubes and/or rails. The document transport system should be designed alongside the storage and retrieval system as part of the materials handling study. It is normally much easier to design and develop automated document handling systems when the office is located in a new building, but it is often possible to fit a system into an existing building with all the inherent constraints.

9.5 QUALITY CONTROL IN THE OFFICE

The biggest single "quality question" is always: Are we doing the right thing? Only if this is answered satisfactorily should any attention be given to the way in which something is being done.

Quality control is not generally applied to office work. There seems to be an implicit assumption that office workers do not make mistakes. This is simply not true – office workers are no different from any other category of workers, in that they too lose concentration and make errors and defective work. These errors can be costly: if they are spotted, they cost money to put right; if they are not spotted, they can be much more costly in supplying incorrect information to others in the organization or to customers or clients. However, errors introduced by the workers are often a small proportion of total errors. Most errors are system errors where the system fails to work adequately, with the result that delays, misunderstandings and misrouting occur.

It is therefore important to ensure that the systems, procedures and methods of working used in offices are designed to minimize errors and that some form of control of errors is instituted, especially where the results of any error may be significantly costly or damaging. Good systems and procedures prevent errors, leaving quality control techniques to pick up the small number that do occur. It is possible to implement specific quality control techniques such as spot checking and random sampling and, for some activities, this may be deemed necessary. However, it is just as important to pay attention to the "human factor" involved in determining quality. This factor also leads to system errors since the workers are an integral part of, and probably the most important part of, the system in operation.

One important source of error is a lack of – or inadequate – training of the personnel involved. People generally work without error, but only if they know exactly what is expected of them, they are given the appropriate tools, equipment and support, and they are properly trained in the techniques and skills required. If all of these are true, the "system" has done its job. The workers should also have confidence in their ability to deliver and will carry out their work with the minimum of error – confidence breeds competence.

Recent initiatives such as total quality management and customer service programmes have highlighted the importance of each stage of a procedure in the determination of overall quality of the end product or service. It is important that the culture of the organization makes people want to provide a high-quality service in their own sphere of activity and lets them feel that their own activity is important to the organization and its overall quality delivery.

SECTION IV
WORK MEASUREMENT

10
Time Study

10.1 WHAT IS TIME STUDY?

Time study is a work measurement technique for recording the times of performing a certain specific job or its elements carried out under specified conditions, and for analysing the data so as to obtain the time necessary for an operator to carry it out at a defined rate of performance.

10.2 TIME STUDY EQUIPMENT

If time studies are to be made, certain items of equipment are essential. Basic time study equipment consists of:

- A stopwatch
- A study board
- Time study forms

The study person will need to carry the timing and recording devices whenever a time study is made. In addition, in the study office, there must be facilities for assisting with the analysis of the time study. These may vary from a small calculator to a personal computer.

Other measuring instruments will be required from time to time to obtain data on the work being measured – most work study offices will have (access to) such devices as tape measures, steel rules, micrometers, spring balances, and so on.

In addition, the office should have a clear, reliable clock with a second hand for recording study start and finish times.

Stopwatch There are two main types of watch in general use for time study – the mechanical and the electronic. Mechanical watches can again be subdivided into the flyback and non-flyback types, with a third type – the split-hand stopwatch – in less common use. Electronic stopwatches may be part of a specially designed study board or data capture device.

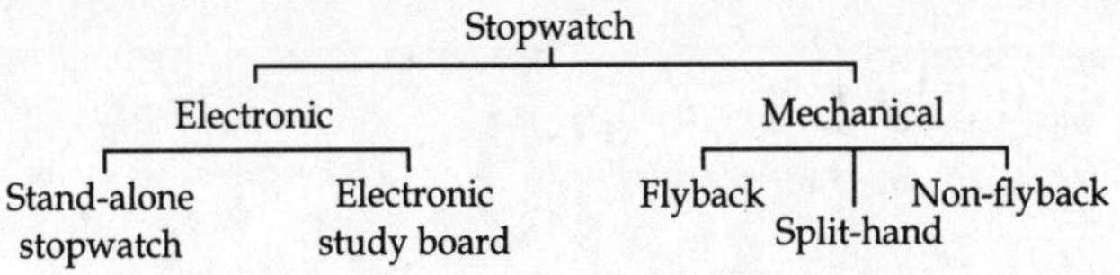

Fig. 10.1: Classification of stopwatch.

Following three types of graduated scales are available for mechanical-type watches:

- Per revolution records a minute with each interval indicating one-fifth of a second. The small hand records 30 minutes.
- Per revolution records a minute with each interval indicating 1/100th of a minute. The small hand in this case also records 30 minutes.
- Per revolution records 1/100th of an hour and each interval indicating 1/10,000th of an hour. The small hand records one hour in 100 divisions.

The watches with decimal minutes as their main scale and a scale graduated in seconds and fifth of second known as the auxiliary scale at the outside of the main scale, are other variants of the mechanical watches.

Figure 10.2 shows a flyback decimal-minute stopwatch. This is probably the type in most general use at the present. For each revolution of the main hand, the small dial makes $1/30^{th}$ of a revolution. Therefore, the complete turn by the small hand is made in 30 minutes. The watch has a slide (A) and a winding-knob (B). The movement is started and stopped by the slide. The function of the winding-knob is to make both the hands of the watch to flyback to zero. The hands don't stop at zero but continue to move again immediately. However, if the slide is used to stop the watch, then both hands stop immediately at their respective positions and start again from the same position once the slide is released. The flyback watch is preferred mainly for "cumulative" timing.

Fig. 10.2: A decimal-minute stopwatch.

Pressure on the winding-knob controls a non-flyback type watch. Application of pressure at first starts the watch; the application of the pressure for the second time stops it; the hands return to zero after the application of pressure for the third time. The watch is suitable only in case of cumulative timing.

In case of a split-hand type of watch, pressing a secondary knob causes one of the hands to stop at its position whereas the other continues to measure the time. The stopped hand returns to the moving hand when the knob is pressed for the second time. The two hands then move together. The accuracy of reading is increased using the split-hand type watch.

It is easier to read a split-hand type watch. However, it is more expensive, complex and troublesome to repair. Equally good results can be derived using inexpensive, light watches by giving proper training to the time study person. The flyback watch with the main dial graduated in 1/100th of minute and smaller dial recording 30 minutes is found to be most preferable for time study until unless instructions to use a specific watch to be used is made.

The watch is a delicate instrument and must be treated with care. Winding of watches before each study and running the watch overnight should be done. The watches should be sent to watchmaker for cleaning and routine overhaul at regular intervals.

The Study Board

A flat board that is used for keeping the time study forms is known as the study board. The board is made from suitable plywood or from a suitable plastic sheet. The size of the board should be larger than the largest time study form. Further the board should be rigid in construction. The board must be provided with a fitting to hold the watch to ensure a proper reading and to relax the hands of the work study person relatively free. The watch is normally placed on the top of the board at the right hand side for right handed people. This ensures that the board may be rested on the left forearm, the bottom edge of the board against the body. The forefinger or the middle finger of the left arm can be used to operate the watch. Figure 10.3 shows the arrangement for the same.

The board can be tiring to use in case the board is either too long or too short in respect to the length of the arm. Hence, most of the study persons customize the size of the board after a sufficient practice.

Electronic stopwatches and study boards

An electronic stopwatch (Fig. 10.4) performs exactly the same role as a mechanical one – the recording of element durations. One of the main advantages is that it allows flyback timing to be performed without any loss of accuracy. (With a mechanical watch, the time taken for the hand to return to zero is "lost". With an experienced practitioner, this time is minimal but with a trainee or inexperienced observer, it can be significant and can jeopardize the accuracy of a time study.) With an electronic watch the timing device is running continually and it is only the display that is updated as the "flyback" button is pressed to reset the display to zero. At the end of the time study with most watches, it is possible to read off the total elapsed time.

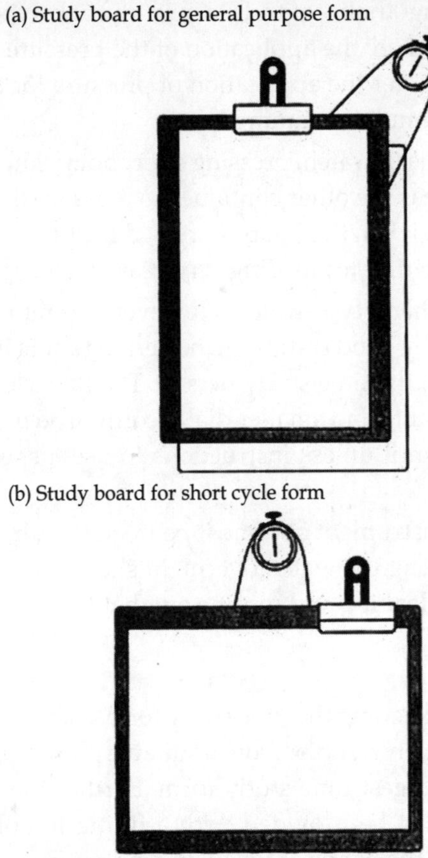

Fig. 10.3: Forms of time study boards.

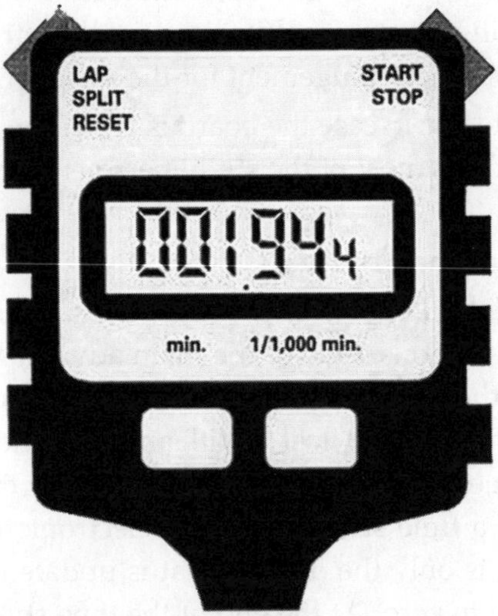

Fig. 10.4: An electronic stopwatch.

Electronic watches can often be used in a number of calibration modes – they can be set to record in fractions of seconds, minutes or hours.

Electronic data capture devices or study boards are units which are used to record activity during a time study and which include an electronic timing device which automatically assigns time to elements.

The most usual procedure is that as work proceeds, the observer keys into the device a code that identifies the element being carried out and then keys in the rating assigned to the element. At the moment of the breakpoint, the observer hits a key to terminate the element. This causes the time to be recorded (but not displayed) and the recording of the next element to begin. The board or data capture unit records all this data (element code, rating and element duration) in its internal memory for later analysis, often via transfer to a personal computer.

There are two types of unit in common use. The first are hand-held computers which have been modified for time study purposes (mainly through the addition of time study software, but the "customization" process may include such things as new legends on the keys) and the second are specially designed electronic time study boards. The first have the advantage that when not being used for time study they may, in addition to other software, be used for other applications.

Conversely, hand-held computers may require the use of a study board as well, to take notes, and combining the two may be difficult and cumbersome. The specially designed boards have the advantage that they are generally easier to use for time study recording. For example, they may have keys labelled "OC" for occasional element, "FE" for foreign element, and so on.

An example of an electronic study board is shown in Fig. 10.5. One of the advantages of electronic data capture is that, because the time is never visible to the observer, it becomes impossible to "clock rate", in other words to be tempted to adjust the rating. Another important advantage is that the observer is required to carry out less writing (if any at all) and can pay more attention to the work being measured. (Notes may have to be made about foreign elements, frequencies, abnormal occurrences, and so on, and thus the electronic study board normally has space for a writing pad.)

10.3 TIME STUDY FORMS

Taking a time study requires the recording of substantial amounts of data. These data are in a regular form consisting of element codes or descriptions, ratings and element durations (perhaps with additional explanatory notes). Although the data could be recorded on plain paper, it is more convenient to use pre-printed forms which ensure that each study is of the same consistent format, that all relevant data are recorded and that filing and retrieval of completed studies is more reliable.

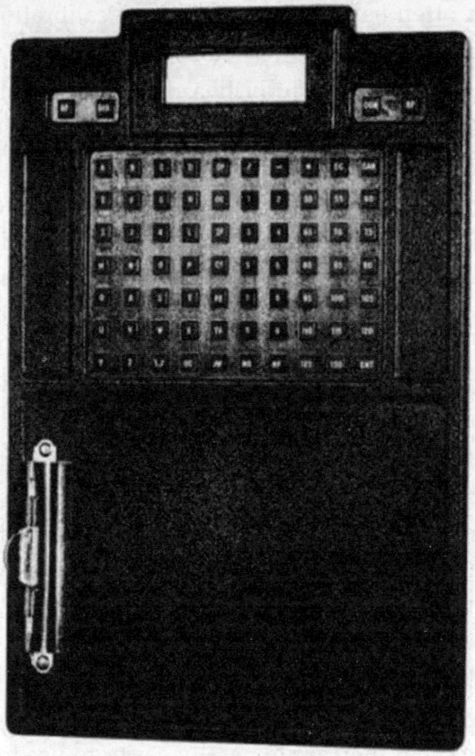

Fig. 10.5: An electronic study board.

Source: GP-1 Time Study Board supplied by Tectime Data Systems, Newcastle-under-Lyme, Staffordshine, United Kingdom.

There are numerous designs of forms; most work study practitioners have their own ideas on the ideal layout. The examples shown in this book represent designs which have been proved to be satisfactory for general work. The principal forms used in time study fall into two groups: those used at the point of observation while actually making the study, and which should therefore be designed or selected to fit the study board in use; and those which are used after the study, as part of the analysis process, in the study office.

Electronic study boards and data-capture devices eliminate most of the need for time study forms. However, it is still important to record notes which relate to the work being observed, especially where it is seen to deviate from normal practice or conditions, and a simple form which has as a minimum recording of the date, time, observer and operator will suffice. Similarly, when it comes to the analysis stage, many of the forms used in the analysis of studies taken with a conventional stopwatch will not be required since the analysis may be carried out by computer. The forms described here are therefore those which would be used by an observer taking conventional time studies with a mechanical or electronic stopwatch and recording the data by hand.

Forms used on the study board

- **Time study top sheet:** As the name indicates, this is the introductory sheet of a study and is on the top. The sheet records all the essential information about a study. The information about the elements into which the operation has been broken down and as well as the breakpoints used are also carried by the time study top sheet. The first few cycles of the study may also be recorded by the sheet. Figure 10.6 shows the example of a time study top sheet. The sheet has spaces in the heading. The work layout sheet should however be drawn on the reverse side of the sheet if the layout is simple, or it should be drawn on another sheet and attached with the time study sheet if the layout is complex.

Time study top sheet	
Department:	Study No.: Sheet No.: of
Operation: MS No. Plant/Machine: No.:	Time off: Time on: Elapsed time:
Tools and gauges:	Operative: Clock No.:
Product/part: No.: DWG No.: Material:	Studied by: Date:
Quality	Checked:
Note: Sketch the workplace layout/setup/part on the reverse, or on a separate sheet and attach.	

Element description	R	WR	ST	BT	Element description	R	WR	ST	BT

Note: R = Rating. WR = Watch reading, ST = Subtracted time BT = Basic time

Fig. 10.6: General-purpose time study top sheet.

- **Continuation sheet:** For further cycles of study, the continuation sheet is used. The sheet is shown in Fig. 10.7. It can be seen that the sheet consists of columns and spaces for study and the sheet number. The same layout should be adopted on the reverse side of the same sheet. The heading is not required on the reverse side of the sheet. The time study top sheet and the continuation sheet are sufficient enough to carry out the study. However, for repetitive operations involving short cycles a specially ruled sheet should be used instead.

Study No.:	Time study continuation sheet				Sheet No.		of		
Element description	R	WR	ST	BT	Element description	R	WR	ST	BT
Note: Reverse side similar, but without upper line of heading.									

Fig. 10.7: Continuation sheet for general-purpose time study (front).

- **Short cycle study form:** A simple type of the form is shown in Fig. 10.8. Such forms work very well for most common short cycle works. A more complicated version of the same is shown in Fig. 10.9 and Fig. 10.10. These forms can be used if the short cycle work is a rule and not an exception.

Short cycle study form		
Department:	Section:	Study No.: Sheet No.: of
Operation:	MS No.:	
Plant/Machine:	No.:	Time off: Time on: Elapsed time:
Tools and gauges:		Operative: Clock No.:
Product/Part:	No.:	
DWG No.:	Material:	Studied by: Date:
Quality:	Working conditions:	Checked:
Note: Sketch the workplace overleaf.		

EL No.	Element description	Observed time										Total OT	Average OT	R	BT
		1	2	3	4	5	6	7	8	9	10				
Note: R = Rating, OT = Observed time, BT = Basic time															

Fig. 10.8: Simple type of short cycle study form.

Short cycle study sheet

Date of study ______

Time finished ______
Time started ______
Elapsed time ______

Study No. ______
Sht. ____ of ____ Sheet

Department ______
Operation ______
Tools used ______

Part name ______
DWG No. ______ Part No. ______
Speed ______ r.p.m. ______
Feed ______ Mm/Min. ______

Basic cycle time ______ Min.
or
Total ave. element time ______ Min.
Rating factor ______
Basic cycle time ______ Min.

Machine and No. ______
Operated Auto ☐ Foot ☐ Hand ☐

Material

Standard
______
______
______

Reason for study
Original study ☐
Method study change ☐
To check estb. standard ☐

Allowances: Personal %, Delay %, Fatigue %, Other % — % — Min.

Standard time per piece ______ Min.

Workplace layout

Description of method

Remarks:

Fig. 10.9: Short cycle study form (Front).

Date of study ____________	Time finished ______ Time standard ______ Elapsed Time ______			**Short cycle study sheet**						Study No. Sht. ______ of ______ Shts.		
Element No.	1	2	3	4	5	6	7	8	9	10	Name of operative	
Standing ☐ Sitting ☐ Moving about ☐											Clock No. ______ Observed by ______ Approved by ______ Foreign elements	
Cycle No.											Symbol	Description
1											A	
2											B	
3											C	
4											D	
5											E	
6											F	
7											G	
8											H	
9											I	
10											J	
11											K	
12											L	
13											M	
14											N	
15											O	
16											P	
17											Q	
18											R	
19											S	
20											T	
Total												
No. of Obs.												
Average												
Rating %												
Basic time												

Fig. 10.10: Short cycle study form (Back).

Forms used in the study office

- **Working sheet:** This sheet is used to analyze the readings that have been obtained from the study. The representative times of each element of the operation is obtained using the working sheet. For performing analysis in various ways, sheets with different rulings may be required. Generally, the time study persons use simple lined sheets having the same size as that of the study sheets for making their analyses.

Short summary sheet			
Department:	Section:	Study No.: Sheet No.: of	
Operation:	MS No.	Date:	
Plant/Machine:	No.:	Time off: Time on:	
Tools and gauges:		Elapsed time: Check time:	
Product/Part:	No.:	Net time: Obs. time:	
DWG No.:	Material:	Unacc. time: UT as%	
Quality:	Working conditions:		
Operative M/F	Clock No.	Studied by: Checked:	
Sketch and note on back of Sheet 1.			

El. No.	Element description	BT	F	Obs.	
Note: BT = Basic time F = Frequency of occurrence per cycle, Obs = No. of observations					

Fig 10.11: Study summary sheet.

- **Study summary sheet:** This sheet summarizes all the information that has been obtained during the course of study. The sheet carries the selected or the derived times for all the elements. Frequency of occurrence of each element is also added to the information carried by the sheet. The detail about the operation that has been recorded is included in the heading at the top of the time study sheet. The summary sheet is clipped at the top of other sheets and is filed with them. Figure 10.11 shows an example of the study summary sheet. The size of the study summary sheet is same as that of the other sheets. The sheet has extra space for addition of extra columns if required to be added for making a summary of a particular study.
- **Analysis of studies sheet:** The results obtained from various sheets of all the study on an operation are recorded on this sheet. The basic time for an element of a particular operation are compiled from the analysis of studies sheet. The size of the sheet is usually larger than the other ordinary study forms. Figure 10.12 shows the analysis of studies sheet.

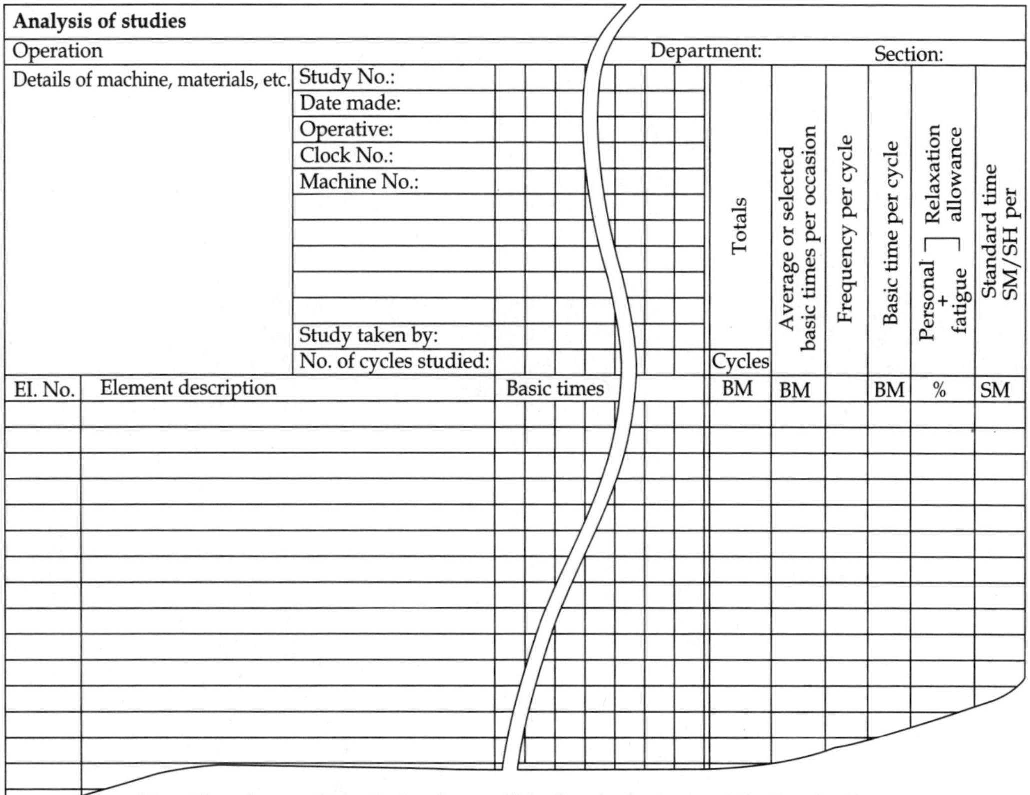

Note: El. = element; BM = Basic minutes; SM = Standard minutes; SH = Standard hours.

Fig. 10.12: Analysis of studies sheet.

10.4 OTHER EQUIPMENT

The stopwatch or electronic data capture device provides the necessary accuracy for all general-purpose work. Where this is not so, for example in highly repetitive, very short-cycle work, then some other measurement technique is more appropriate than time study. Time study can be extended into such areas using films or videos of work. With film, the number of frames can be counted for a short sequence of work to give an accurate time duration – as long as it is validated that the projection of the film is at precisely the same speed as that of the camera that took the film. An alternative, for both film and video, is to record the work with an accurate and detailed timing device kept "in shot" while the recording is taking place. Times can then be read from this timing device when the film or video is replayed at slower speeds.

11
Time Study: Selecting and Timing the Job

11.1 SELECTING THE JOB

As in method study, the first step in time study is to select the job to be studied. Generally speaking, there are a few occasions when a work study person can go into a working area or a department and select a job at random. There is nearly always a reason why a particular job requires attention. Some possible reasons are:

- The job in question is a new one, not previously carried out (new product, component, operation or set of activities).
- A change in material or method of working has been made and a new time standard is required.
- A complaint has been received from a worker or workers' representative about the time standard for an operation.
- A particular operation appears to be a "bottleneck" holding up subsequent operations and possibly (through accumulations of work in process behind it) previous operations.
- Standard times are required before an incentive scheme is introduced.
- A piece of equipment appears to be idle for an excessive time or its output is low, and it therefore becomes necessary to investigate the method of its use.
- The job needs studying as a preliminary to making a method study, or to compare the efficiency of two proposed methods.
- The cost of a particular job appears to be excessive, as may be evidenced by a Pareto type of analysis.

Method study should be performed prior to the study if its purpose is to set performance standards. This is because method study defines and establishes the best way of performing a task. Further, if the method study has not been performed, then there are chances that workers or the technical staff may themselves evolve a much better way of performing a job or a task. The evolved way of doing a job may lead to involvement of considerably less amount of work to achieve the desired results. Depending upon the skill of an operative, there may be variation in the amount of work and the method of performing the same. If an operative is less skilled then there may be increase in the amount of work done and also a more laborious method would be needed to be adopted. The amount and nature of work involved will not be stable until and unless the best way of performing a task has been developed, defined and standardized. The incentive made to the workers may become uneconomical if it is made using the time standard. There may be situations in which the operatives may find the time unattainable while on the other hand the operatives may find that the work can be completed in a much shorter time than set for performing the task. Further in such cases, the operatives may try to restrict their output to maximum, even without taking note of the inquiries that the management would make. This is because they would try to perform the job within the set time standard.

However, a clause permitting for retiming of jobs is necessary to be included in case of collective agreements introducing work study. The retiming may be necessary whenever the work content is altered in either direction. The same clause may be invoked by the management in case a reduction in work content has been made by a worker or management. The retiming can lead to resentment amongst the workers and may even shatter confidence in the workers if done frequently. Therefore, it becomes critical to make sure that the adopted method is right.

There are certain jobs that have very little importance to the enterprise or the abilities of the operatives. In such cases, problem may arise for selection of jobs to be studied. In situations where piece-work system is in place, the time fixed for the jobs may be so liberal that the bonuses and other incentives earned by the workers are so high that it becomes difficult to maintain the incentives if the jobs are readdressed for the timing. Similar resistances/attempts to alter the methods, which should/can be offered by the methods that after alteration will automatically bring about a reassessment of the times allowed. In such situations it may then become unwise to proceed with the studies. The difficulty can be done away by tackling a number of jobs through time study after analyzing on whether the earnings of the workers can be increased by application of time study even if the job to be studied is less relevant to the enterprise.

It is always better to return to the problematic jobs once the study has been made on other important jobs to the enterprise. The establishment of confidence in the work study person should also be taken into account before proceeding for the same. Such problematic jobs must always be negotiated with the worker's representatives. It becomes easier to carry out negotiations once the purpose of the change is fully understood.

11.2 THE APPROACH TO THE WORKER

The relationship between work study person, supervisors and the workers plays a vital role in case of time study in comparison to the work study. On one hand the purpose of method study, i.e., to improvise the method adopted for doing a job is quite obvious to everyone in the enterprise engaged in doing the job, the purpose of time study can be misunderstood if not explained carefully. In case of method study, the purpose may be welcomed by workers whereas in the case of time study the same may be welcomed with unrest if it's misinterpreted completely.

The work study person is assumed to have become familiar in the enterprise while making method studies. Further, the work study person is well known to the workers involved, their representatives and the supervisor. However, if the case is where no time study has been made earlier, then it is a usual practice to bring together the workers' representative and the supervisor to clearly explain the purpose of the time study. The same may be invited to handle the watch. Efforts must be made to address different concerns and questions. This is where the value of work study courses for workers' representatives and supervisors shows itself.

The supervisor and the workers' representative should be asked to identify a most suitable worker amongst the workers to be studied. The chosen worker should have a pace of working which is average or just above the average. Further he or she must be a competent and steady person. Asking the supervisor and the workers' representative for the selection of a competent worker to be studied is a part of good policy. Efforts should be made not to select people temperamentally unsuited to being studied and who cannot work normally while being watched. A number of qualified workers should be selected for the study in case of job being done on a large scale.

A distinction is made in time study practice between what are termed representative workers and qualified workers. A **representative worker** is one whose skill and performance is the average of the group under consideration, and who is not necessarily a **qualified worker.** The concept of the qualified worker is an important one in time study. This person is defined as follows: A qualified worker is one who has acquired the skill, knowledge and other attributes to carry out the work in hand to satisfactory standards of quantity, quality and safety. There is a reason for this insistence on selecting qualified workers. In setting time standards, especially when they are to be used for incentives, the standard to be aimed at is one which can be attained by the qualified worker, and which can be maintained without causing undue fatigue. Because workers work at different speeds, observed times have to be adjusted by factors to give such a standard. These factors are dependent on the judgment of the study person. Experience has shown that accuracy of judgment is attainable only within a fairly narrow range of speeds close to that which is normal for a qualified worker.

The setting of time standard will be more easy and accurate if the study is made for slow or unskilled workers and at the same as that for an exceptionally fast worker. This may help in identifying the unduly large as well as the unduly short time. The unduly large time may be uneconomical while on the other hand the unduly short time may be unfair on the part of slow and unskilled workers which may later on become a subject of complaint. The management should decide on the list of workers on which the study is to be made. After the list is prepared, worker to be studied must be approached with the supervisor and the workers' representative. The worker should then be explained about the purpose of study. The supervisor and the representative can ask the worker to work at the pace that he or she is usually accustomed to. The difficulties encountered while performing a job should be carefully examined by the work study person. Once the worker understands the purpose of the study and hence the study is well established, the procedure need not be explained again to the same worker thereafter. However, while establishing the study for a new worker, the procedures must be followed.

As some workers fear to work with the supervisor standing over them and watching them, the supervisor must be impressed upon to let the worker work alone. The worker must be allowed to get accustomed to the newly established method before setting time standards. Depending upon the complexity and the duration of the operation to be performed, a worker may take quite a long time to reach a stage of consistency. It may even take days or weeks for a worker to perform at a nearly consistent speed. After the stage is reached, one can set time standards. Similarly, the timing should be done for a job performed by a new operative until and unless one becomes thoroughly accustomed to the job.

The position of making observation relative to the operative plays a very critical role in making a proper study. The observation position should be such that, the representative making the observation doesn't interfere or distract the operative performing the job. The representative must also take care of the apprehensive behaviour of the worker that may arise if the worker feels that someone is standing over him or her while he or she is performing the job. Generally, the position will be decided depending on the nature of operation to be performed. However, it is a usual practice to take the observation from the rear and about 2 metres away from the worker. By adopting such a position, it becomes easier for an operative to interact with the representative by making a little head movement. For easier recording and reading the watch, the stopwatch must be held well up in line with the job while the observation is made continuous.

The representative should not conceal his or her position while making a recording. The operative should always be in knowledge of the time study. The practice of performing the time study without the knowledge of the operative is dishonest. It may be a situation that someone else sees it and the news may then spread like wildfire. Therefore, the work study should not have anything to hide.

It is equally important for a representative to be in standing position while making a study. The tendency of doing all the work by themselves should not arise in workers while the representative is making the study. If the worker feels that the representative is in comfortable position then representative may lose workers' respect. Particular position may be adopted by a representative so that it can be maintained for a longer period of time. The standing position can meet the requirements of alertness and concentration required while timing very short elements or cycles.

It is observed generally that the new operative may be bit nervous and may fumble most of the times. The operative may work at a faster pace than required and as a result may cause a number of errors. In such cases, it would be the responsibility of the representative to interact with the operative and put him or her at ease. Further, the operative can be asked to settle down for a bit. It becomes easier to detect any variation in the pace of the worker relative to the natural pace when the work is performed repeatedly. This is because in such situations there will be very little variation of the pace when observed for different number of cycles. When the representative observes that there are wide variations in successive cycle times because of the material being worked upon or the tool used, then the same must be reported to the concerned authorities. However, if the variations are not because of the material or the tool, then it is the actions of the worker that are responsible for the same. In such cases the work study should be discontinued by the representative and should be communicated to the supervisor. The supervisor should be asked to look at the way the job is being performed for correctness. This should be done as a matter of practical diplomacy.

There are situations where technical considerations have got a significant role on a job. It becomes difficult for the work study person to identify the possibility of stretching the time of the job under study. However, if the work study person is an expert then the level of difficulty may decrease. Work where craft skill is involved such as that of turning and screw cutting operation, where feeds and speed have been specified by the process planning department are some of the examples of such situations. Therefore, it is always good to properly establish the method and the conditions under which a work is being carried out. Making such study will greatly reduce the effort required to time the job.

The different problems faced by a representative have been highlighted in the above paragraphs. However, there are many other issues that a representative has to face which one can come to know after experience in the atmosphere where men and the women work there.

11.3 STEPS IN MAKING A TIME STUDY

When the work to be measured has been selected, the making of a time study usually consists of the following eight steps:

- Obtaining and recording all the information available about the job, the operative and the surrounding conditions, which is likely to affect the carrying out of the work.
- Recording a complete description of the method, breaking down the operation into "elements".
- Examining the detailed breakdown to ensure that the most effective method and motions are being used, and determining the sample size.
- Measuring with a timing device (usually a stopwatch) and recording the time taken by the operative to perform each "element" of the operation.
- At the same time, assessing the effective speed of working of the operative relative to the observer's concept of the rate corresponding to standard rating.

- Extending the observed times to "basic times".
- Determining the allowances to be made over and above the basic time for the operation.
- Determining the "standard time" for the operation.

11.4 OBTAINING AND RECORDING INFORMATION

There is some information that must be recorded before starting the proper study. Top of the time study sheet is usually used for recording the observations prior to making a proper study. The proper headings help to ensure that no piece of information is overlooked. The items to be included while designing a time study form are listed below. However, the exact number of items to be included depends on the type and the nature of work being carried out in the enterprise. For example, no space will be required for the "product", etc., in case of non-manufacturing industries such as transport and catering. Space will be required for "tools" in case where work is manual. In such cases, no space will be required for "plant or machine".

A simple instant-print-type camera with flash attachment may be used for recording the details of the workplace. The details can be recorded with greater accuracy. In cases where the time study may be referred later, it is always a good practice to fill-in all the relevant information from the direct observation. Otherwise, a study may become useless after a few months if it carries incomplete information. The different information that needs to be obtained is grouped as follows:

- Information that will make it easier for the study to be found and quickly identified when needed.
  - The study number.
  - Numbering on sheet and the number of sheets.
  - Name or initials of the study person making the study.
  - Date of the study.
  - Name of the person approving the study.
- Information that will make it easier to identify accurately the product or part being processed.
  - Product or part name.
  - Drawing or specification number.
  - Part number.
  - Material.
  - The requirements to be met for maintaining the quality. A standard specification number may be put. Tolerances and surface finish are specified as far as engineering practices are concerned.

    - Issue number is required in cases where drawings are reissued. The situation arises when a product is modified.
- Information that will make it easier to identify the process, method, plant or machine.
    - Department or location where the operation is taking place.
    - Description of the operation or activity.
    - Method study or standard practice sheet numbers (where they exist).
    - Plant or machine (maker's name, type, size or capacity).
    - Tools, jigs, fixtures and gauges used.
    - Sketch of the workplace layout, machine setup and/or part showing surfaces worked (on the reverse of the time study top sheet or on a separate sheet attached to the study if necessary).
    - The settings governing the rate of production of a process or a machine. Examples include machine speeds and feeds to name a few.
- Information to enable the operative to be identified.
    - Operative's name.
    - Clock number.
- Duration of the study
    - The start of the study ("Time on").
    - The finish of the study ("Time off").
    - Elapsed time.
- Working conditions
    - Temperature, humidity, adequacy of the lighting, etc., as a supplement to the information recorded on the sketch of the workplace layout.

Where an electronic study board is being used, it is still important to record the same kinds of identifying data. If the software being used for the study does not allow such data to be keyed into the board, then the data must be recorded on a separate study top sheet, designed for this purpose. This sheet will be similar to a normal time study top sheet but will include a cross reference to an identifying code which is part of the data recorded on the board (such as the study reference).

11.5 CHECKING THE METHOD

The method used by the operative should be checked properly before embarking on a study. A method study should have been already made before fixing timing of the job. Further, a written practice sheet should have been completed too. The standard sheet is merely used for making a comparison of what is being done. The methods used by the operative must be compared with the study sheet that was prepared in the previous study in case if the operative complaints about not being able to obtain the desired output. After making a careful study the work study representative may find that the operative may be using a different method other than that specified. For example, the operative may be using a different tool, different speeds and feeds for a machine or any other settings than that demanded by the process.

The case may have been that of the worn out tool or incorrectness of the profile to which the tool has been sharpened. It would be always wise enough to not proceed for obtaining the time of a process and therefore setting of time standards by using incorrect process conditions.

It may however be difficult to analyze for change in methods in case of jobs of repetitive nature such as work on a conveyor. This is because the change may be due to changes in movement of arms and hands of an operative which are very difficult to be detected through the naked eyes. In such situations special apparatus may be required.

In case of short-run jobs, the time study can be started even without a full-scale method study being conducted. Such jobs are done a few times a year in the working area concerned. The work study person should first put right any obvious inefficiency in such cases. Once the inefficiencies are put right, work study person may then make a careful record of the method adopted for performing a job. The importance of maintaining the record in such cases is realized in the later stages, when the operatives are not able to meet the expected efficiencies.

11.6 BREAKING THE JOB INTO ELEMENTS

An operation is broken down into elements once the study person is satisfied that all the required information about the operation has been recorded. Further, it is also critical to identify the operative needed. The study person must ensure that the method being used is the best possible one in the prevailing circumstances.

Before proceeding further, it would be wise enough to define an element and a work cycle. A distinct part of a specified job that is used for making observation, measurement and analysis is an element and the sequence of the elements required to perform a job forms a work cycle. The beginning and the ending of a work cycle is marked to the same point.

It is necessary to divide a job into elements because of the following reasons:

- The productive and unproductive work is separated.
- The accuracy would be more while assessing the rate of working than would have been possible if the assessment would have been made over a complete cycle. This is because the operative may tend to perform different elements of a job at different pace and therefore may not be possible for the operative to work at the same pace throughout the cycle.
- It makes it possible to identify the different types of elements to be identified which will aid in deciding the appropriate treatment to be accorded to a particular element depending on its type.

- A more accurate allocation of the fatigue allowances can be made to the elements involving a high degree of fatigue if isolated properly.
- The elemental approach will help in checking the method so that the subsequent omission or insertion of elements may be detected quickly. This may become necessary if at a future date the time standard for the job is queried.
- A detailed work specification may be produced if the job is broken down into elements.
- The frequently recurring elements such as the operation of machine controls, loading and unloading of job from the fixtures, etc., may be timed accurately.

Types of Elements

There are eight different types of elements. These have been defined below with their respective examples:

- **Repetitive element:** The elements that occur in every work cycle of a job are categorized as repetitive elements. Examples: locating of workpiece in its fixture, putting aside a finished product or a component.
- **Occasional element:** The elements that don't occur in every work cycle are occasional elements. The frequency of their occurrence is rather irregular. Examples: instructions from supervisor, setting control mechanisms of a machine. These elements are considered to be useful part of job. The final standard time of the job will include occasional elements.
- **Constant element:** The basic time for constant elements remains constant. Examples: switch on machine; gauge diameter; screw on and tighten nut; insert a particular cutting tool into machine.
- **Variable element:** The basic time for variable elements is variable. The variation depends on some characteristics of the product, equipment or process. Examples: using handsaw to saw logs in which case the time varies with diameter and harness of the log, sweeping of floor where the time is dependent on the area swept.
- **Manual element:** The elements of job performed by a worker are the manual elements.
- **Machine element:** Any element of a job that is performed automatically by any process, physical, chemical or otherwise that, once started, cannot be influenced by a worker except to terminate it prematurely. Examples: anneal tubes, fire tiles; form glass bottles; press car body shell to shape; most actual cutting elements on machine tools.
- **Governing element:** An element occupying a longer time within a work cycle than that of any other element which is being performed concurrently. Examples: turn diameter on a lathe, while gauging from time to time; boil kettle of water, while setting out teapot and cups; develop photographic negative, while agitating the solution occasionally.
- **Foreign element:** An element observed which does not form a part of the operation(s) being studied. Examples: in furniture manufacture, sanding the edge of a board

before planning has been completed; degreasing a part that is still to be machined further. It will be clear from the definitions given above that a repetitive element may also be a constant element, or a variable one. Similarly, a constant element may also be repetitive or occasional; an occasional element may be constant or variable, and so on, for the categories are not mutually exclusive.

11.7 DECIDING ON THE ELEMENTS

The general rules that need to be followed while breaking a job into elements includes the following:

- The elements should have definite beginnings and endings. This aids in elements being identified easily. Once the beginnings and endings are defined, it becomes repeatedly recognized. The sound for example that of stopping machine, putting down tool can mark the beginnings and endings. Further, a change of direction of hand or arm can also be used as defining the beginnings and endings of an element. These are more appropriately referred to as break points. These points should be described clearly on the study sheet. Thus, one can define a break point as an instant at which one element of a job ends and the other begins.
- For convenient timing, the efforts must be made to make the elements as small as possible. There is a varied opinion with regard to choosing of smallest practical unit that can be timed using a stopwatch. However, the smallest practical unit that can be timed is considered to be about 0.04 min. This can be varied between 0.07 to 0.10 min for less trained observers. It is general practice that very short elements should succeed the longer elements. This aids for accurate timing and recording. Long manual elements should be rated about every 0.33 min.
- Efforts should be made that the chosen manual elements will represent unified and recognizably distinct segments of the operation. This can be made clearer with an example which involves reaching, moving and positioning the wrench to tighten a nut. It is possible in this instance to identify three distinct operations: reaching for a wrench and then grasping it in the hand, shifting the wrench to the desired location, positioning the wrench properly in hand in order to tighten the nut. All these three actions will be performed by the worker as one natural set of motion. One may use a break point at the instant where the fingers touch the wrench which will break the whole set of actions into two distinct elements. However, it is better to consider the different set of motions as a whole and define the element as "get wrench".
- It is always vital to separate manual elements from machine elements. However, doing so may be difficult and cumbersome for short cycles. This separation is necessary to derive standard data.
- Variable and constant elements also should be separated.
- There are certain elements that do not occur in every cycle and are known as occasional and foreign elements. These elements should be timed separately from the other elements.

The type and nature of manufacturing operation and the results desired decide the necessity for a fine breakdown of elements. For example, the assembly operations in the light electrical and radio industries will generally have short cycle of operations with short elements. The amount of detail for a proper description of the element will depend on a number of factors, for instance:

- Less detailed element descriptions is required for small batch jobs than that required for long running jobs.
- Place to place movements will require less description than that for hand and arm movements.

Checking of the element description should be done through a number of cycles. After the prerequisites are done, the timing should be initiated.

11.8 SAMPLE SIZE

Here we are not concerned with a proportion but with finding out the value of the representative average for each element. Our problem, therefore, is to determine the sample size or the number of readings that must be made for each element, given a predetermined confidence level and accuracy margin. Here again, we can apply a statistical method or a conventional method. For the statistical method, we have first to take a number of preliminary readings (n'). We then apply the following equation for the 95.45 confidence level and a margin of error of ± 5 per cent:

$$n = \left(\frac{40\sqrt{n'\sum x^2 - \left(\sum x^2\right)}}{\sum x} \right)^2$$

where,

n = sample size we wish to determine

n' = number of readings taken in the preliminary study

£ = sum of values

x = value of the readings.

An example will make the point clear. Let us suppose that we take five readings for a given element, and find that the value of the elapsed time in 1/100th of a minute is 7, 6, 7, 7, 6. We can then calculate the squares and the sum of the squares of these numbers:

x	x^2
7	49
6	36
7	49
7	49
6	36
$\sum x = 33$	$\sum x^2 = 219$

Therefore, n = 8.81 or 9 readings.

Since the number of preliminary readings n' that we took is less than the required sample size of nine, the sample size must be increased. However, we cannot simply say that four more observations are needed. When we add the values obtained from these four additional observations, the values of x and x^2 will change, and this may affect the value of n. Consequently, it may be found either that a still larger sample is required, or that the sample taken was in fact adequate or more than adequate.

If we choose a different confidence level and accuracy margin, the formula changes as well. Normally, however, we choose either the 95 or the 95.45 confidence level.

The statistical method of determining the sample size is valid to the extent that the assumptions made in deriving the formula are valid – in other words, that the observed variations in the readings are due to mere chance and are not made intentionally by the operative. The statistical method can be cumbersome, since a given work cycle is composed of several elements. As the sample size will vary with the readings for each element, we can arrive at different sample sizes for each element within a given cycle, unless of course the elements have more or less the same average. As a result, we may have to calculate the sample size, in the case of cumulative timing, by basing it on the element that will call for the largest sample size.

Some authors, and companies such as General Electric, have therefore adopted a conventional guide for the number of cycles to be timed, based on the total number of minutes per cycle (Table 11.1). It is also important that the readings be continued over a number of cycles in order to ensure that occasional elements (such as handling boxes of finished parts, periodical cleaning of machines or sharpening of tools) can be observed several times. In conducting the study, the table of random numbers may be used to determine the times at which the readings are to be taken.

Table 11.1: Number of recommended cycles for time study.

Minutes per Cycle	**To 0.10**	**To 0.25**	**To 0.50**	**To 0.75**	**To 1.0**	**To 2.0**	**To 5.0**	**To 10.0**	**To 20.0**	**To 40.0**	**Over 40**
Numbers of cycles recommended	200	100	60	40	30	20	15	10	8	5	3

11.9 TIMING EACH ELEMENT: STOPWATCH PROCEDURE

Timing of the job can begin once the different elements of the job have been written down. The two principal methods of timing with stopwatch are:

- Cumulative timing
- Flyback timing.

In **cumulative timing** the stopwatch runs continuously throughout the study. The beginning of the first element of the job marks the beginning of the stopwatch. The stopwatch is not stopped until the entire job has been completed. The recording of the time is made at the end of each element of the job. The successive subtraction of time is done to arrive at the individual element time. The cumulative timing ensures that all the time is recorded during a job.

In **flyback timing** the timing for each element of the job is obtained directly. The hands of the stopwatch are returned to zero as the element of a job commences. The stopwatch is then allowed to start immediately for recording the time for the next element.

A wrist watch or any wall clock can be used to take an independent check of the overall time of the study. The same can come in handy if retiming is considered as it also serves in noting the time of the day at which the study was made. For example, when the operatives are fresh in the first hour or two in the morning the cycle time for a repetitive job will be shorter in comparison when the recording has been made late in the afternoon.

With the stopwatch in hand, the study person in the case of flyback timing; walks to the clock at nearly exact minute, i.e., the next major division say an hour or one of the five minutes points. The stopwatch is started and the exact time is then noted on the study sheet in the space represented by the heading "time on". After the time has been noted, the study person with the watch running comes to the place where the study is being conducted. The hands of the stopwatch are then snapped back when the timing for the first element begins and the time elapsed for completion of an element is noted down on the study sheet. The stopwatch is allowed to run until the time elapsed for the last element for the last cycle is noted down. The hand of the stopwatch is then snapped back to zero and is allowed to run continuously until the work study person reaches the clock again for noting down the completion time of the work. The stopwatch is then finally stopped. The "time off" space in the study sheet is used to enter the final clock time. The time recorded in the "time on" and "time off" are known as the "check times". The "elapsed time" is then obtained by subtracting the clock reading at the beginning of the study from the clock reading at the end of the study and the same is entered on the form.

The "recorded time" is the sum total of the times of all the elements, the check times and the ineffective time. The same is also recorded on the study sheet. There are certain factors due to which the "recorded time" doesn't agree to that of the elapsed time. The factors may be due to the time lost in returning the hands of the stopwatch to zero, bad reading or missed elements. However, if the difference is more than ± 2 per cent then it's a usual practice to discard the study.

In the case of cumulative timing, since the stopwatch is only read and not snapped back, the two times, i.e., the elapsed time and the recorded time must be identical. There will be no effect on the overall time if some occasional element is not recorded. This advantage of cumulative timing is explored by many trade unions. Further, the cumulative timing is more accurate than the flyback timing and gives no opportunity for altering times in favour of management. However, the cumbersome task of subtraction to arrive at the individual element time is one of the disadvantages of the cumulative timing. The process of subtraction also increases the time taken in working up the study in later stages.

However, for experienced study person, the flyback timing is as accurate as cumulative timing and is therefore widely used. It is believed that the work study person achieves a fair degree of accuracy when trained using the cumulative method. Generally ILO suggests the employment of cumulative method for training purpose for the following reasons:

- The experience suggests that the work study person will achieve more accuracy in handling stopwatch while training on the cumulative method in comparison to that for flyback method.
- Since the foreign elements and interruptions are included, the overall time will not be affected if the inexperienced work study person fails to record some of the element times.
- With the cumulative method, it is difficult to manipulate the rating of the operative. This is because only watch readings and not actual times are recorded. However, the reverse is true for the flyback method.
- Since no time is omitted in case of cumulative timing, the same, if used as a basis for incentive plans, will be readily accepted by the workers and their representatives. Further, it would be easier to introduce the time study in an enterprise or an industry.

The errors are inevitable in the flyback, method, and may arise due to the delay that occurs when the hand is snapped back to zero. In case of small elements the percentage of error is more. Therefore, for shorter elements in particular the cumulative timing is more effective in comparison to the flyback timing method while on the other hand for longer elements, the flyback timing can be more safely used. The confidence of the worker plays a critical role too and shouldn't be overlooked.

Electronic stopwatches have the benefit of allowing times for individual elements to be recorded on a flyback basis, without any error introduced by the mechanical flyback mechanism of a conventional watch. It thus offers the same levels of accuracy as cumulative timing without the inconvenience of performing the subtractions. It is, however, still possible to misread the watch and a check on the sum of all recorded times against the total elapsed time should still be carried out. With electronic study boards and data capture devices, the study person does not make readings of element times – these are automatically recorded as the study person identifies the element break points. No errors are therefore introduced by the recording process.

There is a third method of timing which is employed for short-element short-cycle work, and which may indeed be the only way of getting accurate times with a stopwatch, for elements which are so very short that there is not enough time for the study person to read the watch and make a recording on his or her study sheet. In this situation, the method used is known as differential timing. With differential timing, elements are timed in groups, first including and then excluding each small element, the time for each element being obtained subsequently by subtraction. For example, if the job consists of seven short elements, the study person may time numbers 1 to 3, and 4 to 7 for the first few cycles, recording only these two readings per cycle. The timing is then recorded for 1 to 4 and 5 to 7 for a few cycles, and so on. If differential timing is applied in this fashion, either the cumulative or the flyback method of watch manipulation may be used.

We have now discussed all the preliminaries to making a time study, from the selection of the job, through the recording of all relevant data, the breakdown of the job into elements and the examination of the methods employed, to the recording of the actual element times. In the next chapter we shall discuss the means of modifying these observed times to take into account variations in rates of working.

12
Time Study: Rating

12.1 THE QUALIFIED WORKER

The workers with fast pace and slow pace of working should be avoided while making a time study. Therefore, it is a usual practice to perform the study on a number of qualified workers. One may define a qualified worker to be the one who has acquired the skills, knowledge and other attributes to perform a given job or task under satisfactory standards of quality, quantity and safety.

Varying human abilities are required to perform jobs of different natures. Visual acuity, mental alertness and concentration may be required to perform certain jobs while most jobs require physical strength. It is obvious that all the workers in the enterprise will not have all the possibilities to perform jobs. The management will also be able to arrange training programmes only for the selected few.

It is totally a complicated process to acquire skills. Following attributes highlight the differences between an experienced worker and the inexperienced one:

- An experienced worker performs a job with smoothness and the movements are consistent.
- Rhythm while performing a job is acquired by an experienced worker.
- The response to the signals by an experienced worker is more rapid.
- The difficulties are easily anticipated by an experienced worker and more ready to overcome them.
- An experienced worker is in more relaxed state of mind while performing a job. The job is carried without giving the appearance of conscious attention.

A good deal of time may be taken by a worker to translate into an experienced and skilled worker for performing a job. In one particular case, it was discovered that a worker took around 8000 cycles of job to perform at a constant pace. The time then taken by the worker to perform the task was just half as that when required when the job was tried for the first time. Therefore the time standard would turn out to be wrong if the standards are set on the basis of worker who is an inexperienced one. There are certain jobs that can be learnt very quickly.

It would be ideal on the part of study person to be sure enough that only properly qualified workers are chosen for performing the job while the study is made. However, it is difficult to do so in practice. It may be possible that none of the workers can be said to be completely qualified to perform the task under study, though this may be done by carrying out training programmes. In other cases, there may be only few workers to carry out the task under study and therefore cannot be considered to be average or representative of the group. One may define a representative worker as the one who has the required skill and attributes to perform the job and the performance is average of a group under consideration. The same may not be referred to as a qualified worker.

There may be situations where the whole group is made of mainly qualified workers. In such cases there may be one or perhaps many workers who could be considered representative workers. The time normally taken by the average worker/s to perform an operation, working in an ordinary fashion provided that there is sufficient motivation to carry on with the job is known as standard time.

12.2 THE AVERAGE WORKER

The term average worker has been coined by statisticians and is not more than an idea. The truly average worker is no more than an idea. None of the individuals are exactly alike. However, variations in measurable characteristics such as height for a number of people belonging to a particular country or area form a typical pattern. These variations when represented graphically tend to form a normal distribution curve. For instance if one considers characteristics such as that of height in western European countries, one will find that the average height of a man is about 172 cm. A large number of men in the crowd will have their height between 170 cm and 175 cm. The total number of men that have height greater or smaller than this will become fewer and fewer as those heights approach the extremes of tallness and shortness.

The same applies to the performance of the operatives. Figure 12.1 shows this conveniently. If there are about 500 workers who are qualified to perform the same operation by similar methods and conditions, the operation being under the control of the workers, the distribution of the time taken by the workers is shown by Fig. 12.1. The times have been divided into groups at intervals of four seconds for further simplification of the figure. Table 12.1 shows the groups in which the different workers fall.

On analysis, it can be seen clearly that the percentage of times that are less than 46 seconds is around 32.4 per cent while the percentage of times that are more than 50 seconds is around 34.8. The largest single group of times (32.8 per cent) lies between 46 and 50 seconds. Therefore, from the analysis one can surely say that for the group of 500 workers the average time taken for the performance of the job is between 46 and 50 seconds. The average may be say 48 seconds. Further, the time taken by any average worker to perform the job would be 48 seconds. The same time may not hold for any other industry or enterprise. For a factory that runs under better conditions and pay their workers well, the average time may be less than 48 seconds, say 44 seconds, whereas the average time may be more than 48 seconds for the factories that are poorly run and have less able workers.

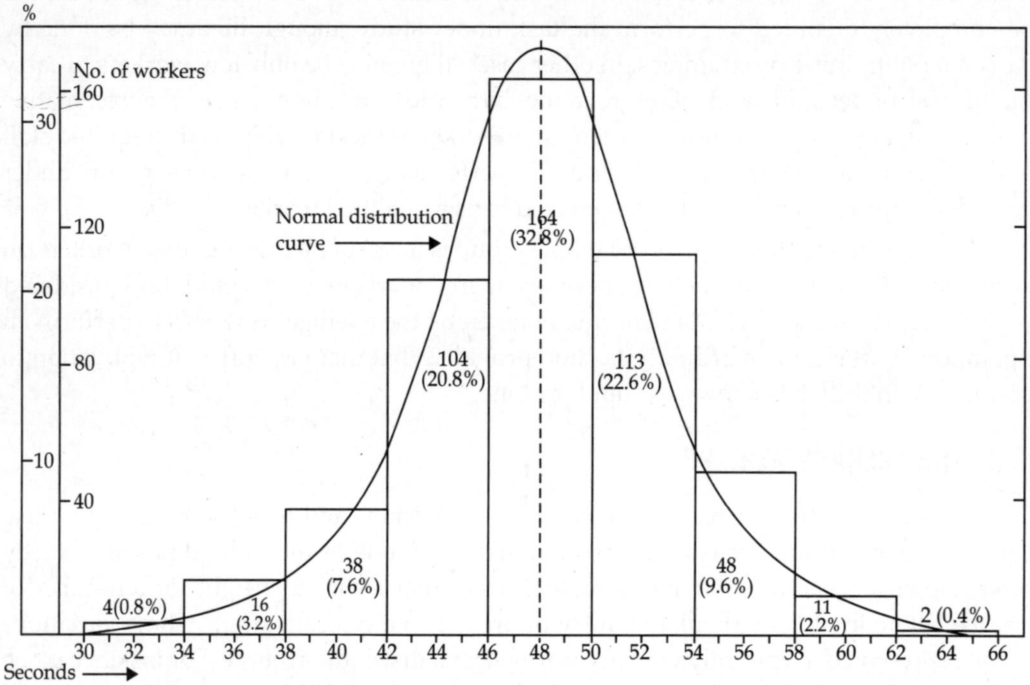

Fig. 12.1: Distribution of times taken by workers to perform a given job.

A "normal distribution curve" will result if a curve is drawn to fit this distribution. The curve will tend to be more symmetrical about the peak value if large sample is considered. However, the same can be altered by the introduction of special conditions. For example, the right-hand side of the curve would probably become shorter in case the slow workers are transferred to some other work. This is because the number of workers returning very long times will decrease.

Table 12.1: Specimen performance distribution.

Time Group (Sec.)	Number of Workers (out of 500)	% of total workers	
30-34	4	0.8	32.4
34-38	16	3.2	
38-42	38	7.6	
42-46	104	20.8	
46-50	164	32.8	32.8
50-54	113	22.6	34.8
54-58	48	9.6	
58-62	11	2.2	
62-66	2	0.4	

12.3 STANDARD RATING AND STANDARD PERFORMANCE

The time standards can be used for a number of purposes such as that of programme planning, as a basis for incentives, etc., in any enterprise. The time standards must be such that the same can be achieved by the majority of workers in the enterprise. It would be of no use to set standards that are very high as this would make it difficult to achieve different purposes. Further, if the too low times standards are set that are easily achievable even by the slowest worker will not be conducive to the efficiency.

It is fair enough at this stage to ask how a work study person obtains such a fair time from time studies.

As mentioned previously the time study should be conducted only on some of the qualified workers. However, it is tedious and cumbersome to obtain individual time of all the workers and plot them in the manner as shown in Fig. 12.1. This, if done, will result into average time. Unfortunately, this is hardly ever possible. Timing a job for an average qualified worker is also not easy since it is not possible for a worker to work consistently from day to day or even from minute to minute. Some means for assessing the rate at which a worker works needs to be adopted by a work study person. Further, there must be methods of relating the pace of the worker to the standard results. The process is referred to as **rating.** Therefore, one may define rating as the means by which the workers' pace of doing job is assessed and compared to the observers' concept of standard pace. Thus rating is a comparison of the workers' pace with the standard result. One may define a standard rate of working as the rate at which qualified worker will work naturally at a job using the correct method. This rate is usually referred to as the **standard rating**. On a rating scale this rating is denoted by 100.

An operative will be able to achieve the so-called **standard performance**, if the standard pace is maintained by the worker while taking the appropriate relaxation. Therefore, standard performance may be defined as the rate of output that is achieved by qualified workers without any over-exertion as an average over the working shift or day. Further, the output should have been achieved following the correct method of doing the job and given that the workers are self-motivated. On standard rating and performance scales, the standard performance is denoted as 100.

For instance, in United Kingdom and United States, the standard rating is equivalent to the speed of the limbs of a worker with average physique, walking without a load on a level ground in a straight line at 6.4 kilometers per hour. The rate is expected to be maintained by a worker having a right physique and one who is accustomed to walking provided that the pauses for rest are taken as and when needed. The standard has been achieved as a result of experience. The standard is so set that an average qualified worker will be able to earn bonus if he or she works at this pace, without any undue strain which would otherwise have risked the workers' health. The pace is normal who walks just towards the destination. Neither the person is sauntering nor hurrying. People with purpose of catching a train don't even walk at this pace.

The standard pace differs from country to country. For instance, the standard pace arrived at will be different for European and North American countries than the rest of the world. However, there is little evidence in general that suggests that different localities with different environmental conditions will require different standards for rates, given that the workers are adequately nourished, feel trained and motivated. The standard rate described above could be used to provide a datum for comparing the performance of workers in different parts of the world which then can be used to determine the adjustments that would be required. Dealing with a pack of cards in 0.375 minutes is another example of working at a standard rate.

It will take a few fours for a qualified worker to show the required consistency. On the other hand, those involved in the manual work will generally work at their normal working rate which will not match at all with the standard rate. This is because some people work at a pace faster than others. Further, depending upon the complexity and arduousness of elements involved in a job, the standard rate of performance will differ and the speed of the motions of the limbs will not always be that prescribed by the standard rate. The standard rate is achieved by the worker as the cumulative outcome of all the elements of a job for different periods of work at varying paces.

In cases where time standards are used as a means to provide incentives to the workers, it must be ensured by the management that the workers' representatives are satisfied that the time standards set should be such that an average qualified worker will be able to earn 20-35 per cent above the time rate by achieving the standard performance. If there is no target and incentive for the workers that may drive them to yield higher outputs, then they may tolerate some small amounts of ineffective time within their element of work. In many cases it is also possible that the workers reduce their performance over an hour or so, i.e., well below the level of standard performance. The workers will motivate themselves to produce high output only when they are given appropriate incentives. The workers will try to get rid of small amounts of ineffective time and even narrow the gaps between their productive movements. The workers will also try to alter their pattern of movements to achieve a higher output. Figure 12.2 illustrates diagrammatically the effect of elimination of ineffective time under the influence of incentives.

The case is that of operatives working on a lathe that have to gauge their workpiece from time to time. The gauge lies placed in the locker which is besides them. In instances where the workers have no reason to hurry, they will turn their whole body round to pick up the gauge, turn back to the lathe, gauge the workpiece and then turn the whole body again to put the gauge back to the location from where it was picked. Further, they will carry each and every of these elements at their natural pace. In the case where incentives are provided to the workers, they will try not to turn their whole body instead they will just stretch their arms out and perhaps will have a glace round to check the position of the gauge on the locker, pick up the gauge, gauge the workpiece and then place the gauge back in the locker with a hand movement. In both the instances, there will not be any deliberate stopping of the work. However, in the second case some of the movements would have been eliminated which is required with a viewpoint of furthering the operation. Figure 12.3 illustrates the effect of putting a whole working area or a plant on an incentive.

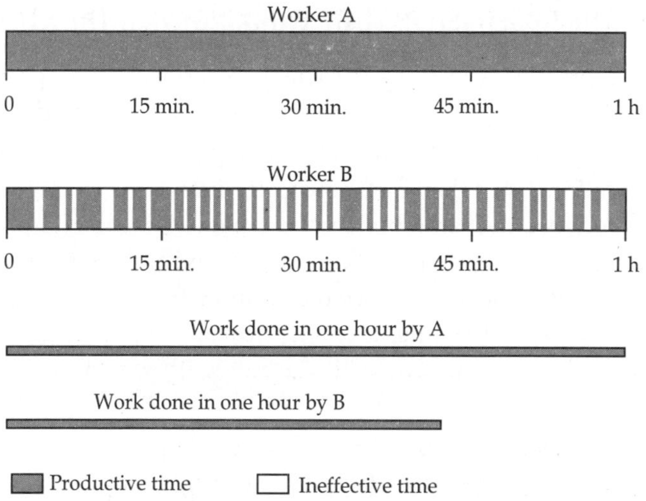

Fig. 12.2: Effect of ineffective time on performance.

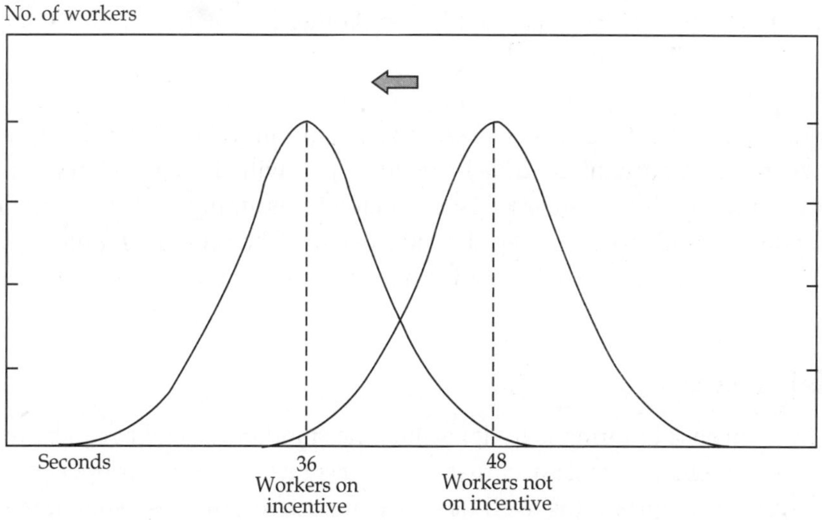

Fig. 12.3: Effect of a payment-by-results incentive on the time taken to perform an operation.

It is quite obvious that providing incentives to workers in proportion to the output will not make an unskilled worker to become skilled as the naturally skilled worker. Further, the slow worker will not perform at a rate faster than the naturally faster worker. However, if the whole working area is put on a well-designed incentive plan and provided that the working conditions are same, then this would result in every worker tending to work at a more consistent rate. The small amount of ineffective time will be eliminated and there will be reduction in the average time for the job. The normal distribution curve will move to the left while retaining the shape. Figure 12.3 shows this change wherein the peak of the curve now comes at 36 seconds instead of 48 seconds.

12.4 COMPARING THE OBSERVED RATE OF WORKING WITH THE STANDARD RATE

By long periods of practice and with sufficient experience, it is possible to compare accurately the observed rate of working with the theoretical standard.

Let us take the case of walking. In this instance, if people are asked to judge the rate at which a person is walking then they may categorize it as slow, average or fast. However, with little more experience the same bunch of people will be able to predict a numerical value of the rate at which a person is walking say for example 3 miles an hour or 5 miles hour an hour. With a little more experience the accurate number may be predicted say for instance 2 ½ miles an hour or 4 ¾ miles an hour. However, in order to be at such a level of accuracy one needs to have in mind a particular rate with which the observations can be compared and hence results can be arrive at.

Similar kind of experience is required by a work study person when he or she does the rating. However, the training required to arrive at results may be for a longer duration. This is because of the complexity involved in the operations. Instances of walking may be used in earlier stage of training which bears very little resemblance to most of the jobs that are required to be rated. In later stages, films and other live demonstrations may be used to train the work study persons.

The confidence required by a work study person in the rating of job will come through long experience and practice. The work study person may find himself or herself in a situation where it may be required to back the arguments with the management, supervisors or workers' representatives. Unless this is done with assurance, all the aforementioned parties may lose confidence in the work study person. Therefore it is quite essential that the time standards must be set only after gaining training under expert guidance and long practice.

12.5 WHAT IS RATED?

The very first purpose of rating is to determine the standard time that can be maintained by the average qualified worker and that can be used as a basis for proper planning and control as well as for providing well-designed incentive schemes. Therefore, the main concern of the work study person is the speed at which workers carry out their work relative to the normal speed defined by the work study person. Most of the authorities agree that the stopwatch can measure the time taken to carry out different elements of a job and hence determining the speed of working.

The speed is the effective speed at which a job is performed. Therefore, speed is not mainly the speed of movement of a worker. This is because an unskilled worker may try to work at an extremely fast rate and yet take longer than a skilled worker who appears to be working at a relatively slower pace. A lot of unnecessary movements are performed by unskilled workers which have been already done away by a skilled worker after long hours of practice. Experience and knowledge can help a work study person in acquiring accurately the effective speed of a worker. An inexperienced study person may suggest that a worker is performing at a higher speed by observing too many rapid movements. At the same time he or she may underestimate the speed of a worker who may appear to be slow in performing a job but with economical motions involved.

There are jobs where muscular effort is also involved. So a definite question arises whether effort should be rated. As far as jobs with little efforts, the need for rating effort doesn't arise at all. However, for jobs with muscular effort, definitely effort must be rated. It is very difficult to rate effort. The result of exerting effort is usually only seen in the speed.

The amount of effort which has to be exerted and the difficulty encountered by the operative is a matter for the study person to judge in the light of experience with the type of job. For example, if an operative has to lift a heavy mould from the filling table, carry it across the working area and put it on the ground near the ladle, only experience will tell the observer whether the speed at which it is being done is normal, above normal or subnormal. Those who had never studied operations involving the carrying of heavy weights would have great difficulty in making an assessment the first time they saw such an operation.

Operations involving **mental activities** (judgment of finish, for example, in inspection of work) are most difficult to assess. Experience of the type of work is required before satisfactory assessments can be made. Inexperienced study persons can be made to look very foolish in such cases, and moreover can be unjust to above-average and conscientious workers. In any job the speed of accomplishment must be related to an idea of a normal speed for the same type of work. This is an important reason for doing a proper method study on a job before attempting to set a time standard. It enables the study person to gain a clear understanding of the nature of the work and often enables the elimination of excessive effort or judgment. The rating process is thus brought nearer to a simple assessment of speed. In the next section some of the factors affecting the rate of working of the operative will be discussed.

12.6 FACTORS AFFECTING THE RATE OF WORKING

Variations in actual times for a particular element may be due to factors outside or within the control of the worker. Those outside this control may be:

- Variations in the quality or other characteristics of the material used, although they may be within the prescribed tolerance limits.
- Changes in the operating efficiency of tools or equipment within their useful life.
- Minor and unavoidable changes in methods or conditions of operation.

- Variations in the mental attention necessary for the performance of certain elements.
- Changes in climate and other surrounding conditions such as light, temperature, etc. These can generally be accounted for by taking a sufficient number of studies to ensure that a representative sample of times is obtained.

Factors within the operative's control may be:

- Acceptable variations in the quality of the product.
- Variations due to the individual's ability.
- Variations due to the attitude of mind, especially the attitude to the organization for which he or she works.

The times of similarly described elements of work are affected to a great extent by the factors that are within the worker's control. Some of these factors are:

- The movements of the worker have some pattern and therefore by affecting the pattern of worker's movement the times of elements can be altered.
- The pace with which an individual worker performs a job.
- The pattern of worker's movement as well as the pace of doing a job.

Keeping in mind the above factors, it becomes essential for a study person to have a clear idea of the pattern a qualified worker needs to follow while he or she performs the movements. Further, the work study person should be able to provide the necessary variations in the pattern followed whenever the qualified worker encounters a totally different range of conditions. A detailed study of the work involving a highly repetitive set of elements which are likely to run for long periods is required which can be done using different techniques of the method study. Workers should be given proper training with regard to the pattern of movements that must be followed for such cases. The number of factors on which the pace of the worker depend are:

- The amount and nature of physical effort demanded by the work.
- The care required on the part of the worker.
- Experience and training.

The pace of performing a job will be slow for work involving a greater physical effort. The pace will also be affected by the ease with which the physical effort has been made. The pace will be slow for the effort made by the workers in the direction which is not convenient for them, while the pace will be relatively faster for effort of the same magnitude made in a convenient direction. For instance, the effort applied while pushing a car. One can do so either by pushing the car from behind or by pushing the same car with one hand on the steering wheel through the window. One should always be able to distinguish between the slowing up of pace due to effort and slowing of pace due to fatigue.

In certain situations the rating may be superfluous. Such circumstances arise, for instance, when the workers are heavily loaded. In such cases the workers will have to exert considerable physical effort throughout and the same will be performed at their best natural pace. Therefore, it will be adequate to determine the average of the actual times taken during a number of observations. A work study person may end up making a false rating if number of observations is not made. One such case was shown in an ILO study of earth moving operations made in India. The workers carried a load of up to 38 kg in basket over their head. The workers did not dawdle with the heavy load. The workers were anxious to get rid of the load by reaching the end. Therefore, they performed the task at their best natural pace. They achieved their goal by taking very rapidly a large number of short strides. Doing so, it appeared that they are almost going to break out into a trot at any moment. It was found that the loaded walk took a great amount of time in comparison to the leisurely unloaded walk. The work study person would have ended up in making a false rating if he or she lacked adequate experience. The jobs involving such heavy load and hence increased masculine effort are common in factories and industries. Carrying sacks, picking the sack and then putting them down is one such instance that includes heavy loadings in factories and industries. All such jobs are generally carried out by the workers at the best natural pace.

The pace of doing a job may reduce if increased care is taken in carrying out the job. Placing a peg with parallel sides in hole is an example which requires more care than is the case while placing the peg which is tapered.

The study person should be able to recognize the fumbling and hesitating nature of a worker. The introduction of minor method variations such as that of fumbling and other foreign elements such as that of hesitation may be eliminated if adequate training and experience is added to the workers' natural skills and dexterity. Assigning a lower rating can be helpful in considering very slight deviations from the standard method but further training is usually required to eliminate the aforementioned foreign elements.

Too high ratings must not be adopted by the study person in the following cases:

- The situations in which a worker is worried or looks hurried.
- Cases where a worker is being more careful than required.
- The study person finds a job to be relatively more difficult.
- The pace of the study person is very fast, as in case of recording a short element.

On the other hand, too low ratings must not be adopted by a study person in the following situations:

- The situations where a worker makes a job to appear comparatively easier.
- The cases where smooth, rhythmic movements are adopted by a worker.
- When a work study person expects a pause in the work but the worker does not do so.
- In situations where heavy manual work is performed by a worker.
- The study person is tired.

The above factors should be taken into account by a work study person while making ratings. The task of rating becomes much easier if a good method study has been made prior to making the ratings. The rating becomes a matter of simply judging pace by a proper method study which simplifies the job and therefore less number of elements to be assessed.

12.7 SCALES OF RATING

It is necessary to have a numerical scale for making a comparison between the observed rate of working and the standard rate. The basic time, i.e., the time which a qualified and motivated worker may take to carry out the element at standard rating, then can be obtained by multiplying the observed time by a factor which is the rating itself.

A wide variety of scales of rating are in use. The common ones are the 60-80, 75-100 and 100-133 scales, and the British Standard scales which are termed the 0-100 scale.

Table 12.2 shows examples of various rates of working on the scales mentioned.

Table. 12.2: Various rates of working on the principal rating scales.

Scales				Description	Comparable waking speed	
60-80	**75-100**	**100-133**	**0-100 Standard**		**(min)**	**(km/h)**
0	0	0	0	No activity		
40	50	67	50	Very slow; clumsy, fumbling movements; operative appears half asleep, with no interest in the job.	2	3.2
60	75	100	75	Steady, deliberate, unhurried performance, as of a worker not on piece work but under proper supervision; looks slow, but time is not being intentionally wasted while under observation.	3	4.8
80	100	133	100 (Standard rating)	Brisk, business-like performance, as of an average qualified worker on piece work; necessary standard of quality and accuracy achieved with confidence.	4	6.4
100	125	167	125	Very fast; operative exhibits a high degree of assurance, dexterity and coordination of movement, well above that of an average trained worker.	5	8.0
120	150	200	150	Exceptionally fast; requires intense effort and concentration, and is unlikely to be kept up for long periods; a "virtuoso" performance achieved only by a few outstanding workers	6	9.6

The lower figures in case of the 60-80, 75-100 and 100-133 scales denotes the rate of working of an operative on time rates of pay. The higher and in each case one-third higher corresponds to the rate known as the standard rate that the qualified worker would be motivated to apply themselves to their work, as for instance by an incentive scheme. The underlying assumption while preparing the scales was that workers on incentive tend to perform about one-third more effectively than the other workers.

Since the scales are linear, there is no need of denoting an intermediate point between zero and the figure chosen to represent the standard rating. Whichever scale is used, the derived final time standards should be equivalent. This is because the nature of work doesn't change even though different scales are used to make an assessment of the rate of doing a work.

12.8 HOW THE RATING FACTOR IS USED

Standard performance is delineated in Fig. 12.4. A factor less than 100 say 90 or 75 may be adopted as a standard if the study person decides that an operation is being carried out at a relatively less effective speed. On the other hand, a standard over and above 100, say 110, 115 or 120 would be used if it is decided by the work study person that the effective speed of doing the job is comparatively more than the effective speed. During the first weeks of their training, study persons are unlikely to be able to rate more closely than the nearest ten.

Study No.	**Time study continuation sheet**				Sheet No.		of		
Element description	R	WR	ST	BT	Element description	R	WR	ST	BT
Note: Reverse side similar, but without upper line of heading.									

Fig. 12.4: Standard performance.

The following mathematical equation must have been always true if the study person's ratings were always impeccable, provided that the element is a constant element type and is always performed in the way it is intended to be:

Observed time × rating = a constant

An example, expressed numerically, might read as follows:

Cycle	Observed Time		Rating		Constant
1	0.20	×	100	=	0.20
2	0.16	×	125	=	0.20
3	0.25	×	80	=	0.20

From the above calculations one may find that 0.20 × 100 is shown equal to 0.20 rather than 20. This is because rating is always calculated in comparison to the standard rating (100). The amended time is then a fraction where assessed rating is the numerator while standard rating forms the denominator.

The basic time for an element is then obtained by the following mathematical equation:

$$\text{Observed time} \times \frac{\text{Rating}}{\text{Standard rating}} = \text{Basic time}$$

For example:

$$0.16 \times \frac{125}{100} = 0.20 \text{ min}$$

The above calculated basic time is the time that would be taken to perform an element of a job if performed at standard rate, instead of the faster one actually observed.

The example below shows that basic time lower than that of the standard would be achieved in case where the operative was judged to be working slowly:

$$0.25 \times \frac{80}{100} = 0.20 \text{ min}$$

The multiple, observed time × rating is rarely constant when taken over a large number of readings. This may be because of the number of following reasons:

- The work content of the element has variations.
- There may be inaccuracies in taking down and recording the observed times.
- The ratings calculated may be inaccurate.
- Variations due to rating to the nearest five points.

12.9 RECORDING THE RATING

Rating must be done for each element of an activity when it is performed before recording the time and irrespective of the previous or succeeding element. Recording of rating is difficult in case of very short elements. Every cycle or the complete study may be rated in case of work with repetitive nature. This is done when the short cycle study form is used.

The rating should be recorded for an element when it is in progress and the same should be noted before the time is taken. If the practice is not followed then there may be risk that previous time and ratings for the same element will be influential in the process of assessment. This is one of the reasons for placing the "Rating" column to the left of "watch reading" column on the time study sheet. The element time in case of the cumulative timing doesn't occur as a separate figure until subtractions have been made which is advantageous. This is because; if the same would have occurred with a separate figure then it might tempt the study person to "rate by the watch".

Since the rating of an element represents the assessment of the average rate of performance for that element, the longer the element the more difficult it is for the study person to adjust this judgment to that average. The rating for long elements should be done every half a minute, though timed as a whole upto the break points.

A sufficient accuracy may be obtained in the final results if the rating is done to the nearest five. Long practice and training will result into greater accuracy.

Referring back to the figures in this chapter, the discussion was made for filling-in of two columns namely "watch reading" and "rating" on the same line. The readings are continued for a number of cycles at the end of which the clock is allowed to run until it has been synchronized with the one when started. The "time after" can then be noted and recorded. The study is then at an end. The next step, after thanking the operative for his or her cooperation, is to work out the basic time for each element of the job.

13
Time Study: From Study to Standard Time

13.1 SUMMARIZING THE STUDY

In this chapter we will see how the study which has been taken up by the work study person is worked upon. How the results obtained from the study through analysis of study sheets are entered will also be discussed. Later on, it will be further discussed how the standard times obtained from the entries on the analysis of study sheets are compiled.

The entries made on the time study top sheet and the continuation sheets are made using a pencil. All the entries made so far on the time study top sheet and the continuation sheets have been written in pencil. Pencil will also be used for the heading details in the top of the sheet shown in the data blocks, the first entry on the study sheet: "time before", the last entry: "time after" and the two entries for each of the watch reading: the rating and the watch itself. The column headed "R" will contain the ratings. This column will also consist of numbers such as 95, 115, 80, 75, 100, 105, and so on. Until the study person has obtained sufficient experience, the ratings should always be entered in steps of ten such as 80, 90 and so on. The watch readings in decimal minutes will be contained by the column headed "WR". Most of the entries will comprise only two figures. This is because the watch readings would have been made at an interval of half a minute or less. The rating and the timing for the long elements are done every half a minute during the performance of the same and also the break point signaling its end. The entries will comprise three-figure entry whenever a full minute has been crossed. Generally, the decimal points are omitted. This is done to save the amount of writing that the study person has to make. Further, by doing so the chance of ambiguity diminishes.

Let us make the above discussion clear through an example assuming that the "time before" was 2.15 minutes. Then the first entry on the study proper made will be 215. Now if the watch was read 2.27 minutes after it was started, the entry that would be made will be 27. Further, the entries will be 40, 52 and 308 if the watch was read at 2.39, 2.51 and 3.07 minutes after it was started. The entries in two and three figures will continue down the sheet until ten minutes have elapsed. After this the entries made will comprise four figures. Generally, the study person continues to make entries in three and four figures until an interval of another ten minutes have elapsed. The study will be terminated by making the "time after" entry. The "time off" reading will also be made at this time and noted in the data panel on the study top sheet. There may be watch readings without accompanying ratings in case where certain delay and stoppage has occurred. Rating of the same is of course not possible since they are not work.

It must be ensured that the entries made in pencil are not erased. This can be done by making this a working rule. However, there may be possibility that the study may contain an error and the same may be corrected without invalidating the study. In such situations, the corrections should be made in ink over the original entry made through pencil. This ensures that the correction was made in the study office and not at the place of study. The part of the study in which there is a doubt of making correction should be ignored. The need may arise to scrap the study and make a fresh one.

A different colour pencil or ink must be used for carrying out all the subsequent work on the study sheet; this will aid in differentiating between the initial recordings. The procedure is made a standing rule by many departments. This will help in eliminating any doubt about the initial readings and the subsequent calculations. Further, besides having the advantage of orderly processing of data, the practice also helps to maintain confidence of workers. The representatives also have faith in the process and therefore have no doubt in the manner in which the studies have been made.

13.2 THE STUDY SUMMARY SHEET

Some amount of work is required to be done before the study summary sheet is completed. This consists of making some simple calculations which may be done by a clerk. The study person then can get on with something else. Until and unless a work study person is well acquainted with all the different procedures as that of instructing the clerk and checking the calculations easily and quickly, the study person is expected to do everything personally.

The data at the head of the study summary sheet is the first thing to be done. Everything in ink must be neatly copied from the study sheets. The elapsed time is then calculated from the data entered for time off and time on. The elapsed time should agree with the final watch reading, when cumulative is practised. If the two are not equal then there is error which must be investigated. The error must be cleared up before proceeding for further work study. This is because a work study will be required to be scrapped off due to a serious error. Once scrapped, the work study needs to be started again. The check time is calculated by summing up the "time before" and "time after". The net time is then obtained by subtracting the "check time" from the elapsed time. When using flyback timing, this should equal the sum of all the observed times. And in case cumulative time is being practised then this should be equal to the sum of all the subtracted times. The sum of all the element times recorded should be added up and compared for agreement with the net time, in case the flyback timing is being practised. This check should be done before proceeding for further studies. The error in comparison should be within 2 per cent. The tolerance in error is provided because it is unlikely that there will be exact agreement.

The check cannot be made in case of cumulative timing until the subtracted times have been obtained and totalled. The accuracy with which the subtractions have been made is checked using the comparisons made. If in any case the error occurs, same should be investigated and corrected. This should be done before work of extension is undertaken.

The study person lists all the repetitive elements on the body of the study summary sheet. This is done in order of occurrence of the elements. The break points used are also noted down on the reverse side of the sheet.

There may be certain variable elements in some of these repetitive elements which will have to be treated in a manner different from the constant elements. A fresh table below the full list of repetitive elements is used for these variable elements. The list of any occasional elements is made below the list of variable elements. The contingency elements of work if any are also noted along with the list of occasional elements. The list is followed by the list of foreign elements and ineffective time. The sheet should then provide for a summarized record of everything observed during the study.

Enter Frequencies

The frequency with which each element occurred is also entered against each of the elements listed on the study summary sheet. The entry made against repetitive elements will read 1/1 or 2/1, etc., since these occur at least once in every cycle. The entry 1/1 indicates that the element occurred once in every cycle while the entry 2/1 indicates that the element occurred twice in every cycle. The occasional elements such as that of sharpening of tools may occur only once every ten or 50 cycles. The entry in such cases will be 1/10 or 1/50. The entries are made in the column headed "F".

The observations taken during a study is the source of deriving frequencies. The representative sample of occurrences for occasional elements gives a true picture of the frequency of occurrence. However, this may not be possible to include in the study which otherwise would have made the study long. Although this can be considered unimportant, in terms of its effect on the overall standard time that will be developed – since the time for such an element will be a very small proportion of the overall time – it is important in gaining the confidence of the workers. If, when examining a study, they see a frequency which they know from experience to be incorrect, they will lose confidence in the study and may use that small point as the basis of a challenge of the entire study. For such elements, it is necessary to confirm the frequency with the supervisor or by analysis of historical records. For example, with an element such as "Replace tool", it should be possible to find the number of tools issued from the stores in a given time period and to relate this to the number of components produced in the same period. A frequency of occurrence of the element "change tool" can then be determined.

13.3 EXTENSION: THE CALCULATION OF BASIC TIME

The next task of making calculation on the time study sheets should only be done by the study person, once the following tasks have been accomplished:

- The entries in the heading block of the study summary sheet.
- List of all the elements involved in the job.
- Entries for the frequencies.
- If necessary, a sketch of layout of the workplace on reverse side of the sheet. A great deal of time and money may be saved by employing a simple instant-print-type camera. A simple scale, such as the rod painted in 1 cm bands, should be included in the photograph.

A different coloured pencil or ink should be used while making the entry for the results of calculations. The colour should be different from that used for making observations at the workplace. The study person may however directly proceed to extension when flyback timing has been used.

In case of the cumulative timing, the subtraction of each watch reading from the one following it is required before obtaining the observed timing for each element. These calculations are entered in the column titled "ST" which stands for subtracted times. The entry is made in the third column on the time study sheet. In the rest of the chapter, a single term "observed time" will be used to mean for both the "subtracted time" and the "observed time". This is because, the subtracted time obtained in case of cumulative timing is same as that of the observed time in case of the flyback timing.

The basic time is derived from the observed time and the same is entered in the column titled "BT" on the time study sheet. Basic time may be defined as the time for carrying out an element of work at standard rating, i.e.,

$$BT = \frac{\text{Observed time} \times \text{Observed rating}}{\text{Standard rating}}$$

The calculation for deriving the basic time from the observed time is known as extension. The effect of extending an observed time for an element to the basic time is shown graphically in Fig. 13.1.

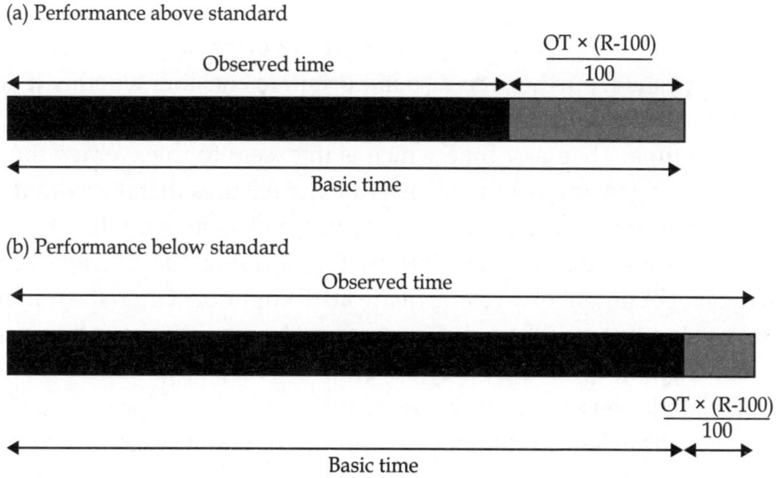

Fig. 13.1: Effect of extension on the time of an element.

The Selected Time

The time that is representative of group of elements or group of times for an element is known as the selected time. The selected time may be observed or basic and the same should be denoted as selected basic time or selected observed time.

Constant Elements

There are a number of reasons for which the results of all the calculations of the basic time for any single constant are same. The representative time for each element should be obtained from all the basic times which have been entered on the time study sheets. The same will be recorded against the element description on the study summary sheet. The same will then be transferred, as the end result of the study, to the analysis of studies sheet.

Working sheet is used to carry out the calculations required to arrive at the selected basic time. The working sheets are then stapled to the time study sheets when completed. A simple calculator or computing equipment can be used to increase the accuracy in the calculations and reduce time.

Examining and selecting of a representative time for a constant element can be done by various methods. The most common of all the methods is making a straight average of the different element times obtained, i.e., sum of all the basic times of a constant element is divided by the number of occasions on which the element was recorded. Before, making the calculation, it is mandated to scrutinize the list of all the basic times, eliminating excessively high or low times, i.e., which are outside the normal range. These ringed times are sometimes styled "rogues"; they should be examined carefully.

Error in timing may result into an exceptionally high time. However, in case of cumulative timing an error of this kind on careful analysis of the study can be revealed. This is obvious from the shortening of the next element which is a result of extensively long time of the preceding element. An error can be made in the extension accounts for another cause of high time. Higher work content caused as a result of variations in material being worked upon or in the method adopted for working is perhaps the most common cause for an extensively long time. Once the source of error has been identified, then the cause must be established. Further, it is also important to consider whether it occurs rarely or frequently. It is also usual practice to eliminate the basic time from the total time and derive the average time. Then any time which is in excess to the average time should be carried down to contingencies. Following this practice ensures that the extra time has been accounted for although it has been treated as contingency, which is what it actually is. It is also advised not to exclude any calculations for deriving the average time if minor variations in the work content of an element are at all common. Often the minor variations can be treated as signals to alert the study person. However, if the minor variations are hard to eliminate then the time study may be continued for a large number of observations so that the calculated average of all the basic times may be sufficiently representative. Efforts should be made at best to eliminate the variations and hence reasons must be found for the variations.

On the other hand, the examination for short time should also be done with great care. This also indicates the error on the part of study person. The shorter time may also indicate that minor method improvement was adopted which resulted in a much shorter time. If this is the case at hand then, the method study should be undertaken again. While doing so special attention should be made to the working method used.

The approach is suitable only for situations where the exceptional times are rare or infrequent and if frequent then only minor in character. Frequent large variations are indicative of elements' nature being variable rather than being constant and it must be treated as such.

An example of a time study made on one element: "Picking a book, inspection, initial back end paper" was observed for 31 times. The basic times calculated are shown below:

Basic minutes

27	26	28
26	25	25
27	29	27
27	28	27
26	28	26
27	27	25
26	27	26
25	26	26
26	27	**49**
27	26	26
		28

It can be seen from the above calculated basic times that the basic time of 0.49 minutes has been emphasized while making the study. This may have occurred when a faulty book was encountered, examined and rejected. The total basic time calculated comes out be 7.97 minutes if the basic time of 0.49 minutes is excluded. The average comes out to be 0.266 minutes per occasion. Numeral 266 will be entered on the study summary sheet and will be carried to the analysis of studies sheet. However, the basic time obtained for the element will be rounded off to the nearest two figures at the end of the study. In this case it is 0.27 minutes. The excess for the emphasized numeral is 0.49 - 0.27 = 0.22 minutes. This excess will be carried down to the contingency record.

It is simple to teach and understand the selection by averaging in this way. This practice is readily accepted by the practitioners and the workers. The averaging gives a more accurate result then obtainable from other methods when the total number of observations made on an element is relatively small. The work content, however increase substantially when short elements have been observed for a large number of times. In order to reduce the calculation time other methods for selection have been devised.

One method is to form a distribution table against the ratings. For the element in the aforementioned example this can be done as below in Table 13.1:

Table 13.1: Ratings and basic times.

Rating	80	85	90	95	100	105
Observed times	31	32	30	28	28	27
		31	30	30	27	
		30	30	27	27	
		31	26	28	26	
		31	27	27	27	
			28	26	28	
			29	29	27	
			29			
			29			
			29			
Total	31	155	258	195	190	27
Basic Times	25	132	232	185	190	28
					Total	792

The basic time of 0.49 minutes which was emphasized in the earlier table has been excluded in the tabulation above. Totaling of the observed time is done for each of the ratings. The corresponding ratings are then multiplied with the totalled observed basic times under them. The sum total then yields the basic time. In this case, it comes out to be 7.92 minutes. This total when divided by 30 yields 0.264 minutes. The result is comparable with that obtained by averaging method.

The selection can be made by adopting a third method that employs constructing a plot. This method also eliminates the need to extend each observed time. This is shown in Fig. 13.2. The entries are made in the form of crosses or dots. Thus two entries are made for each observation made in the two sections of the plot. The time scale is represented by the left-hand axis. The range of times observed is marked on this scale, for example, in this case from 26 to 32. The ratings observed are marked on the scale at the top of the right-hand part, in this case from 80 to 105. To construct the plot, the study person starts the study, makes a cross against the observed time which is then followed by a second cross but under the observed rating.

When the study is completed, the plot will show the frequency distribution of the observed time. A curve fitting procedure is then followed which results in a straight line passing through the plotted points of frequency distribution. The basic time is then selected by entering the right-hand side of the plot and starts to move vertically downwards under the 100 rating until the straight line is intersected.

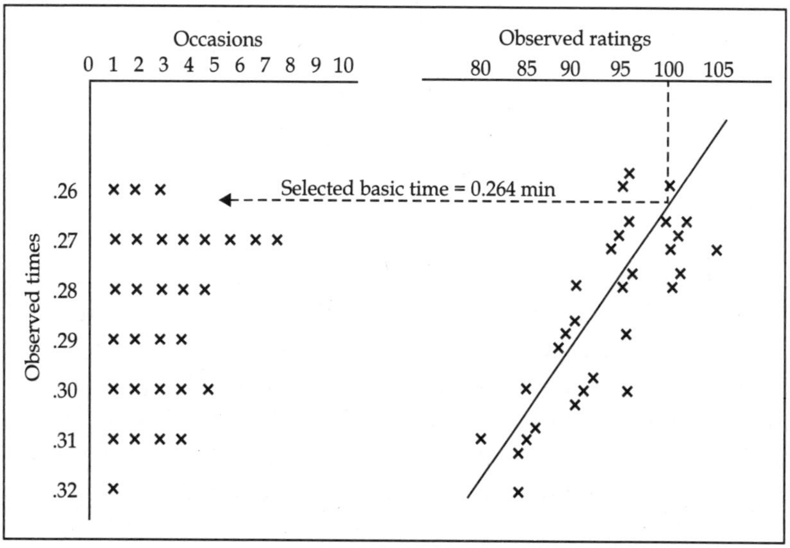

Fig. 13.2: A graphical method of selecting basic time.

The left-hand side of the plot is essential to check whether the distribution follows the normal pattern. The method should not be used if there is any aberration. The distribution patterns produced will each have a significant meaning attached to it. For instance, this may be indicative of the variations in the work, the operatives' rate of working, etc. However, one should restrict oneself from such analysis until unless some experience has been gained. It is advisable to not consider this method until enough experience has been gained.

Variable Elements

For variable elements there is lot of difficulty in making an analysis. The difficulty arises in finding out the cause that causes the basic time to vary and also there may be situations where several elements at once may have to be undertaken for the study. An example of task where such situation arises is that of cutting a wooden plank with the handsaw. The width of the plank causes a variation in the basic time needed to make the cut. The thickness of the planks is another factor that causes the variation in the basic time. The cut will take more time if the saw requires sharpening. Continuing the observation while working with a blunt saw will be disregarded.

The basic time is extended to the observed time while making treatment to the variable element. The analysis sheet in case of the variable elements takes the form of a graph where the basic time is plotted against the unknown variables. The analysis of studies sheet will have the prepared graph attached to it.

A variable that yields a straight line on entering the basic times should be taken as the basis for the plot. In situations where the variability with time is not arithmetically linear, a logarithmic paper can be used. The end product of the variation of the main variable with the time may be a smooth curve. This situation arises when it is quite impossible to discover a straight line variation between the main variable and the time. Basic times for the element will then be selected by reading off the curve at the appropriate point on each occasion on which a standard time has to be compiled.

The nature of the treatment that the study person will give while studying the cross-cutting of planks would depend on whether the operation is carried out rarely or more often during the day. In case the task is performed a number of times each day, then a series of graphs will be required to be built. Each graph will be different depending on the thickness of the wood considered. The relationship between the main variable and the time if established to be linear will aid in establishing a formula. Then taking into account a factor, will lead to the calculation of the basic time. However, if the operation is carried out rarely then the study person would plot the basic times against the product of width of plank and the thickness of the plank. By doing so the study person combines the two main variables. The study person would then try to establish a factor to take into account the hardness of the wood.

A relatively more number of observations would be required in case of a variable element than that for the constant element. This should be planned before embarking on the calculation of the basic times. This is necessary so that all the different conditions and variables likely to be encountered could be recognized. It is also advisable to discover the basis against which to plot the times. This can be done by conducting trial plots against different possibilities, until the indicator of the cause of variable time is recognized.

Each of the methods described has its own merits and demerits. Hence, prescription of any of the method to yield a satisfactory output depends on these merits and demerits. A close attention to the analysis of working methods is necessary at this juncture of method study to discover the reasons behind the variation in basic times.

13.4 COMPLETING THE STUDY SUMMARY SHEET

Once the calculations have been completed, the study person makes the entries into the study summary sheet. This helps in maintaining a clear and concise record of all the gathered observations and information. The selected basic time of the constant element is entered against each of the constant elements. Further, the number of times the observations have been made for the particular constant element is also entered. Similarly, in case of variable element, the relationship between the basic time and the controlling value is entered against the respective element. In some cases where the graph sheets have been used for the analysis, the reference to such graphs should be recorded in the study sheet. The study finally concludes with any of the occasional or any of the foreign elements which may have appeared during the study.

It is also advisable to show the calculations made for any of the contingency elements and hence any of the contingency time extracted. In order to have a basis for comparing of one contingency with the other, the contingency basic time is usually expressed as a percentage of the total basic time of the repetitive work observed during the study.

The ineffective time must be totalled and entered in the summary sheet. The ineffective time is the time period during which no work has been done which may be because of the rest and relaxation of the operatives.

13.5 ELECTRONIC TIME STUDY

The above procedure applies equally to studies taken with an electronic stopwatch. Where the study has been taken with an electronic study board or data capture device, the procedure will be different and will depend on the degree of sophistication of the system being used.

In the simplest systems (and as the first stage in more complex systems) the recording device simply prints out (via a small in-built printer or after connection to an external printer) a listing of all the observation data in terms of element identification, rating and elapsed time, together with basic summary data such as total elapsed time and possibly average rating. These data are then handled just as if the study had been taken with a conventional stopwatch. It is important that this basic record of the study data is maintained as part of the study file so that the source of subsequent time values can be identified and validated. Equally, the system should ensure that the basic computerized record is tamper-proof, especially before this first printout of data is taken.

Most electronic systems offer additional functions and take the user through subsequent stages of extension, frequency allocation, and so on. Although much of this is automatic (such as the extension of observed times to basic times), the system must offer the analyst the opportunity to identify and ring out "rogue times" referred to earlier in section 4, and omit them from subsequent analysis. The analyst will also need to input element frequencies and allowances if the calculation of a standard time is to be carried out. Electronic time study systems take the drudgery out of analysis but the responsibility for that analysis and the results of it rests with the study person.

Many systems transfer the data from the recording device to a personal computer for this analysis stage. This has the advantage of releasing the study board for further studywork. It also allows the transfer of data over telephone lines so that studies taken at a remote site can be transmitted to "base" for the analysis and reporting stages to be carried out. (Another advantage is that the analysis software has to be provided only once – if it were part of the study board itself, the analysis facility would be duplicated in each device.) This allows the situation to be established where a team of study persons can take a large number of studies in a relatively short space of time and have those studies analyzed by a separate analysis team or support officer. It is important though that the person taking the study should examine any such analysis before final results are derived from it and issued, and "signs off the analysis as being validated". The final result of this process will be a study summary sheet containing the same data as for a manually taken study. This sheet may be produced directly by the system, after the input of all relevant data by the analyst, or by the analyst using data output from the system.

An example of such a summary sheet, produced by the Tectime System in the United Kingdom, is shown in Fig. 13.3. When the system in use is a full-time study system, it will also allow the continuation of support into other areas such as the merging of several studies of the same job and the establishment of work content and standard times for such work. The principles to be followed are exactly the same as those for manually derived study data.

Tectime Data Systems Ltd. Demonstration Package	Summary to standard time for study MANUFACT/SOCK1 by cycles		Singleman V5 System
Study name: Sock-1	Job Ref: Socks	Second Ref: A — Analyst: P.S.	Operator: K. Hayes
Date: 01/02/91	Start time: 06.00:00	Finish time: 15.31:00	Elapsed time: 57L70
Site: Number 3	Section: CORTESE	Dept:	Area: CORTESE
Remarks: 316 dozen produced 1 3/24 damages/grades			
Job on file: FACTORY - STRAGHTENING - LOADING OPERATIVE - HOLD UPS - LINKED TO MACHINES			
Unit A: Pair of socks — 2000.00			

Element Code	type	Total obs. time	Total bm's	Total obn's	Bm's obn	Frequency	Bm's cycle	RA %	Sms.
1.	Repetitive Pick up sock from bench adjacent to m/c Open and present to m/c	406.220	402.627	3727	0.106	2/1	0.216	12.00	0.242
2	Repetitive Pick up first sock and load onto form Reject and place aside	0.680	0.664	5	0.133	2/100	0.003	12.00	0.003
3	Repetitive Load 1st – Reject and place aside Load next	4.450	4.314	21	0.205	2/100	0.004	12.00	0.005
5	Repetitive Obtain full bag of work and empty onto bench	2.510	2.340	8	0.293	2/500	0.001	12.00	0.001
CY1	Contingency Relevant talking	2.720	2.710	4	0.677	4/2000	0.001		
CY2	Contingency Clean machine	0.650	0.650	1	0.660	1/2000	0.000		
CY10	Contingency File nails	2.220	2.220	2	1.110	2/2000	0.001		
IF1	Ineffective Operative not working	14.710		1					
IF3	Ineffective Operative at break	71.520		3					
IF4	Ineffective Operative in restaurant	50.810		4					
IF5	Ineffective Personal needs	3.650		1					

Totals Box	Observed time Min.	%Total	Basic time Min.	% Total	Standard time Min.	% Total	
Repetitive	413.85	73.9	409.94	98.7	0.25	100.0	Average rating = 99.06
Contingency	5.59	1.0	5.58	1.3			
Ineffective	140.69	2.51					
Total time	560.14		415.52		0.25		
Total SMs		4.000%	0.2509				
Contingency		3.000%	0.0100				
Policy			0.0075				
Total SMV			0.2664				
Parts per hour @ 100:			223.6204				

Fig. 13.3: An example of a study summary sheet produced using electronic capture devices.

How Many Studies?

The study should be made for each of the different conditions of working. For instance, the changing atmospheric conditions during the work performed in different shifts.

The study for the work involved in starting and shutting a particular study should also be studied. A separate work value may be needed for the startup and shutdown activities. Alternatively, allowances can be used to take into account these activities while making calculations for the individual jobs. For instance, inking up the machine may be required for the presses in the industries employing printing. In industries where special clothing is required, a separate time may be required. Further, for cleaning workplace and the machines, allowances need to be provided.

Thus, studies will have to be made for all the incidental and ancillary activities. A plot for the cumulative average basic time for the study made on element is one of the methods of determining the number of cycles required to be observed for making the calculations of basic times. The cumulative average is obtained by the addition of the product of the basic time and the number of observations made for the first study to that of the second study and then dividing the sum by the total number of observations made for both the studies. In the similar fashion the plot is made for the successive studies made. When the plot settles down at a constant level then it is suggestive of adequate number of studies for that element. An example is shown in Fig. 13.4.

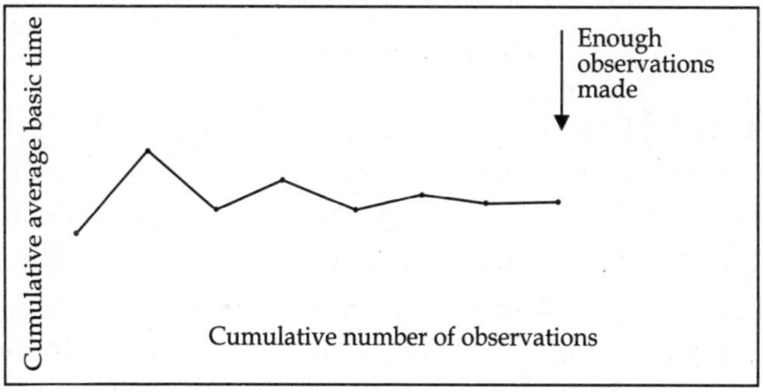

Fig. 13.4: Cumulative average basic times for a constant element.

13.6 THE ANALYSIS OF STUDIES SHEET

Figure 13.5 shows an example of an "analysis of studies sheet." As soon as the study has been completed, the results obtained are copied from the study summary sheet and entered on the "analysis of studies sheet." The form in the example shows the recording of all the elements forming a job. Further it also provides the full details of the repetitive and occasional elements. The form also records for any of the repetitive and contingency times observed. Graphs are appended to the sheet to record the results obtained from studying variable elements.

Analysis of studies									
Operation				Department:			Section:		
Details of machine, materials, etc.		Study No.:		Totals	Average or selected basic times per occasion	Frequency per cycle	Basic time per cycle	Personal + fatigue Relaxation allowance	Standard time SM/SH per
		Date made:							
		Operative:							
		Clock No.:							
		Machine No.:							
		Study taken by:							
		No. of cycles studied:		Cycles					
El. No.	Element description		Basic times	BM	BM		BM	%	SM

Note: El. = element; BM = Basic minutes; SM = Standard minutes; SH = Standard hours.

Fig. 13.5: Analysis sheet.

The final representative times is calculated for each element. This is done after ensuring that enough observations have been made for an element. The overall weighted average score is obtained for each element. The calculation doesn't take into account any entries which are found to be erroneous after making subsequent work study.

The basic time per cycle, per job or per operations is then easy to calculate once the final representative times have been calculated. This is done by multiplying the time per occasion by the frequency per cycle for the occurrence of each element. In case of variable elements, appropriate graphs may be used to obtain the basic time. A straight line relationship can also be used to arrive at the basic time for the variable elements.

The allowance necessary for any contingencies is also calculated on the analysis of study sheet. This is done only when provisions have been made to consider the contingencies. First the calculation is made for the total percentage that the contingencies make up in the total work observed. If the percentage is same both for the contingencies and that devoted to repetitive and occasional elements, then the contingencies are to be recorded in basic minutes. However, if the percentage for the contingencies is small, then the basic time is recorded in terms of percentage. If the percentage comes out to be 4 to 5 per cent higher, then analysis is made to inquire the causes for the contingencies and to eliminate the same.

In order to arrive at standard time, certain allowances are required to be added to the basic time. In the subsequent sections different allowances have been discussed. Before doing so, however, it is necessary to state clearly what is meant by two terms which have been mentioned frequently in the preceding pages but which have not yet been precisely defined: namely **work content** and **standard time.**

13.7 WORK CONTENT

In the chapters at the beginning of this book, the term "work content" was used frequently to describe what the words themselves suggest: the amount of work which has to be done to complete a job or operation, as distinct from any ineffective time which may occur. In time study practice, however, the word "work" is accorded a meaning which is slightly different from its usual meaning in ordinary English usage. An observer who was familiar with the word only in its usual sense would say, when watching operatives at their jobs, that when the workers were actually doing something they were working, and that when they were resting or doing nothing they were not working. In time study practice, however, we are concerned with measuring work in numerical terms, and for this purpose the word "work" is extended to include not only the physical labour performed but also the proper amount of relaxation or rest necessary to recover from the fatigue caused by that laborious task. We shall see later that relaxation allowances are made for other purposes besides recovery from fatigue; but for the moment the important point is that, when in time study we speak of "work" and set out to measure it, we define work to include the appropriate relaxation allowance, so that the amount of work in a job is taken to be not only the time needed at standard performance to do whatever the job requires but also the additional time which is considered necessary for relaxation.

The work content of a job or operation is defined as: basic time + relaxation allowance + any allowance for additional work, e.g., that part of contingency allowance which represents work.

13.8 ALLOWANCES

We have seen that, during the method study investigation which should be carried out before any job is timed, the energy expended by the worker in performing the operation should be reduced to a minimum through the development of improved methods and procedures, in accordance with the principles of motion economy and, wherever practicable, by mechanization. Even when the most practical, economic and effective method has been developed, however, many jobs will still require the expenditure of human effort, and some allowance must therefore be made for recovery from fatigue and for relaxation. Allowance must also be made to enable a worker to attend to personal needs; and other allowances (e.g. contingency allowances) may also have to be added to the basic time in order to give the work content.

The determination of allowances is probably the most controversial part of work study. For reasons that will be explained later, it is very difficult to determine precisely the allowances needed for a given job. What should therefore be attempted is an objective assessment of the allowances that can be consistently applied to the various elements of work or to various operations.

The fact that the calculation of allowances cannot be altogether accurate under all circumstances is no excuse for using them as a dumping ground for any factors that have been missed or neglected in making the time study. We have seen how the study person can go to great lengths to arrive at fair and accurate time standards. These should not be spoilt by the hasty or ill considered addition of a few percentage points here and there "just in case". Above all, allowances should not be used as "loosening" factors. The difficulty experienced in preparing a universally accepted set of precise allowances that can be applied to every working situation anywhere in the world is due to various reasons. The most important among them are:

- **Factors related to the individual.** If every worker in a particular working area were to be considered individually, it might well be found that a thin, active, alert worker at the peak of physical condition required a smaller allowance to recover from fatigue than an obese, inept worker. Similarly, every worker has a unique learning curve or a rate of learning which can affect the manner in which the work is conducted. There is also some reason to believe that there may be ethnic variations in the response to the degree of fatigue experienced by workers, particularly when engaged in heavy manual work. Undernourished workers take a longer time than others to recover from fatigue.
- **Factors related to the nature of the work itself.** Many of the tables developed for the calculation of allowances give figures which may be acceptable for light and medium work in industry but which are inadequate when applied to operations involving very heavy and strenuous work, such as work beside furnaces in steel mills. Moreover, every working situation has its own particular attributes which may affect the degree of fatigue experienced by the worker or may lead to unavoidable delay in the execution of a job. Examples of these factors are: whether a worker has to perform the work standing up or sitting down, and posture during work; whether force has to be exerted to move or carry loads from one place to another; whether the work itself results in undue eye or mental strain, and so on. Other factors inherent in

the job can also contribute to the need for allowances, although in a different way, for example, when protective clothing or gloves have to be worn, or when there is constant danger, or when there is a risk of spoiling or damaging the product.

- **Factors related to the environment.** Allowances, in particular relaxation allowances, have to be determined with due regard to various environmental factors such as heat, humidity, noise, dirt, vibration, lighting intensity, dust, wet conditions, and so on. Each of these will affect the amount of relaxation allowances needed. Environmental factors may also be seasonal in nature. This is particularly so for those who work in the open air, such as workers in the construction industry or in shipyards. It should now be more clear to the reader why it is so difficult to devise an internationally accepted scheme of allowances to meet every working situation in the world. It should also be stated here, in very clear terms, that the ILO has not adopted, nor is it likely to adopt, any standards relating to the determination of allowances.
- **Relaxation allowances**. Relaxation allowance provides an operative for recovering from the physiological and psychological effects occurring due to performance of a job under specified conditions, i.e., provides for recovering from fatigue. Therefore by providing rest and pauses the consequences of fatigue can be avoided. Further, the relaxation allowance also allows operatives to give attention to their personal needs. The nature of the job is a factor in deciding for the amount of allowance to be given.

Allowances for fatigue are normally added **element by element** to the basic times, so that a work value for each element is built up separately, the element standard times being combined to yield the standard time for the whole job or operation. In this way it is possible to deal with any extra allowance which may be required to compensate for severe climatic conditions, since the element may sometimes be performed in cool weather and sometimes when it is very hot. Allowances for climatic conditions have to be applied to the **working shift** or **working day** rather than to the element or job, in such a way that the amount of work which the worker is expected to produce over the day or the shift is reduced. The standard time for the job remains the same, whether the job is performed in summer or winter, since it is intended to be a measure of the work that the job contains.

There are two major components to relaxation allowances: **fixed allowances** and **variable allowances.**

- **Fixed allowances** are composed of:
  - Allowances for **personal needs.** The personal needs such as washing, going to lavatory, etc., can be met by an operative by making use of this allowance. Usually this ranges between 5 to 7 per cent.
  - Allowances for **basic fatigue.** The allowances for basic fatigue are always a constant. The allowance particularly takes care to take into account the energy expended while carrying out work. Usually, this is about 4 per cent of basic time.

This is considered to be adequate for a worker who carries out the job while being seated, who is engaged in light work in good working conditions and who is called upon to make only normal use of hands, legs and senses.

- **Variable allowances:** These are added to fixed allowances when working conditions differ markedly from those stated above, for instance because of poor environmental conditions that cannot be improved, added stress and strain in performing the job in question, and so on.

  As mentioned above, a number of important studies have been carried out by various research organizations trying to develop a more rational approach to the calculation of variable allowances. There are an enormous number of relaxation allowance tables in existence. Most management consultants in all countries have their own tables.

  For the various reasons mentioned earlier in the chapter, when using one of the standard scales it is always preferable to check the amount of relaxation time they yield by carrying out whole-day studies at the workplace, noting the amount of time which the workers actually spend in relaxation (in one form or another) and comparing this with the calculated allowance. Checks of this sort do at least show whether the scale is, in general, too tight or too loose. Relaxation allowances are given as percentages of the basic time. As mentioned earlier, they are normally calculated on an element-by-element basis. This is particularly the case when the effort expended on different elements varies widely (for example, where a heavy workpiece has to be lifted on or off a machine at the beginning and end of an operation). If, on the other hand, it is considered that no one element of a job is any more or any less fatiguing than any of the other elements, the simplest course is to add up all the elemental basic time first and then add the allowance as a single percentage to the total.

- **Contingency allowances:** In order to account for the delays in the work, a small allowance known as contingency allowance is included in the compilation of the standard time. However, due to their occurrence being infrequent and irregular it becomes uneconomical to measure them. Besides providing for the unavoidable delays, the allowance also takes into account the minor extra work. Thus a contingency allowance is split into two parts: allowance that attracts for fatigue allowance and the allowance for the delay. Since contingency allowances are small, therefore these are usually expressed as a percentage of the total repetitive basic minutes in the job. Contingency allowances should only be allowed for cases where a study person finds it impossible to eliminate them. Further, where allowed, they should not be greater than 5 per cent. Care is to taken that such allowances do not act as loosening factors, i.e., these should not lay any obstruction to a proper time study. Contingency allowance in fairness should be given in the enterprises where production work is not well organized.

- **Policy allowances:** In order to provide for satisfactory level of earnings, an increment in the form of a policy allowance is applied to the standard time. This increment is different than the bonus increment. Policy allowances should only be used under specified circumstances and caution must be taken while doing so. This is because; the policy allowance is not the genuine part of the standard time. Therefore, it is dealt with separately in comparison to the basic times. If policy allowance is used at all, then it should be arranged in addition to standard times. The policy allowances aid in lining up the standard times with the requirements of wage agreements between the employer and the trade unions.
- **Special allowances:** These allowances are provided for activities that are not part of the normal operation but without these activities it is difficult to achieve the satisfactory performance of the work. Such allowances classify themselves as special allowances. The nature of special allowances may be temporary or permanent. Therefore care must be taken to specify the nature of such allowances. Time study must be used to determine these allowances wherever possible.

Start-up allowance is provided to compensate for the time that is taken by the work at its start, i.e., before the beginning of the production. For taking into account the waiting time occurring at the end of the day, a **shut-down allowance** may similarly be given. A **cleaning allowance** is given to take into account the time given for cleaning of the machine or the workplace. **Tool allowance** is an allowance of time to cover the adjustment and maintenance of tools.

There are certain allowances that are normally given per occasion or per batch. **Setup allowance** is one such allowance. The setup allowance is usually given to take into account the time required for preparing a machine or process for production. The time may be required to make alterations in the setting of a machine after the production run is completed. For such cases, a **dismantling allowance** may be given.

In cases where production of defective products is inherent in a process, a **reject allowance** may be included in a standard time. An **excess work allowance** may be given as an addition to the standard time, to compensate for extra work occasioned by a temporary departure from standard conditions.

For the workers involved in acquiring skills and developing the ability, **learning allowances** may be given to trainee operatives. Similarly, for the operatives engaged in instructing a trainee a **training allowance** is usually given. Very similar is an **implementation allowance,** given to workers asked to adopt a new method or process to encourage them to attempt an enthusiastic implementation of the new ways and prevent their loss of earnings by doing so.

A **small batch allowance** is required to enable a worker working on small batches to decide what to do and how to go about it (from instructions, by experience, or by trial and error) and then to work up to a standard performance by practice and repetition. The calculation of this allowance will depend on whether it is a one-of-a-type batch or not, on the length and batch size or run length, and on the frequency of similar work and its degree of complexity.

13.9 THE STANDARD TIME

It is now possible to obtain a complete picture of the standard time for a straightforward manual job or operation, one which is considered to attract only the two allowances which have so far been discussed in detail: contingency allowance and relaxation allowance. The standard time for the job will be the sum of the standard times for all the elements of which it is made up, due regard being paid to the frequencies with which the elements recur, plus the contingency allowance (with its relaxation allowance increment). In other words: Standard time is the total time in which a job should be completed at standard performance. The standard time may be represented graphically as shown in Fig. 13.6.

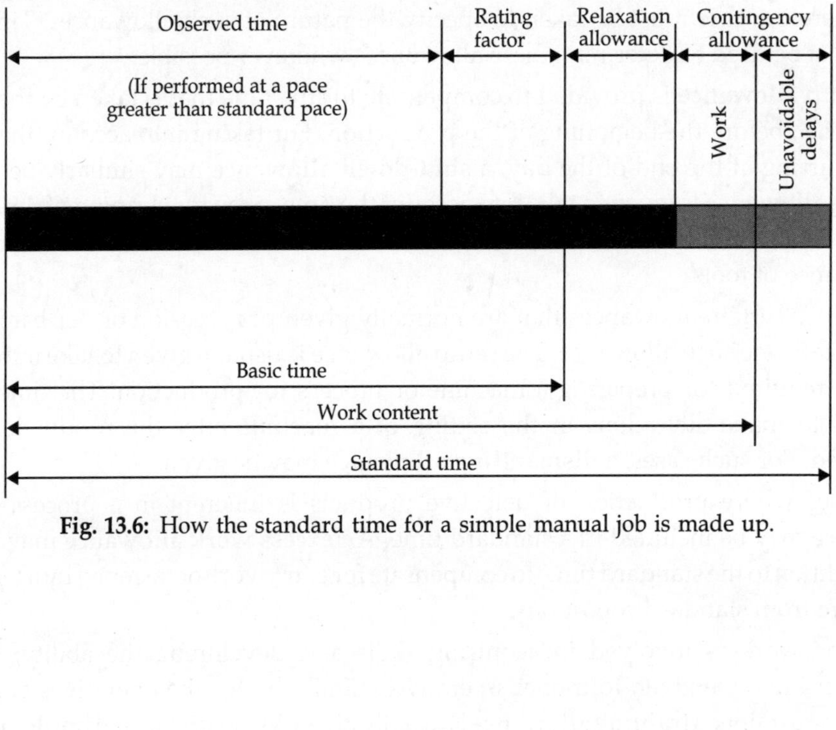

Fig. 13.6: How the standard time for a simple manual job is made up.

14
Predetermined Time Standards

14.1 DEFINITION

Predetermined time standards (PTS), also referred to as predetermined motion time systems (PMTS) or synthetic time standards, are advanced techniques which aim at defining the time needed for the performance of various operations by derivation from pre-set standards of time for various motions and not by direct observation and measurement. These techniques are not normally considered suitable for trainees to use until they have gained a real understanding of, and considerable experience in, work study practice. They will also require specialized PTS training. The essential nature of these standards will be explained in this chapter.

A predetermined time standard is a work measurement technique whereby times established for basic human motions (classified according to the nature of the motion and the conditions under which it is made) are used to build up the time for a job at a defined level of performance.

The nature of PTS systems can be easily illustrated by reference to a simple work cycle, such as putting a washer on a bolt. The operator will **reach** the washer, **grasp** the washer, **move** the washer to the bolt, **position** it on the bolt and **release** it.

Many operations consist, broadly speaking, of some or all of these five basic motions. To these are added other body motions and a few other elements. Table 14.1 illustrates the components of basic PTS. By examining a given operation and identifying the basic motions of which it is composed, and by referring to PTS tables which indicate standard times for each type of motion performed under given circumstances, it is possible to derive a standard time for the operation as a whole.

Table 14.1: Components of a basic PTS.

Motion	Description
REACH	Move hand to destination
GRASP	Secure control of object with fingers
MOVE	Move object
POSITION	Line up and engage object
RELEASE	Let go of object
BODY MOTIONS	Leg, trunk movements

14.2 ORIGINS

The pioneer of motion classification was Frank B. Gilbreth, whose "therblig" subdivisions of hand or hand and eye motions were the key concept in the development of motion study. Two main ideas underlying Gilbreth's approach were that the act of making a detailed critical analysis of work methods stimulates ideas for method improvement; and that the evaluation of alternative work methods can be achieved by a simple comparison of the number of motions, the better method being the one requiring fewer motions.

The credit for adding the time dimension to motion study is attributed to A. B. Segur, who in 1927 stated that "within practical limits the time required for all experts to perform true fundamental motions is a constant". Segur developed the first predetermined time standards, calling his system "motion time analysis". Little is known publicly about the system since he exploited it as a management consultant and bound his clients to secrecy.

The next important development was the work of J. H. Quick and his associates, who originated the "work factor system" in 1934. Like Segur's system, this was exploited on a management consultancy basis and little information was published about it. However, it was eventually adopted by a large number of companies and is now in active use.

A considerable number and variety of PTS systems were produced during and following the Second World War. Among these was a system which has become very widely used throughout the world, Methods-Time Measurement (MTM). Because of its importance, MTM will be used here to illustrate the way in which predetermined time standards are arrived at.

MTM was first developed by three men working on the system at the Westinghouse Electric Corporation in the United States: H. B. Maynard, G. J. Stegemerten and J. L. Schwab. Their findings were published, and thus, for the first time, full details of a PTS system were made freely available to everyone. MTM has also set up, in various countries, independent non-profit-making MTM associations to control the standards of training and practice and to continue research into and the development of MTM. These associations have established an international coordinating body, the International MTM Directorate. In 1965 a simplified form of MTM, known as MTM-2, was developed, and this led to a rapid increase in the use of the system. In addition, a number of other systems were also derived for particular categories of work such as maintenance work or office work which were intended to permit a faster and easier derivation of standard times.

14.3 ADVANTAGES OF PTS SYSTEMS

PTS systems offer a number of advantages over stopwatch time study. With PTS systems one time is indicated for a given motion, irrespective of where such a motion is performed. In stopwatch time study, it is not so much a motion as a sequence of motions making up an operation that is timed. Timing by direct observation and rating can sometimes lead to inconsistency. A PTS system, which avoids both rating and direct observation, can lead to more consistency in setting standard times.

Since the times for the various operations can be derived from standard time tables, it is possible to define the standard time for a given operation even before production begins, and often while the process is still at the design stage. This is one of the great advantages of PTS systems, as they allow the work study person to change the layout and design of the workplace and of the necessary jigs and fixtures in such a way that the optimum production time is achieved. They also make it possible, even before starting the operation, to draw up an estimate of the cost of production, and this could obviously be valuable for estimating and tendering purposes or for budgeting. PTS systems are not too difficult to apply and can be less time consuming than other methods when time standards for certain operations are determined. They are particularly useful for very short repetitive time cycles such as assembly work in the electronics industry.

14.4 CRITICISMS OF PTS SYSTEMS

In view of the value of PTS systems, it is surprising that it took so long for them to become part of general work study practice. The main reason for this delay is probably the considerable number and variety of systems that have been produced, together with the fact that many of them could be obtained only by employing consultants. At present, over 200 such systems exist. This proliferation has led to complaints from management, trade unions and work study specialists.

Furthermore, any PTS system is rather complicated. It is not easy to learn, and a work study person needs a good deal of practice before being able to apply it correctly. The task of learning enough about the various systems to be able to judge their claims and their relative merits is an almost impossible one. For example, some systems do not go into sufficient detail in defining a certain motion. They might, for instance, give the same time for the movement both of an empty cup and of one full of water, or for the movement of a dry brush and of one laden with paint, which must be moved with care. PTS systems cannot also cope readily with movements made under abnormal conditions, for example, movements made when the worker is wearing protective clothing or when the movements are made in an abnormal position, such as a worker reaching to a confined space behind a pipe. The situation was made more complicated by the lack of freely available information on many systems, whose tables were considered to be the property of their developers and were thus not available for publication.

Some work study researchers also questioned the basic assumptions of PTS systems. In part, these criticisms were justified, although some appear to have arisen through misinformation or misunderstanding. PTS systems do not, as was claimed, eliminate the need for the stopwatch, any more than they eliminate method study or work sampling. Machine time, process time and waiting time are not measurable with PTS systems, and occasional or incidental elements are often more economically measured by using other techniques. In fact, it is difficult to obtain 100 per cent coverage in a plant using only a PTS system, and for certain operations such as batch production or non-repetitive jobs the use of such a system can be an expensive proposition.

One type of criticism stems from a too literal interpretation of the basic assumption of Ṡegur, quoted above. In fact, absolute constant times are not implied. The times indicated in PTS tables are **averages,** and the limits associated with the averages are small enough to be neglected in all practical circumstances.

Another common criticism is that it is invalid to add up times for individual small motions in the way required by PTS systems because the time taken to perform a particular motion is influenced by the motions preceding and following it. It is unfair to criticize the more important PTS systems on these grounds, because not only were these relationships clearly recognized by their originators but also special provision was made to ensure that the essential correlations were maintained. In the case of MTM, for example, this was achieved by establishing subdivisions of the main classes of motions and by creating special definitions and rules of application to ensure their essential linking. The relationships are also preserved in simplified systems such as MTM-2.

It has also been declared that the direction of the motion influences the time, for example, it takes longer to cover the same distance when moving upwards than when moving downwards. No PTS system isolates this variable. MTM researchers would agree that the direction of the motion is an important variable. However, they argue that in a single work cycle the operative will not be reaching only upwards, nor always away from the body, nor making only anticlockwise turns: he or she will reach downwards or towards the body or make clockwise turns also, and so justify the use of average values.

14.5 DIFFERENT FORMS OF PTS SYSTEMS

A work study person is likely to encounter a number of different forms of PTS systems, and will therefore find it useful to understand the main ways in which the systems vary, as well as differences as regards levels and scope of application of data, motion classification and time units.

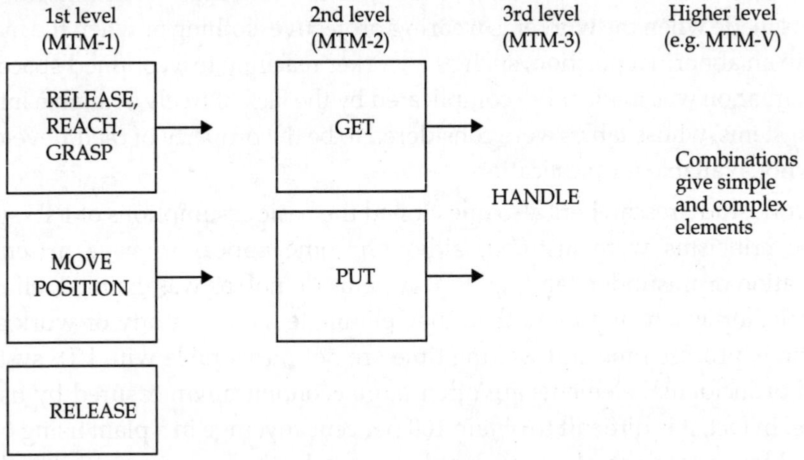

Fig. 14.1: PTS data levels: Basic motions.

Data Levels

Figure 14.1 illustrates data levels by means of the official International MTM systems: MTM-1, MTM-2 and MTM-3.

The first level comprises the motions *RELEASE, REACH, GRASP, MOVE, POSITION, RELEASE.* At the second level these motions are combined: in MTM-2, for instance, the motions are *GET* and *PUT.* At the third level, the motions have been further combined as *HANDLE,* to give a description of the complete work cycle. Beyond the third level there are as yet no completely clear-cut rules, and methods of classification vary according to the work area for which the data are intended.

Scope of Application of Data

PTS systems vary as regards the universality of their application. It is difficult to explain this concept exactly, but Table 14.2 attempts some clarification. First of all there are systems of universal application, which cover all work anywhere.

This is so for motion data at the MTM-1, 2 or 3 levels and for the Work Factor systems. Second, there are data which relate to a main occupation, for example, office work, maintenance work or some kinds of production work. Examples of these are Master Clerical Data for the office and MTM-V, the Swedish MTM Association data for machine shops. Finally, there is the least general category: the specific data systems which are developed for use in particular factories or departments. These data are not transferable without validation studies.

Table 14.2: Scope of application of data.

Degree	PTS System	Scope of Application
1-Universal	MTM-1,2,3; Work Factor	Transferable throughout the world and applicable in all manual work areas
2-General	Master Clerical Data (office); MTM-V (machine shops)	Transferable but within a work area
3-Specific	Standard data for particular departments in a plant	Not transferable without validation studies

Motion Classification

PTS systems provide information about manual work cycles in terms of basic human motions. There are differences between the criteria adopted for the classification of these motions. Broadly speaking, there are two main sets:

- object-related classification; and
- behaviour-related classification.

The object-related classification is employed in the majority of PTS systems (including Work Factor, Dimensional Motion Times and MTM-1) and virtually all the data systems relating to main occupational groups or specifically designed for use within a plant. In an object-related system, reference may be made to characteristics of parts (such as grasping a 6 × 6 × 6 mm object), or to the nature of the surrounding conditions (such as reaching out to an object which is jumbled up with other objects, or reaching out to an object which is lying flat against a surface). The classification is, however, not entirely object-related since motions such as Release Load or Disengage have behavioural definitions.

Unlike most systems, MTM-2 employs exclusively behavioural concepts. This is also true of MTM-3, Master Standard Data and a few less known systems. The behaviour-related systems classify motions according to what they look like to an observer: for example, a movement of the empty hand for a distance of between 5 and 15 cm followed by a grasping action made by a simple closing of the fingers defines the *GET* motion in the MTM-2 system (see below).

Time Units

No two PTS systems have the same set of time values. This is partly due to the fact that different systems have different motion classes and the time data therefore refer to different things. Again, the choice of the basic unit (fractions of a second, minutes, hour) may vary, and some systems follow the practice of adding contingency allowances to motion times, whereas others do not. A final major cause of variations arises from the differences in the performance level implied in the time data. The methods adopted for standardizing, normalizing or averaging the motion times are not uniform. Consequently, PTS time data are divided into one of two sets: work factor systems, which express their data in minutes; and MTM systems, expressed in time measurement units (tmu) which represent one hundred-thousandth of an hour or about one twenty-eighth of a second. The MTM time values, which were derived mainly from film analysis of a variety of industrial operations (the method was to count the number of "frames" occupied by each motion), were standardized using the well-known "Westinghouse" or "Levelling" system. The times are stated to be those which are achieved by an experienced operative of average skill, working with average effort and consistency under average conditions. The performance level, MTM 100, is therefore somewhat less than BSI 100. A public statement on this by the United Kingdom Institute of Management Services and the MTM Association suggests that MTM 100 equals BSI 83.

Other Considerations

Some important properties of PTS systems are much less easy to establish and to compare than the aspects discussed in the previous subsections. Examples of these are the precision and accuracy of the time data, speed of application, methods description capability, and learning time. The lack of reliable, detailed information and, to some extent, the lack of agreed design criteria hamper comparison of these properties.

14.6 USE OF PTS SYSTEMS

The system most likely to be used by the work study person is MTM-2. The following categories constitute the MTM-2 system. Each will be explained in detail in the following subsection.

Category	**Code**
GET	GA GB GC
PUT	PA PB PC
REGRASP	R
APPLY PRESSURE	A
EYE ACTION	E
FOOT MOTION	F
STEP	S
BEND AND ARISE	B
WEIGHT FACTORS	GW PW
CRANK	C

Table 14.3: MTM-2 data card.

	Time in tmu					
Code	GA	GB	GC	PA	PB	PC
- 5	3	7	14	3	10	21
-15	6	10	19	6	15	26
-30	9	14	23	11	19	30
-45	13	18	27	15	24	36
-80	17	23	32	20	30	41
GW: 1 per 1 kg					PW: 1 per 5 kg	
A	R	E	C	S	F	B
14	6	7	15	18	9	61

The MTM-2 system provides time standards ranging from 3 to 61 tmu. These are shown on the data card reproduced in Table 14.3. As stated above, one tmu equals one hundred-thousandth of an hour.

MTM-2 Categories

- *GET(G)*

  GET is an action with the predominant purpose of reaching out with the hand or fingers to an object, grasping the object and subsequently releasing it.

  The scope of *GET*

  - Starts : with reaching out to the object;

- Includes : Reaching out to, gaining control and subsequently releasing control of the object;
- Ends : when the object is released.

Selection of a *GET* is done by considering three variables :

- Case of *GET*– distinguished by the grasping action employed;
- Distance reached;
- Weight of the object or its resistance to motion.

Cases of *GET* are judged by the following decision model:

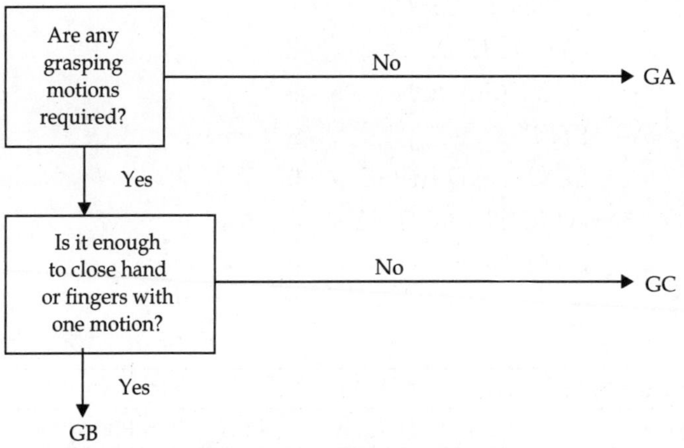

Fig. 14.2: Decision model.

An example of GA is putting the palm of the hand on the side of a box in order to push it across a table.

An example of GB is getting an easy-to-handle object, such as a one-inch cube, which is lying by itself.

An example of GC is getting the cover of a page of this book in order to turn it over.

Distance is a principal variable in *GET,* and five distance classes are provided. Distances are judged by the upper limits of the classes, which are 5, 15, 30, 45 and over 45 cm. The code 80 is assigned to the highest class. Distances are estimated from the path of travel of the hand, less any body assistance.

cm		Code
Over	Not over	
0.0	5.0	– 5
5.0	15.0	– 15
15.0	30.0	– 30
30.0	45.0	– 45
45.0	–	– 80

- GET WEIGHT (GW)

  GET WEIGHT is the action required for the muscles of the hand and arm to take up the weight of the object.

  The scope of *GET WEIGHT*
  - Starts: with the grasp on the object completed;
  - Includes: muscular force necessary to gain full control of the weight of the object
  - Ends: when the object is sufficiently under control to permit movement of the object.

GET WEIGHT occurs after the fingers have closed on the object in the preceding *GET*. It must be accomplished before any actual movement can take place. When the weight or resistance is less than 2 kg per hand, no GW is assigned. When resistance exceeds 2 kg, 1 tmu is assigned for every kg including the first two.

- PUT(P)

  PUT is an action with the predominant purpose of moving an object to a destination with the hand or fingers.

  The scope of PUT
  - Starts: with an object grasped and under control at the initial place;
  - Includes: all transporting and correcting motions necessary to place an object;
  - Ends: with object still under control at the intended place.

  Selection of a *PUT* is done by considering three variables:
  - Case of *PUT*– distinguished by the correcting motions employed;
  - Distance moved;
  - Weight of the object or its resistance to motion.

  Cases of PUT are judged by the following decision model:

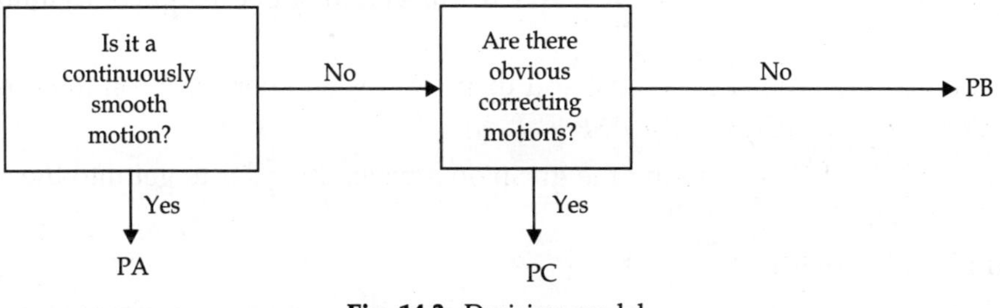

Fig. 14.3: Decision model.

An example of PA is tossing aside an object.

An example of PB is the action of putting a 12 mm ball in a 15 mm diameter hole.

An example of PC is inserting a Yale or similar key in a lock.

A correction is not likely to be confused with a short PA. A correction is a very short unintentional motion at the terminal point; a PA is purposive, usually of easily discernible length.

The motion distance is handled in a similar manner to *GET.*

When there is an engagement of parts following a correction, an additional *PUT* will be allowed when the distance exceeds 2.5 cm.

- PUT WEIGHT (PW)

  PUT WEIGHT is an addition to a *PUT* motion depending on the weight of the object moved.

  The scope *of PUT WEIGHT*

  - Starts: when the move begins;
  - Includes: the additional time, over and above the move time in *PUT,* to compensate for the differences in time required in moving heavy and light objects over the same distance;
  - Ends: when the move ends.

  PW is assigned when resistance to movement exceeds 2 kg per hand.

  Weights are calculated as in *GET WEIGHT.* Between 2 kg and 5 kg, 1 tmu is allowed and coded PW 5 ; between 5 kg and 10 kg 2 tmu are allowed and coded PW 10 ; and so on.

- REGRASP

  REGRASP is a hand action with the purpose of changing the grasp on an object.

  The scope of *REGRASP*

  - Starts: with the object in the hand;
  - Includes: digital and hand muscular readjustment on an object;
  - Ends: with the object in a new location in the hand.

  A single *REGRASP* consists of not more than three fractional movements.

  Digital and muscular readjustments, while performing an *APPLY PRESSURE,* are included in *APPLY PRESSURE.* A *REGRASP* should not be assigned in combination with *APPLY PRESSURE.*

  If the hand relinquishes control and then secures another grasp on the object, the action will be a *GET,* a *REGRASP.*

  An example of R is changing the grasp on a pencil in order to get into the position for writing.

- APPLY PRESSURE (A)

  APPLY PRESSURE is an action with the purpose of exerting muscular force on an object.

  The scope *of APPLY PRESSURE*

  - Starts: with the body member in contact with the object;
  - Includes: the application of controlled increasing muscular force, a minimum reaction time to permit the reversal of force and the subsequent releasing of muscular force;

   - Ends: with the body member in contact with the object, but with muscular force released.

  The minimum dwell time covers mental reaction time only. Longer dwells, in holding actions, must be separately evaluated.

  APPLY PRESSURE applies to the action of exerting muscular force on an object to achieve control, to restrain or to overcome resistance to motion. The object is not displaced more than 6 mm during the action of *APPLY PRESSURE.*

  APPLY PRESSURE, which can be performed by any body member, is recognized by a noticeable hesitation while force is applied. An example of A is the final tightening action made with a screwdriver or spanner.

- EYE ACTION (E)

  EYE ACTION is an action with the purpose of either: recognizing a readily distinguishable characteristic of an object; or: shifting the aim of the axis of vision to a new viewing area.

  The scope of EYE ACTION

   - Starts: when other actions must cease because a characteristic of an object must be recognized;
   - Includes: either: muscular readjustment of the lens of the eyes and the mental processes required to recognize a distinguishable characteristic of an object; or: the eye motion performed to shift the aim of the axis of vision to a new viewing area;
   - Ends: when other actions can start again.

A single eye focus covers an area 10 cm in diameter at 40 cm from the eyes. Recognition time included is sufficient only for simple binary decision. An example of E is the action of determining whether a coin is showing head or tail.

- FOOT MOTION (F)

  FOOT MOTION is a short foot or leg motion when the purpose is not to move the body.

  The scope of *FOOT MOTION*

   - Starts: with the foot or leg at rest;
   - Includes: a motion not exceeding 30 cm that is pivoted at the hip, knee or instep;
   - Ends: with the foot in a new location.

  FOOT MOTION is judged by the decision model for *FOOT MOTION* and *STEP.*

- STEP (S)

  STEP is either : a leg motion with the purpose of moving the body; or : a leg motion longer than 30 cm.

  The scope of *STEP*

- o Starts: with the leg at rest;
- o Includes: either: a motion of the leg where the purpose is to achieve displacement of the trunk; or: a leg motion longer than 30 cm;
- o Ends: with the leg at a new location.

STEP or *FOOTMOTION* is judged by the following decision model:

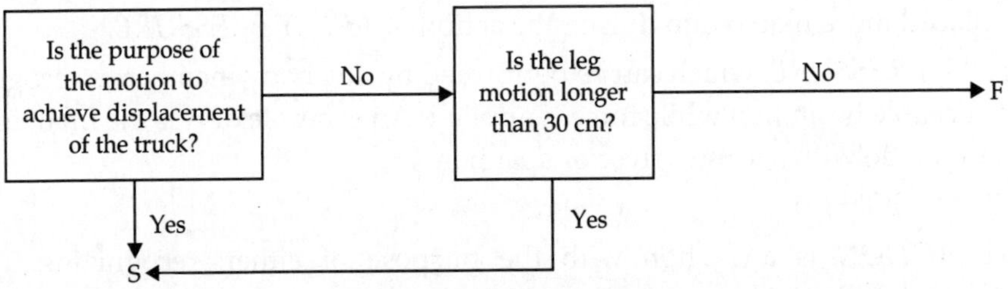

Fig. 14.4: Decision model.

To evaluate walking, count the number of times the foot hits the floor. An example of F is depressing a foot pedal in a car. An example of S is making a single step to the side to enable the arm to reach further.

- BEND AND ARISE (B)

  BEND AND ARISE is a lowering of the trunk followed by a rise.

  The scope of *BEND AND ARISE*
  - o Starts: with motion of the trunk forward from an upright posture;
  - o Includes: movement of the trunk and other body members to achieve a vertical change of body position to permit the hands to reach down to or below the knees and the subsequent arise from this position;
  - o Ends: with the body in an upright posture.

  The criterion for *BEND AND ARISE* is whether the operative is able to reach to below the knees, not whether he or she actually does so. Kneeling on both knees should be analyzed as B.

- CRANK (C)

  CRANK is a motion with the purpose of moving an object in a circular path of more than half a revolution with the hand or finger.

  The scope of *CRANK*
  - o Starts: with the hand on the object;
  - o Includes: all transporting motions necessary to move an object in a circular path;
  - o Ends: with the hand on the object when one revolution is completed.

  There are two variables to consider in applying the *CRANK* motion:
  - o The number of revolutions;
  - o Weight or resistance.

The time value of 15 tmu per revolution may be used for any crank diameter and applies to both continuous and intermittent cranking. *CRANK* applies to motions in a circular path whether or not the axis of cranking is perpendicular to the plane of rotation.

The number of revolutions should be rounded off to the nearest whole number.

The weight or resistance influences the time for moving an object. The rules of adding GW and PW to *PUT* motions also apply to *CRANK*. PW applies to each revolution, whether continuous or intermittent. GW is applied once only to a continuous series of revolutions, but to each revolution where these are intermittent.

No correcting motions as applied to *PUT* are included in *CRANK*. If correcting motions occur in putting the object at the intended place an extra *PUT* must be allowed. An example of C is turning a hand wheel through one revolution.

Training Requirements

In the preceding subsection, the essentials of the MTM-2 system were outlined. To obtain an adequate understanding of the system, however, a trainee will require at least two weeks of formal training in MTM-2 theory and practice, followed by guided application on the shop floor with an MTM instructor. A trainee who is already competent in work study practice should reach a reasonable standard in the use of MTM-2 after about a month of guided application. MTM-1 will require a longer training period. It is helpful if part of this training can be carried out in a plant where MTM standards are already in use. When trainees find that their own analysis compare closely with established standards, their confidence is rapidly built up. Without guidance, it is very difficult for a trainee to learn how to use MTM adequately.

Most PTS training courses end up with an examination in which the trainee carried out a measurement study of a real or simulated job, sometimes on film. Only if a specified pass mark is obtained in this examination is the trainee validated to apply the PTS in question at the place of work as a consultant in that particular PTS system.

14.7 APPLICATION OF PTS SYSTEMS

PTS systems can be applied in three main ways:

- Direct observation of the motions used by the operative;
- Mental visualization of the motions needed to accomplish a new or alternative work method;
- From analysis of a film/video taken of the operative at the place of work.

The overall approach adopted when one of the PTS systems, such as MTM-2, is used for direct observation is not very different from that adopted for making a time study. Indeed, a person experienced in the procedures described in that chapter – selecting the job, approach to the worker, recording job information, breaking down into elements, allowances, compiling total job times – is well equipped to become a good PTS practitioner. The main difference in the approach is that at the point in the total time study procedure where the observer is ready to time and rate the work cycle, he or she will instead make an MTM-2 analysis and then enter the motion times on the analysis sheet from the MTM-2 data card. The calculation of allowances, completion of the documentation and issuing of the job times are then done in much the same way as in a time study. If the same type of summary sheets can be used, so much the better. The study summary sheet and the short cycle study form can be adapted to summarize the information from the MTM-2 analysis sheets.

Choosing the Operative

In the choice of operative to be observed, it is just as desirable to have a cooperative, good-average worker for PTS analysis as it is for time study. Exceptionally fast or abnormally slow performances are difficult for time study specialists to rate, and they present problems for PTS analysts too. The super-skilled operative combines and overlaps motions in a manner beyond the capabilities of the average worker, while an abnormally slow or reluctant operative will make separate, one-handed, hesitant motions which the average operative will perform smoothly and simultaneously. The rules and motion combination tables of the MTM system, like those of other systems such as work factor, do provide information for adjusting the observed motion pattern to that applicable to the good-average worker; this additional work can, however, be avoided by an intelligent choice of operative in the first place. Of course, an experienced PTS analyst may also study extreme performances with advantages. The performance of an exceptionally fast operative may give clues as to how all operatives might be trained to reach a higher-than-average performance level, and the study of slow operatives would show where difficulties are encountered and whether further training can eliminate these.

Recording Job Information

In recording job information, it is important to remember that distance is a significant variable in PTS systems. The plans for the workplace layout should therefore be accurately drawn to scale. This will help in judging or checking the length of motions shown in the analysis.

Breaking Down of Elements

In PTS systems, the division of the operation into work elements follows the same principles as for time study. The division can be made much finer, if required, because the difficulty of timing short elements does not arise. If necessary, the break points can also be changed easily and without having to retime the cycle. This flexibility is illustrated in Table 14.4, which shows a common work cycle – that of fitting a nut and washer on a stud. For example, if a change of method eliminates the need for a washer, the appropriate motions

Table 14.4: Fitting a nut and washer on a stud.

Element	tmu	Code	Description
Fit washer	23	GC30	Washer
	30	PC30	To stud
	3	PA5	On stud
Fit nut and turn down by hand	10	GB15	Nut
	26	PCI 5	To stud
	6	2PA5	Engage threads
	42	6GB5	
	18	6PA5	Turn down nut
Tighten nut using spanner	23	GB30	Spanner
	30	PC30	To nut
	6	PA15	Turn nut
	14	A	Tighten

(GC30, PC30, PA5) and time (56 tmu) can easily be removed from the analysis. Finger turns can also be readily separated from spanner turns and, indeed, from the fitting actions and subsequent turns.

Allowances and Job Times

There is no problem of rating with a PTS system such as MTM-2, since the times have been rated once and for all. All that needs to be done is to add up the motion times and transfer the totals to the study summary sheet. If times are to be issued at BSI 100 and not MTM 100, the tmu total from the study summary sheet should be multiplied by 0.83. (This means that, if times are issued in standard minutes, the total tmu can be divided by 2,000.) It should be understood that the general relationship between the scales applies only to the time totals, and most definitely not to the individual motion times shown on the MTM data cards. Converting individual motion times is quite improper since these are not improved uniformly when a higher performance of a cycle time is achieved.

The times for low control motions (such as GA and PA) are improved only a little compared with those for the highly complex motions (such as GC and PC). The issue is, however, more complicated than this because one would also need a different set of motion combinations when considering a different performance level. Some sophisticated MTM users prefer to issue values at MTM 100.

Relaxation and other allowances are added in exactly the same way as for time study, in order to give the total job time.

Visualization

When the work study person does not have the opportunity of observing the work cycle, for example, when designing a new work method or constructing alternative methods during method study of an existing job, he or she must mentally visualize the motions needed. Figures 14.5 and 14.6 give an example of a PTS problem which can be solved by visualization of the various motions involved, as can be seen from Fig. 14.7.

The ability to visualize motion patterns depends on the study person's intelligence and practical experience. The more familiar he or she is with work study, the more readily the person can picture the motions necessary to pick up and fit parts together, as well as visualize which motions can be performed together easily and which motions are difficult to carry out simultaneously.

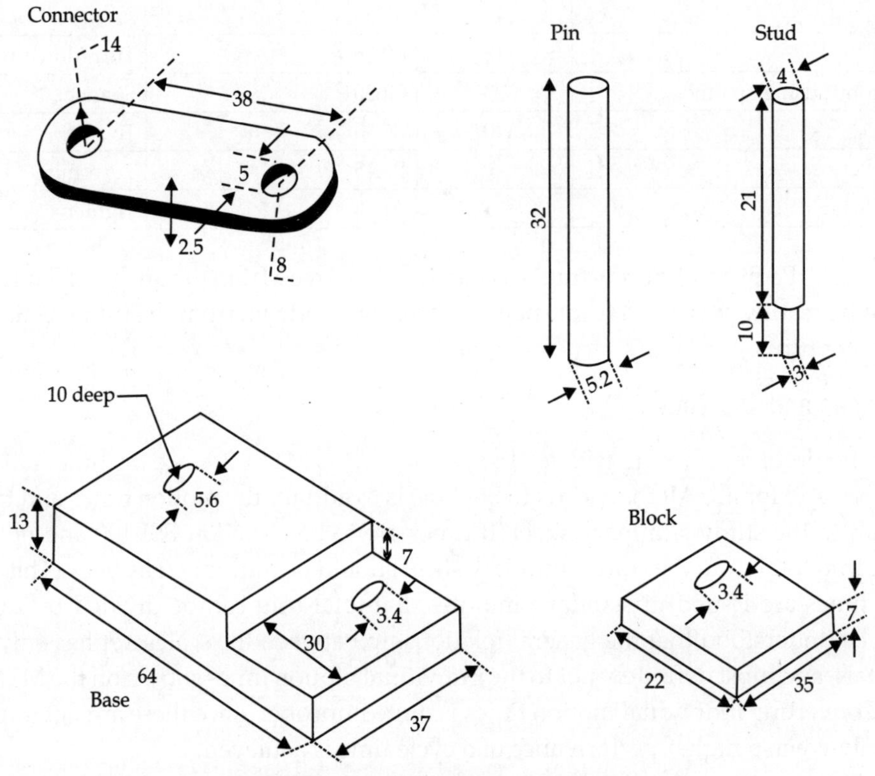

Fig. 14.5: Base assembly (Measurements in mm).

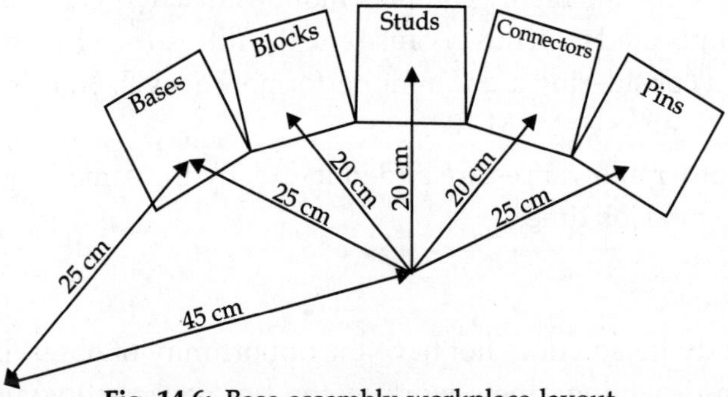

Fig. 14.6: Base assembly workplace layout.

In designing work methods, it is helpful to use a methods laboratory. However, when motion analysis is undertaken there is a need for caution, just as there is with time standards. The experiments with new methods will probably be performed by the work study person or by colleagues, and it is important that they should bear in mind that their own performances will generally fall far short of those which will be achieved by the regular shop floor operatives. Even where shop floor operatives are assisting in the methods laboratory, their performance of a new work cycle will fall short of the standard they will achieve when they have had sufficient practice in working the cycle under shop floor conditions. In both these instances the rules for work design, particularly those of the motion combination possibilities expected of the average experienced operative, must be used to arrive at a correct shop floor method. It is in the work design process that a work study person who chooses to use an MTM-2 system, for example, will reap the benefit of a full training in the detailed MTM-1 system on which MTM-2 was founded. However, at the very minimum the classification details of MTM-1 together with the basic motions which make up the MTM-2 motions and the rules covering the motion combination possibilities of the basic motions must be understood, particularly in relation to practice opportunity, area of normal vision and difficulty of handling.

With this knowledge it will become evident, for example, that in designing the workplace for the parts to be kept in tote pans, a separate GC with either hand will be required. It will also be apparent that even expert operatives cannot perform these motions simultaneously, since each motion involves a kind of minute searching and selecting activity, because the objects are jumbled up together. Similarly, the work study specialist will know that putting loose fitting round plugs into round holes can be done with both hands simultaneously, provided that the workplace is designed so that the targets are within the area of normal vision as defined above under *EYE ACTION.* The rules provide many such guidelines.

PTS Systems and the Broader Techniques

The nature and value of PTS systems should now be reasonably clear. If a work study person intends to become a specialist, for example, in MTM, full training in MTM-1 and MTM-2 and in all the advanced techniques outlined in this book will be necessary. In the more general case, where both work study and other jobs will probably be undertaken as well (such as production planning and control — a common combination in small plants, particularly in the developing countries), an MTM-2 training may be sufficient. However, it is most important that the study person should not lose sight of the fact that the PTS technique is a fine precision tool. Before getting down to minute detail, it should first be seen what can be accomplished by using the broader, simpler approaches. In companies where work study practice has not yet been introduced, intelligent broad thinking will usually reveal ways of bringing about considerable initial improvements in productivity.

Job description: Assemble base (See sketches of parts and layout)	Ref.:
	Sheet No. 1 of 1
	Analyst:
	Date:

Left-hand description	LH	tmu	RH	Righ-hand description
Get base from box	GC30	23	G–	Get pin from box
		14	GC5	
Put base on bench	PA30	30	PC30	Locate pin to base
Get block from box	GC30	23	G–	Get stud from box
		14	GC5	
Move block stud	P–	30	PC30	Locate stud through block
Assist location	P–	26	PC15	Fit assembly to base
		23	GC30	Get connector from box
Assist location	GB–	30	PC30	Locate to stud
Locate to pin	PC5	21		
Pick up assembly	GB15	10		
Place on conveyor	PA80	20		
		264		

Fig. 14.7: MTM-2 analysis sheet, base assembly.

I. REACH—R							
Distance (cm)	Time (tmu)				Hand in motion		Case and description
	A	B	C or D	E	A	B	
2 or less	2.0	2.0	2.0	2.0	1.6	1.6	A. Reach to object in fixed location, or to object in other hand or on which other hand rests
4	3.4	3.4	5.1	3.2	3.0	2.4	
6	4.5	4.5	6.5	4.4	3.9	3.1	
8	5.5	5.5	7.5	5.5	4.6	3.7	
10	6.1	6.3	8.4	6.8	4.9	4.3	
12	6.4	7.4	9.1	7.3	5.2	4.8	B. Reach to single object in location which may vary slightly from cycle to cycle
14	6.8	8.2	9.7	7.8	5.5	5.4	
16	7.1	8.8	10.3	8.2	5.8	5.9	
18	7.5	9.4	10.8	8.7	6.1	6.5	
20	7.8	10.0	11.4	9.2	6.5	7.1	
22	8.1	10.5	11.9	9.7	6.8	7.7	C. Reach to object jumbled with other objects in a group so that search and select occur
24	8.5	11.1	12.5	10.2	7.1	8.2	
26	8.8	11.7	13.0	10.7	7.4	8.8	
28	9.2	12.2	13.6	11.2	7.7	9.4	
30	9.5	12.8	14.1	11.7	8.0	9.9	
35	10.4	14.2	15.5	12.9	8.8	11.4	D. Reach to a very small object or where accurate grasp is required
40	11.3	15.6	16.8	14.1	9.6	12.8	
45	12.1	17.0	18.2	15.3	10.4	14.2	
50	13.0	18.4	19.6	16.5	11.2	15.7	
55	13.9	19.8	20.9	17.8	12.0	17.1	
60	14.7	21.2	22.3	19.0	12.8	18.5	E. Reach to indefinite location to get hand in position for body balance or next motion or out of way
65	15.6	22.6	23.6	20.2	13.5	19.9	
70	16.5	24.1	25.0	21.4	14.3	21.4	
75	17.3	25.5	26.4	22.6	15.1	22.8	
80	18.2	26.9	27.7	23.9	15.9	24.2	

Fig. 14.8: Time measurement application data in tmu (Based on metric weights and measures) [REACH-R].

II. MOVE–M

Distance (cm)	Time (tmu) A	B	C	Hand in motion B	Wt. allowance Weight (kg) upto	Static constant (tmu)	Dynamic factor	Case and description
2 or less	2.0	2.0	2.0	1.7	1	0	1.00	
4	3.1	4.0	4.5	2.8				
6	4.1	5.0	5.8	3.1				
8	5.1	5.9	6.9	3.7	2	1.6	1.04	
10	6.0	6.8	7.9	4.3				A. Move object against stop or to other hand
					4	2.8	1.07	
12	6.9	7.7	8.8	4.9				
14	7.7	8.5	9.8	5.4				
16	8.3	9.2	10.5	6.0	6	4.3	1.12	
18	9.0	9.8	11.1	6.5				
20	9.6	10.5	11.7	7.1				
					8	5.8	1.17	
22	10.2	11.2	12.4	7.6				
24	10.8	11.8	13.0	8.2	10	7.3	1.22	
26	11.5	12.3	13.7	8.7				B. Move object to approximate or indefinite location
28	12.1	12.8	14.4	9.3				
30	12.7	13.3	15.1	9.8	12	8.8	1.27	
35	14.3	14.5	16.8	11.2	14	10.4	1.32	
40	15.8	15.6	18.5	12.6				
45	17.4	16.8	20.1	14.0				
50	19.0	18.0	21.8	15.4	16	11.9	1.36	
55	20.5	19.2	23.5	16.8				
					18	13.4	1.41	
60	22.1	20.4	25.2	18.2				C. Move object to exact location
65	23.6	21.6	26.9	19.5				
70	25.2	22.8	28.6	20.9	20	14.9	1.46	
75	26.7	24.0	30.3	22.3				
80	28.3	25.2	32.0	23.7				
					22	164.4	1.51	

Fig. 14.9: Methods-Time Measurement application data in tmu (Based on metric weights and measures) [MOVE – M].

IIIA. TURN – T

Weight (kg)	Time (tmu) or degrees turned										
	30°	45°	60°	75°	90°	105°	120°	135°	150°	165°	180°
Small (0) to (1)	2.8	3.5	4.1	4.8	5.4	6.1	6.8	7.4	8.1	8.7	9.4
Medium (1) to (5)	4.4	5.5	6.5	7.5	8.5	9.6	10.6	11.6	12.7	13.7	14.8
Large (5.1) to (16)	8.4	10.5	12.3	14.4	16.2	18.3	20.4	22.2	24.3	26.1	28.2

IIIB. APPLY PRESSURE – AP

Full cycle			Components		
Symbol	tmu	Description	Symbol	tmu	Description
APA	10.6	AF + DM + RLF	AF	3.4	Apply force
			DM	4.2	Dwell, minimum
APB	16.2	APA + G2	RLF	3.0	Release force

Fig. 14.10: Methods-Time Measurement application data in tmu (Based on metric weights and measures) [TURN-T, APPLY PRESSURE-AP].

15
The Use of Time Standards

15.1 DEFINITION OF THE WORK COVERED BY TIME STANDARDS

The record on detailed scale must be made after the completion of study work for each and every method, tools and equipment used, that has a bearing on time. The importance is realized in the fact that any changes in the work content will also affect the planning and costing. However, in cases where the time standards are used for setting of incentives, the scale and magnitude of importance also increases. In cases where time standards are used for making incentives, it is a general practice to not change the time standards that have been set. This could be a exception in situations when the work content of an operation is changed, or in situations where there is a change in the organization of the work.

It is a general practice to prepare two documents in situations where time standards are to be used as the basis for an incentive scheme. These two documents define and describe completely the way of compilation of the time standards and the conditions of working to which the time standard has been referred. The two documents are referred to as the **technical setup** and the **work specification**.

15.1.1 The Technical Setup

The technical setup delineates the results of the study work undertaken in the form of summary which may be tables, and graphs. The document also carries the description of how all the time standards have been derived. However, there is no reference to the rates of pay to workers or any matter that relates to the contract between the employee and the employer. The information regarding the calculation of fresh time standards is also present in the technical setup document. The case for setting new time standards may arise when there are changes in the jobs or the working conditions. Thus, a technical setup document consists of all the relevant information for calculation of time standards. An information system data bank for the purpose of storing such information may be adopted.

Since the setting of time standards varies from sections to sections in an enterprise, a separate setup for each of the technical sections of the enterprise is needed. For instance, there would be different setups for sprayers, operators of the shot-blast machines and so on, in a vitreous enameling shop.

The technical setup document should carry all the data on which it is based. This also includes the following:

- Flow process charts showing the improved methods developed
- Analysis of studies sheets
- Relaxation allowance calculation sheets
- Data from predetermined time standards (PTS)
- Curves and graphs relating to standard data.

The importance of the technical setup document and all the other documents attached to it may be realized in the situation of disputes. In cases of disputes, there would be essential evidence available from the technical setup document. Technical setups are normally filed in the work study department, where they are available to the management or to the workers' representatives whenever they may be needed.

15.1.2 The Work Specification

A work specification is a document that carries information related to the job or operation performed, the way in which it has been performed, the workplace layout, the machines, tools and appliances used for carrying out the job or operation, the responsibilities and duties of the worker. The standard time is usually carried by the work specification document. Thus, in contrast to the technical setup document, the work specification document carries the basic data on which the contract between the employer and the employee depends for incentivizing the scheme.

The nature of the job or the operation concerned dictates the amount of detail necessary in a work specification. In cases where machines having broadly similar operations are employed for performing a large number of jobs, only the variations may be noted in detail. Such a case is often encountered in the machine shop work in the engineering industry.

On the other hand, the specification of work may be lengthy and details may be required in cases where the whole plant or the department will run for an indefinite period of time and that too unchanged. For instance, it may include specifications for the alternatives of types of materials used.

The work specification should cover the following points that embrace the standard method laid down as a result of method study:

- Details of the products or workpieces, including:
  - Specification of drawing, or title and product number
  - Specification of material
  - Sketches of surfaces or parts to be treated.
- Details of the plant or machine on which the operation is performed, including:
  - Size or type, make, register number
  - Speeds and feeds and other equivalent data

- Tools, jigs and fixtures
- Sketch, where not available, of workplace layout.

- Operation number and general description of the work covered
- Quality standards, including:
  - Grade quality
  - Tolerances and finish
  - Gauging requirements, gauges and other inspection apparatus
  - Frequency of inspection
  - Action for items failing the quality standard.
- Grade and sex of labour, including:
  - Indirect and direct labour
  - Part-time assistance by supervisors or inspectors.
- Detailed description of all work involved, including:
  - Constant and variable elements, repetitive elements
  - Occasional elements
  - Indirect work.
- Details of time standards, including:
  - Standard time for each job, element, or operation
  - Allowed time for all indirect work
  - Percentage relaxation allowance.
- Clerical procedure to be carried out by operatives in recording output and booking waiting time
- Conditions under which the time standard is issued, and any special provisos

The nature of the work dictates the manner in which the established time standards are made clear to the operatives. For instance, if the operation or job is performed by a single worker, then he or she may be informed about the time standards by the work study person. Generally, lengthy explanations are avoided by the workers, once the work study has been accepted. The standards may be posted on the notice board, in situations where a large number of workers are employed on the same type of job. In batch production the standard time is generally written or printed on the work ticket, job card or process layout.

15.2 THE STANDARD UNIT OF WORK

Generally, the following forms are used for setting of time standards:

- *X* minutes per piece
- *Y* minutes per 100 (or per 1,000) pieces
- *Z* minutes per tonne, metre, square metre, etc.

Sometimes the above may be converted into hours if needed. The above value represents the output at standard performance. Since each unit of time consists of the relaxation time, hence the total time allowed in minutes or hours is not indicative of the continuous work. The ratio of the relaxation time to the total work will depend on the nature of the work. The relaxation time may be as high as 50 per cent in cases of extremely heavy work such as that of furnace tending.

The measurement and comparison of productivity can be done using the standard minute. This, may be represented by the ratio:

$$\text{Performance} = \frac{\text{Work ouput in standard minutes}}{\text{Input of labour time in minutes}} \times 100$$

15.3 PRODUCTION PLANNING AND THE UTILIZATION OF PLANT AND HUMAN RESOURCES

Poor planning of the work flow and flow of orders is one of the main aftermaths of ineffective time. An ineffective timing may often lead to one order not following the other or the plant and the labour is not continuously employed. It is necessary to know the following in order to effectively plan a programme of work.

- What is to be done or made.
- Quantity involved.
- The operations necessary to carry out the work.
- The equipment, plant, and tools needed.
- Types of labour required.
- The expected time duration of each operation.
- The required quantity and types of equipment.

The sales office or the commercial department can generally supply the information related to the first and second items in the above list. Planning department is responsible for providing the information regarding items 3, 4 and 5 of the list. A part of the information for the said items may also be acquired from the method study. The work measurement can supply information on item 6. The information on item 7 is supplied from plant department records or those of the department concerned.

The information gathered will help in clearly stating the required and the available capacity. These must be expressed in terms of time. Requirements will be stated as:

Number of operations of each type to be performed × Expected time for each operation

The actual time that an operation is likely to take is of primary interest when planning a programme. This depends on the conditions in the plant which includes the state of labour management. Where this is the case and the work study application has had time to settle down, these times should be those of the average performance of the shop or department as given by the production records over a period. This may even apply to an individual machine or process. It is the only realistic basis for such calculations.

The times are arrived at by multiplying the standard times by:

$$\frac{100}{\text{Average performance}}$$

While calculating the available plant and labour capacity, much importance is given to the time being allotted for cleaning, dismantling, setting up, change-overs and so on. The capacity is usually expressed in work minutes or machine minutes depending on whether it is calculated for plant or the machine.

The matching of production or operational requirements to capacity in this way makes it possible to:

- Show an insufficiency of any type of plant or labour
- Show an excess of capacity in any type of plant or labour
- Give accurate estimates of delivery dates

The management can prevent any hold-ups from occurring with the availability of the above information. Alternatively, it can start looking for work to fill up spare capacity.

15.4 ESTIMATING PRODUCTION COSTS

The success or failure of a firm in a competitive market may depend on the accuracy with which it is able to price its products. Unless the manufacturing time of the product is accurately known, the labour cost cannot be estimated, and many indirect costs dependent on time – such as plant depreciation, fuel and power consumption, rent, and the salaries of staff and supervision – cannot be accurately determined.

If the management can rely on the accuracy of the costing, appropriate prices can be fixed. If these are below those of the firm's competitors, the management can be happy in the knowledge that it is underselling them in safety; if they are above, the cutting of costs can be undertaken with more assurance than would otherwise be the case and with a knowledge of the margins available to be cut.

Standard and actual labour costs per 100 or per 1000 standard minutes of production are frequently calculated each week from the weekly control statements. Since the actual labour cost per 100 standard minutes takes into account both direct and indirect labour costs, it is the more useful figure to use for estimating production costs.

As indicated in this chapter, the estimation of costs of special projects can be adjusted in terms of a range that varies between normal time and crash time. In this process, knowing the time it takes to perform every activity is of primordial importance in the decision-making process. Special projects are usually costly ventures and many are subject to a tendering process. Hence a proper process of estimation based on ascertained times can make the difference in obtaining an order and in making a profit.

15.5 STANDARD COSTING AND BUDGETARY CONTROL

The standards of labour costs can be set using the information from the work measurement. The information also provides a means to control these costs. The budgetary control of the labour budget can also be set on the basis of these standards. The information provided for budgetary control comprises the indirect expenses, sales budget and therefore helps to predict the capacity of labour that would be available for the entire period of budget.

The actual performance figures can also be derived using the standards. The need for such accurate standards cannot be overstressed. One of the main causes of the poor decisions and hence the total failure of many industrial enterprises is the absence of less information on the cost.

15.6 INCENTIVE SCHEMES

Several features inherent in the techniques form the basis of using work measurement as a basis for incentive schemes. These features are namely:

- Recording of the times is done by accurate practical means and are based on direct observations.
- To ensure that the standard times are truly representative, enough observations are made both for the repetitive and occasional elements of the work. This also leads to taking into account the random occurrences.
- In case a situation of examination occurs, the management or workers can make use of the full records that have been retained after the study.
- Any of the management-labour negotiations on performance standards can be undertaken on the basis of times and associated data.
- Properly applied method study followed by work measurement enables management to guarantee the time standards with reasonable assurance that it is not exposing itself to the risks of perpetuating uneconomic rates.

The bonuses earned by the workers should be known by them as quickly as possible for the success of any of the incentive schemes. The information pertaining to the same must be made available the day after it has been referred. The same may be shown in the form of money units, or as an average number of standard units produced per hour. The workers, in many firms are acquainted with their performances which enables them to raise any queries on the spot.

The value of this practice to an incentive scheme is as follows:

- The effect of the operatives' own actions on their earnings is brought home to them while the events concerned are still fresh in their mind.
- Any queries on the amount of bonus due can be taken up and corrections made, if necessary, **before** the wages are made up.

- The posting of the figures daily on the notice board, where this has been agreed to by the workers and their representatives, adds interest and may stimulate a competitive spirit.
- The confidence in the workers increases if there is a repeated confirmation by the management to the workers for the calculations made by management. The difference of opinion can then be discussed which instills fairness of the system.

15.7 ORGANIZATION OF AN INFORMATION SYSTEM ASSOCIATED WITH WORK MEASUREMENT

A system of recording of operatives' work output and times should back the work measurement when the measurement is associated with an incentive scheme. A central point in the plant which may be the accounts department should be used to compile the figures related to times and work output. At the central point, these figures could be processed to determine the bonuses earned by each worker or operative. The statistics then could be used by the management to control the performance and costs of the entire plant.

One of the main functions of work study is to devise a system suitable for use in the organization. There are some characteristics that a devised system must have. These are the following:

- should be able to provide full and accurate information;
- should ensure that the required information is entered as a daily routine and at the same time transmitted with the minimum delay for further processing;
- should be simple to operate and comprehend. This is to ensure that the system is full proof and can be carried on by comparatively unskilled clerical staff; and
- should be economical as to computer use or paperwork.

Table 15.1: Minimum data required for work measurement and labour control records.

Information	Source
Hours of attendance of each operative	Clock card or time sheet
Standard time for each operation	Job card or work study compiled standard data
Times of starting and finishing each operation	Job card or work sheet
Quantities produced	Job card or work sheet
Scrap or rectification: quantities and times	Scrap note or rectification slip
Waiting time and non-productive time sheet of actual performance	Waiting time slips or daily work

The control statements are the sheets or printouts which summarize the output and performance information. Generally, there would be three levels of control statements at different intervals and serving different purposes. The results of the previous day working can be indicated to the supervisor through a daily statement which may be prepared daily for each of the sections of the organization. A weekly control statement may be prepared for the entire department of the plant. This can be done once a week. A single sheet frequently has space for the record of 13 weeks of work, a fresh line being used each week, so that the current week's results can be compared with those of earlier weeks during the same quarter. The control statement which goes to the top management is usually made up monthly, on either a departmental or a whole-plant basis.

In any system of recording associated with work measurement and an incentive system, the minimum data given in Table 15.1 must be recorded and eventually transmitted for incentives and wages calculations.

It should be noted that the rapid proliferation of mini-computers and the availability of suitable software packages have rendered the establishment of a control system quick, less cumbersome and less costly. In addition, it has also enabled the management to gain an insight into ineffective times and their causes, and the productivity of various departments or of the plant as a whole.

SECTION V
ENTREPRENEURIAL DEVELOPMENT

16
Entrepreneur and Entrepreneurship

16.1 INTRODUCTION

The presence of entrepreneurship has been felt for a long time. However, in the recent years it has emerged as though a new discovery has been made. It is a general description that any person who owns and runs a business is an entrepreneur. In other words, an entrepreneur is a person who is responsible for organizing, operating and bearing the risk of an organization. Further, an entrepreneur perceives the needs and demands of the market and then in order to meet the perceived demands, he/she brings together manpower, material and the required capital.

Entrepreneurship is a very old concept that relates to the idea and vision of an entrepreneur as well as the implementation of the same by the entrepreneur. One may also define entrepreneurship as a creative and innovative response to the environment. The process of establishing a new venture is entailed in the concept of entrepreneurship. Further, entrepreneurship is a mixture of a number of skills and traits. These include imagination, the ability to take risk, the ability to make use of the resources required for establishing the new venture.

The culture of entrepreneurship consists of set of norms, values and characteristics that ultimately leads to the efficient growth of entrepreneurship. The entrepreneurship blends itself into the organizational culture that leads to the creation of new opportunities and an environment where these new opportunities could be earnestly pursued. An entrepreneur not only seeks the opportunities but also looks for the ways in order to capitalize on the newer opportunities and ultimately gain control over them. On the other hand, a manager performs in a non-entrepreneurial culture and is only focused on the resources, structure and relation between the market and the organization. The perception of opportunities drives the entrepreneurial managers.

16.2 DEFINING ENTREPRENEUR

The word 'entrepreneur' stems out from the French word 'entrepreneur'. Since the beginning of 16th century, the word 'entrepreneur' has been used to designate people in different fields. In the beginning of 16th century, this word was used for a person who was engaged in military expeditions. The same word was used in the 17th to designate a person involved in civil engineering activities such as that of construction and fortification. It was for the first time, that in 18th century it was used in the field of business to designate a person dealing with the buying and selling of goods.

However, generally there is no accepted definition for the word 'entrepreneur'. Same applies to the model of entrepreneurship which answers the pertinent question of as to what an entrepreneur does. A distinction has been marked in the recent decade between the individual entrepreneurship and corporate entrepreneurship. The differences are made on certain attributes that include creativity, innovation, personal traits, etc.

Scores of literature is available on the models of the entrepreneurial leaders and on the definition of the word 'entrepreneur'. Different authors have put their ideas about the models and definition in their own words. The French economist, Cantillon was the first person to coin the word entrepreneur and defines it as an agent who combines the production resources to meet the market needs and requirements. Furthermore, an entrepreneur was unaware of the price that would be received by the product at the expense of purchase of various resources for producing the same.

An important and crucial function of the economic development is performed by entrepreneurs. Entrepreneurs are responsible for mobilizing capital, exploring of natural resources and carrying on trade. Therefore, an entrepreneur inputs to spell the difference between prosperity and poverty among not only within a nation but also among different nations.

J. B. Say has described an entrepreneur's role as one of combining different factors of production in order to bring these factors together. Thus, according to Say, an enterprise is a system carrying out the combination of productive factors and the person responsible for carrying out these is an entrepreneur.

The significant role played by an entrepreneur has been stressed upon by many theories in economics. The first major author to having highlighted the human agent in the process to economic development was Schumpeter. He believed that the economy was propelled by the continuous efforts of persons "who wanted to promote new goods and new methods of production, or to exploit new sources of materials or new market" not merely for profit but also for the purpose of creating. The word innovation was used by Schumpeter for such an activity. The writer has also emphasized on innovation as a function of an entrepreneur. In the theory of Schumpeter economics, entrepreneur has been regarded as a highly specialized concern.

According to the theory, an entrepreneur is seen as the one who sees new opportunities and exploits their potentiality.

The motivation for making profit for an entrepreneur is not only based on the sole motive to raise the standard of consumption but also on other desires such as that of conquering the competitive market. Thus an entrepreneur tries to maximize the profit on the basis of the innovation skills. An entrepreneur should gain satisfaction in combating the problems using the acquired skills and capabilities.

The role of human resource and in particular the pivotal role of an entrepreneur is crucial for the change and development of the civilization which, in turn, is a result of trade, commerce and industrialization. It is rightly hypothesized by McClelland that one of the psychological factors that engenders economic growth is the entrepreneurial potential. To meet the needs and necessities of a society and henceforth for transformation of the perception of the people in terms of economic thoughts, the need of entrepreneurial achievements and motivation is truly recognized.

The statement as expressed succinctly by Zinkin "No entrepreneur, no development" truly reflects the importance of entrepreneurs to progress of a nation. The four major tasks that an entrepreneur performs have been stated by Kilby. These are:

- **Exchange relationship:** An entrepreneur should have the potential to perceive new opportunities in the market. Further, he/she should be able to gain command over the available resources even if these are scarce. The high potential to market the products and respond to the competition is also vital in exchange relationship for an entrepreneur.
- **Practical administration:** An entrepreneur must have the capability to deal with the bureaucracy and manage the human relations which involves management of customers.
- **Management control:** This comprises the traits of financial and production management.
- **Technology:** An entrepreneur should be sound enough in overseeing assembly of the factory and if needed to upgrade the quality of the process and the product.

An entrepreneur is involved in taking decisions under the conditions of uncertainty for all the above fields of activities. Hence, under the proposed framework by Kilby, an entrepreneur has the following traits:

- The ability to determine the nature and the degree of uncertainty associated with a particular performance of operation or job.
- The potential to make decisions that are appropriate to the attainment of the goal.

Dewing in the early twentieth century described an entrepreneur as one who basically is a business promoter. In other words, an entrepreneur has the ability to transform the ideas into a profitable venture or establishment. For Dewing, an entrepreneur is a person who has the qualities of imagination, judgment and restraint.

According to ILO, entrepreneur is a person who has the ability to perceive and analyse the business opportunities, gather the required input and resources and necessitate appropriate actions to ensure success.

Casson has considered both the functional and indicative definitions while describing an entrepreneur. According to him, an entrepreneur is a person who specializes in taking judgmental decisions about the co-ordination of scarce resources.

Analyses of Danhof's into the role of an entrepreneur reveal that, an entrepreneur "is primarily concerned with changes in the formula of production ... over which he has full control .... He devotes correspondingly little time to the carrying out of a specific formula". The functions of entrepreneur can be divided into three major roles according to the analysis of Danhof: gathering of the relevant information, evaluation of the gathered information with respect to the profit, and initiation of the operation. Danhof's major emphasis is decision making or making of judgment under alternative choices.

Six possible schools of thought on entrepreneurship have been described by Cunningham and Lischerson. The different schools of thoughts are:

- **Great Person School:** According to this school of thought, an entrepreneur is born with a sixth sense to aid him during the early stages of a venture.
- **Psychological Characteristics of School:** This school of thought says that an entrepreneur is helped in start-up stage by the unique values and attitudes possessed.
- **Classical School of Thought:** Explains that innovation is the central characteristic of entrepreneurship which helps the entrepreneur much in early growth.
- **Management School of Thought:** According to this school of thought entrepreneurs are the people who organize an economic venture, manage and assume responsibility to avert any kind of risk. Such functional orientation helps them in early growth and maturity.
- **Leadership School of Thought:** This thought explains the leadership quality of an entrepreneur. They have the ability to adorn their own style in order to meet the needs of the people. Such leadership personality suits them most during early growth and maturity situations.
- **Intrapreneurship School of Thought:** The act of development of independent units and to create market which expands the scope of an enterprise is intrapreneurship. Intrapreneurship is needed by an entrepreneur during the situation of maturity and change.

Looking at the above definitions, one can have a feel that there is a wide array of views on the definition, role and model of an entrepreneur. Entrepreneurs have been considered to be the catalyst for the socio-economic development, irrespective of the definition given to define them. The word catalyst is rightly coined for an entrepreneur as this can be felt in real world too. Many countries that have got a higher percentage of entrepreneurs have grown at a much faster pace compare to the other countries which have lesser percentage of the entrepreneurs. Therefore, motivation to entrepreneurship is a must for any society.

16.3 CHARACTERISTICS OF AN ENTREPRENEUR

An entrepreneur being a highly enthusiastic, energetic and goal achieving individual, has the following characteristics:

- Entrepreneur is a deterministic and resolute individual.
- They are innovative and creative in achieving the desired results.
- They have the attitude to shoulder responsibilities with enthusiasm.
- Entrepreneurs have in them the skills to manage the financial related issues in order to obtain the desired profit.
- Entrepreneurs have the potential to manage the human relations, i.e., can manage bureaucracy at all levels, handle customer complaints and needs.

16.4 CONCEPT OF ENTREPRENEURSHIP

The two terms "entrepreneurship" and "entrepreneur" are often used synonymously, but they are totally different conceptually. According to Arthur H. Cole, entrepreneurship is the purposeful activity of an individual or a group of associated individuals, so called entrepreneur(s), for the initiation of a business venture and to maintain it to always make the venture a profit oriented business unit. This business venture is organized in a manner that while meeting the market needs through the production or distribution of economic goods and services, it also remains to be a profitable unit.

Table 16.1: Comparison between entrepreneur and entrepreneurship.

Entrepreneur	Entrepreneurship
Refers to a person	Refers to a process
Visualizes	Vision
Creator	Creation
Organizer	Organization
Innovator	Innovation
Technician	Technology
Initiator	Initiative
Planner	Planning
Leader	Leadership
Motivator	Motivation
Programmer	Action
Risk-taker	Risk-taking
Communicator	Communication
Administrator	Administration

The topic of entrepreneur has been discussed widely, the discussions ranging from the classical economists to the modern theoreticians. The analysis has led to several pronouncements and observations. Prof. James K. Omps has put his views in this context. He is of the opinion that one of the most critical factor that bothers a nation is the percentage of entrepreneurs in the total population. However, the limited resources, lack of technology and energy shortages are equally important factors that bother a nation.

Entrepreneurship should comprise an act by an individual or bunch of individuals where it brings prosperity to the entrepreneur and his organization by exploiting the opportunities and exploit them for the betterment of a society. The number of high quality innovators in the form of entrepreneurs supplied by a society is one of the important variables for the economic development of any nation. This becomes obvious when it is looked at from the social and macroeconomic perspective. However, the development also depends on the generation of new desires amongst the people of society to accept and demand new innovations. Therefore, a vicious circle is thereby established that results in all-round economic development with improved standard of life.

The concept of entrepreneurship is gaining importance amongst the business management scholars and social scientists. This has been well acknowledged in today's world of liberalization and global competition that the creation of wealth is of much importance than being governed by the societal paradigm.

Benjamin Higgins has defined entrepreneurship as an act to foresee investments and opportunities related to production. The act also consists of organizing of an enterprise to undertake a new production process, raising of the organization capital, handling of manpower and raw materials, selecting of efficient professionals in the form of managers for carrying out day-to-day operations of the enterprise.

According to the views of Peter F. Drucker, entrepreneurship is a practice and not a science or an art. It has got a knowledge base which is a means to an end. He considers entrepreneurship to be a considerably less risky act provided that the entrepreneur is systematic and the elementary and well known rules are not violated. However, if a methodical approach is not adopted then the act of entrepreneurship could turn out to be a complex phenomenon.

Three phases in the entrepreneurship development have been identified by modern writers:

- **Initial phase:** This phase is all about the creation of awareness related to the entrepreneurial opportunities. This could be done using surveys.
- **Development phase:** In the development phase, training programmes are implemented in an efficient manner in order to develop motivation and managerial skill.
- **Support phase:** The support related to infrastructural building to establish a new enterprise and to develop existing units.

16.5 CHARACTERISTICS OF ENTREPRENEURSHIP

Two main characteristics of entrepreneurship were identified by D.C. McClelland. The first one being, doing any job in a systematic and better way and the second involves decision making under the situations of uncertainty and risks. Other experts in the area have enlisted the following characteristics of entrepreneurship:

- **Ability to create enterprise:** Entrepreneurship is an act that involves the establishment and operation of an enterprise. Therefore, it is primarily an economic activity which is concerned basically with the satisfying of the needs of market with the aid of production of goods and services and their distribution.
- **Organizing function:** An entrepreneur is responsible for bringing together the different inputs which are essential for production. This he does by coordinating and controlling the different inputs and at the same time the persons engaged in performing operation in the enterprise.
- **Innovation:** Entrepreneurship is an act of creative response to the changing environment which should be automatic and spontaneous. The act of entrepreneurship should be innovative to create something new which is essential for the success of an economy. The innovation can lead to dynamic change in the society and ultimately lead to conditions for growth of the economy.
- **Risk bearing capacity:** Entrepreneurship has an inseparable element of risk. The different guarantees of rent to landlord, wages to employees are done under the environment of uncertainty to earn profit.
- **Managerial and leadership functions:** The traits of managerial and leadership are also important elements for the successful management of organization. These skills will make the act of entrepreneurship oriented predominantly in the direction of integration of productivity and desire to make profit.
- **Gap filling:** Entrepreneurship is an act of filling the gap between human needs and the available products and services. Necessary corrective measures to fill the gaps can only be taken once the gap identification process has been achieved.

16.6 TYPES OF ENTREPRENEURS

Different writers have given different views on the classification of entrepreneurs. Arthur H. Cole has classified entrepreneurs into three main categories: empirical, rational and cognitive entrepreneurs. On one hand, an empirical entrepreneur hardly introduces anything revolutionary. He follows the principle of rule of thumb. While on the other hand, a rational entrepreneur tries to bring changes that look more revolutionary by keeping himself informed about the prevailing general economic conditions. The third category of an entrepreneur is a cognitive entrepreneur who seeks the advice and services of the experts in the field to introduce the required changes that are aberrations to the existing scheme of things.

One can also classify an entrepreneur into private and public entrepreneurs. A private entrepreneur is solely motivated by the desire to earn profit and therefore would never enter those sectors of the economy where there are less prospects for profits. The examples of this category include the general infrastructure industries. While a public entrepreneur on the other hand is driven by the socio-economic development. For example, the government owned electricity generation and distribution enterprises which a government is required to run irrespective of the profit. However, the role of private entrepreneurs cannot be undermined in the countries which are less developed and lacks the space for private entrepreneurs.

On the basis of the scale of enterprise, one can classify an enterprise as small-scale and large-scale enterprise. The small-scale enterprises are much more pertinent to the less developed countries. Because of the lack of resources, the small-scale entrepreneurs are not in a position to take an initiative for the production on a large-scale and therefore cannot introduce a significant technological change. While on the other hand, a large-scale entrepreneur possesses both the financial support as well as has the backing of the required expertise. As such they are in a position to introduce novel changes. Relatively higher percentage of large-scale enterprises can be found in developed countries. One can surely say that one of the main reasons for the wide technological gap between the developed and developing countries is this classification scheme.

According to Clarence Danhof, entrepreneurs can be broadly classified into the four main classes: innovative, fabian, imitative and drone. An innovative entrepreneur introduces a novel concoction of different input factors by judiciously assembling and synthesizing the information. He has the quality of being an industrial leader. On the other hand, an imitative entrepreneur, also known as an adoptive entrepreneur, makes use of the established innovations by the other innovators. The traits of being timid and cautious are signs of a Fabian entrepreneur. The innovations will only be adopted by such an entrepreneur after the satisfaction that failure to do so may be harmful for the business. A drone entrepreneur restricts his activities to just one or two innovations. He would continue to operate without adopting changes even if the returns obtained are less. Two main aspects can be drawn from the classification scheme of Danhof:

- There would be relatively large number of innovative entrepreneurs than the fabian or drones in the ranks for an economy making technological advancements.
- If there are large number of fabian or drones, then it may be a situation where the economy is not making much technological advancement.

The different classes of entrepreneurs as classified by Clarence Danhof are discussed in below.

- **The innovative entrepreneur:** Joseph Schumpeter has coined the term innovative entrepreneur. The most important function of an entrepreneur as described by Joseph, is innovation. An innovative entrepreneur is regarded as the protagonist in the process of socio-economic development. He is a highly motivated individual and has the ability and potential to foresee potentially profitable opportunities. The talent and innovative skills that are possessed by innovative entrepreneur may be exhibited in any one of the following forms:

(a) The introduction of a new product or a product with new and improved quality with which consumers are not yet familiar.

(b) The introduction of new tools or methods of production that have not yet been tested. This new method or new tool may not be a new scientific discovery but may be, say, a new method to handle commodities.

(c) The venture into a new market in which the manufacturing firm hasn't entered at all previously.

(d) The conquest of a new source of supply of raw materials or semi- finished goods.

(e) The creation of a new venture that leads to breaking up of the monopoly position of an already existing venture.

The term innovator means a person who has the ability to commercialize the inventions for the production of goods and services that not only yield profit but also meet customer satisfaction. Hence, the word should not be confused with inventor in which case a person discovers new things and methods. In other words, an innovator is a person who implements the ideas of an inventor for the betterment of the society in a commercialized way. Thus, an innovator entrepreneur not only indulges in original activities but also goes further to exploit the invention commercially, which is comparatively more in comparison to what an inventor does.

Innovating entrepreneurs are rare in developing countries, although being the most vigorous types. According to the analysis of Schumpeter, the panacea for the economic problems in a developing country is the development of entrepreneurs. Therefore for sustained economic development, an economy must produce innovating entrepreneurs with long time horizon and with the ability and potential to achieve the transformations in a substantial manner.

Peter F. Drucker, describes an innovating entrepreneur as one who is always in hunt for change, responds to it and henceforth exploits it as an opportunity. Innovation is the basic key of entrepreneurship for an innovating entrepreneur. The innovative entrepreneur increases the value and satisfaction obtained from resources by the consumer.

An innovative entrepreneur creates new products or increases the value of an existing product. They have the traits to transform a material into a resource or generate a new productive configuration by combining the existing resources. These classes of entrepreneurs are treated to be mysterious or genius by ordinary few. But, according to Drucker, these are the people with sound knowledge base and are disciplined in their attitude. Further, any person who is purposeful and systematic can become an innovative entrepreneur. Drucker opines that it is not only the big and large business establishments to which the entrepreneurship is confined, but is equally important to both the small business and non-economic institutions.

- **Adoptive or imitating entrepreneurs:** The readiness to adopt innovations pertinent to the business venture is one of the main traits of adoptive entrepreneurs. Depending on the innovator's ability to catch the attention of the society by the innovations, an adoptive entrepreneur after careful observations about the success of the innovation will follow the innovator. Adoptive entrepreneurs do not innovate the changes themselves and therefore are sometimes similar to being revolutionary. The technology and techniques are imitated by the imitative or adoptive entrepreneurs.

  According to Schumpeter, this class of entrepreneur has a prominent role in the developing countries. Adoptive entrepreneurs completely fill the void of the scarcity of resources and capital and the scarcity of innovative innovators for the developing nations.

  Since a developing nation prefers to emulate the technology, skill set and knowledge base available with the advanced countries, the imitative entrepreneurs are most suitable for developing regions.

  These imitating entrepreneurs have the potential to transform the available techniques and technologies to suit their specific purposes. Therefore the need for such kind of entrepreneurs is rightly realized in a country with limited natural resources.

- **Fabian entrepreneurs:** A fabian entrepreneur will always take caution in implementing any change. He is also characterized by the skeptical perspective towards practising any change. Therefore, shyness and laziness are the traits that one can associate with a Fabian entrepreneur. The past practices and traditions dictate their dealings. These entrepreneurs follow the footsteps of their predecessors. They are shy enough to take any kind of risk.

- **Drone entrepreneurs:** The following of traditional methods of production is one of the important traits of a drone entrepreneur. He won't take any steps towards changing the method of production that has been introduced by him. They continue to use their introduced method even if they suffer losses. Due to these factors, it is often the case that their products lose the attention of the market. Further, their adopted methods may also become uneconomical at times. As a result, they may be pushed out of the market.

16.7 ENTREPRENEURIAL TRAITS

True entrepreneur is one who has the capability and potential to carry out the tasks of the organization and coordination of the factors and various inputs of production. This is done in more than their average capacities to handle the different tasks. A true entrepreneur is often regarded as a pioneer, a captain of enterprise. However, there is a scarcity of such a talent pool and hence the shortage of a true entrepreneur in an economy. On the other hand, a new situation in the environment is traceable by the modern entrepreneur. They evaluate the new situation and then manage to make the required adjustments in the economic system. A successful entrepreneur must possess the following characteristics:

- **Mental ability:** Creative thinking and intelligence are two of the most important elements of mental ability. Therefore an entrepreneur must have the intelligence and the analytical mindset to manage the organization. He should intelligently and analytically analyze various problems faced under varied circumstances to deal with them. The changes must be anticipated by an entrepreneur thus necessary decisions must be taken.
- **Clear objectives:** A clear objective according to the nature of business is an important trait for an entrepreneur. He should be clear in his mindset as to the nature and type of goods to be produced and the ancillary activities that are required to be undertaken to produce the same.
- **Business secrecy:** Maintaining secrecy of matters pertaining to business matters is a must for a successful entrepreneur. This can be done by making a proper selection of the subordinates.
- **Human relations ability:** Emotional stability, tactfulness and personal relations are the most important entrepreneurial traits. The main distinction between a successful entrepreneur and failed entrepreneur is made by the way he manages the public or human relations. Good relations with the customers can be gained by continuously winning their confidence. An entrepreneur must have good relations with his customers in order to gain their continued patronage and win their confidence in his product. He must also maintain good relations with his employees, if he is to motivate them to higher levels of efficiency.
- **Effective communication:** A good communication skillset helps an entrepreneur to put his decisions or analysis effectively and with clarity. To-the-point communication which is also crisp and convincing, is one of the secrets behind the making of a successful entrepreneur.
- **Technical knowledge:** An entrepreneur must have a reasonable level of technical knowledge base since he is involved in dealing with the sophisticated technologies.
- **Decision making:** Taking decisions after properly analyzing the different aspects of the business is the key to a successful entrepreneur.
- **Energy:** An entrepreneur is required to work hard for long periods. Further, constant attention is also required for the successful running of the business.
- **Risk-bearing:** An entrepreneur should be prepared to accept failures, since there is no business without the element of risk involved. The failures should be looked at as a challenge and opportunity.

A few more additional traits have been identified by Robert D. Hisrich which has been discussed in the preceding paragraphs:

- **Motivation:** A team is required to be built by an entrepreneur for running a venture. An entrepreneur must try to keep the members highly motivated. An environment for growth and career development must be provided to each and every individual.
- **Self-confidence:** Entrepreneurs should have confidence to face any kind of situation. They must be determined to achieve goals and at the same time inspire others.
- **Long-term involvement:** Continuous and consistent involvement is required on the part of entrepreneurs for the commitment to long-term projects.
- **High energy level:** Success of an entrepreneur demands the ability to work long hours for sustained periods of time.
- **Troubleshooter:** An entrepreneur must be able to identify the cause of any problem and at the same time suggest solutions for the problem. Therefore, an entrepreneur must possess the trait of the proverbial "troubleshooter".
- **Initiative:** The entrepreneur must have initiative, accepting personal responsibility for actions and above all make good use of resources. It is this trait which gives the entrepreneur the courage to risk and learn from failures.
- **Goal-setter:** An entrepreneur must be able to set challenging, but realistic goals. This personal trait can go a long way in the all round progress of a nation.

These personal traits make an entrepreneur a successful person. However, it must be stated that no entrepreneur possesses all these strengths. No entrepreneur is born with all these traits. It is possible for him to acquire these traits if the environment is suitable for this purpose.

16.8 ENTREPRENEURSHIP AS CAREER OPTION

An educated person has broadly two career options. One is called wage or salary employment, wherein people are employed in government service, public and private sectors and get fixed wage or salary. The other option is entrepreneurial employment under which people set up their own ventures. Wage employment does not generate resources and is organized within the existing wealth. Wage employment is self-saturating.

Once availed, it blocks the employment opportunity to others for another 10 years. On the other hand, the latter contributes towards national wealth and has a unique characteristic of self-generation. This starts a chain of activities that create unending employment opportunities. Entrepreneurship promotes small savings in the middle class individuals for investment into new ventures. It also provides an outlet that creates an urge among individuals to attain excellence in product design and related innovation. Thus, entrepreneurship provides a lasting solution to the acute problem of unemployment. The difference between wage employment and entrepreneurial employment is shown in Table 16.2.

Table 16.2

	Wage Employment	**Entrepreneurial Employment**
Nature	Self-saturating	Self-generating
Scope	Limited	Unlimited
Orientation	Routine Types Status Quo Problem Avoiding Dependent Decisions	Creative Innovative Problem Solving Independent Decisions
Contribution	Consumes National Wealth	Generates National Wealth
Earning	Fixed (Subsistence)	Growing (Generating Surplus)

In the context of employment generation, the three terms, i.e., income generation, self employment and entrepreneurship are often used interchangeably. Entrepreneurship refers to identification of innovative ideas, setting up of a new enterprise. Whereas, self employment refers to full time involvement in one's own occupation. One may or may not be bearing the risk, mobilizing inputs, organizing production and marketing the product or service. Income generating activities, on the other hand, are part time, casual and practised with a view of raising additional income. All entrepreneurs are self-employed and income generating persons. But all self-employed and income generating persons may not be entrepreneurs.

17

Qualities, Functions and Role of an Entrepreneur in Economic Growth

17.1 INTRODUCTION

Entrepreneurs play a vital role in the economic development of a country. Primarily, the development of an economy from the perspective of socio-economic development depends to a great extent on its entrepreneurs. An entrepreneur has the required skillset, spirit of innovation and motivation to setup and run his own industry. He is always determined to achieve goals. He seeks opportunities and seizes them to achieve economic gains.

Entrepreneurship is the act of organizing, producing goods and services and their distribution and maintaining the profit earned, by a group of highly motivated individuals who are goal achievers. Adventurism, uncertainty, risk bearing, creativity and innovation are some of the terms that can be used to describe this purposeful act. The act involves the dynamic changes that are required to be made in a process or method of production to meet the requirements of an economy, while maintaining the profit. Entrepreneurship therefore means to achieve objectives by doing things in a new and improvised manner.

17.2 QUALITIES OF ENTREPRENEURS

The major quality that is required to be an entrepreneur is the willingness to work hard. However, many believe that for being a successful entrepreneur one is required to have intelligence such as that of a professor, capacity to foresee the future like an astrologer as eloquent and convincing as a salesman, an auditor's precision, a talent to manipulate the funds and so on. It will be hard to find a person that has all these qualities and therefore no one can be an entrepreneur. Thus, to be an entrepreneur, willingness to hard work is the vital key.

Looking at the prospects of being rewarded in the long term, an entrepreneur takes the risk to work under an environment of uncertainty and establish his own business venture. An entrepreneur incepts an idea and formulates a plan. He then organizes the required inputs and other resources and puts them in the formulated plan to achieve the set goal or objective. Different roles at different stages are required to be played by a person to become a successful entrepreneur.

Some of the essential qualities entrepreneurs must possess are briefly described below:

- **Desire to achieve:** A person should have the desire to achieve the set goals. Dreams are made by most of the people, the dreams of success and achievements. However, they lack in the desire or the need to achieve their dreams by taking appropriate actions. An entrepreneur on the other hand has a strong desire to achieve higher goals.
- **Perseverance:** Entrepreneurs have a quality to be committed to the goals and the course of action to be taken. They get absorbed in it and are not deterred by the problems and difficulties that beleaguer any project. They stick to their plans and work hard until and unless they achieve the desired goals.
- **Moderate risk taker:** Taking high risk and being a gambler are not the traits that characterize an entrepreneur. Entrepreneurs take moderate risk that they think is solvable. They love to take a middle road strategy which is high enough to be exciting and has a fair chance to win.
- **Find and explore opportunity**: An entrepreneur should be aware of the opportunities around him. They should seize these opportunities to manipulate them to their advantage. The difficulties are converted into opportunities using the innovative bent of mindset. Further, they are realistic in their approach. Entrepreneurs carefully plan and anticipate achieving their goals in realizing an opportunity.
- **Analytical ability:** An entrepreneur has a realistic approach about the business undertakings. The personal likes and dislikes are not allowed by them to come in their way. They seek expert advice whenever they require assistance. Emotional attitude is avoided by them in their business or while solving the related problem.
- **Using feedback:** An entrepreneur should always be keen to have an immediate feedback of the course of action to achieve the plan. An accurate data irrespective of the fact that it is favourable or unfavourable is promptly required by an entrepreneur to evaluate their performances. The stimulus is given by mainly the unfavourable data that will motivate them to achieve higher goals.
- **Facing uncertainty:** A successful entrepreneur is always optimistic in the unfamiliar situations. The circumstances may appear to be appealing even though the odds are not clear. An entrepreneur always moves ahead undeterred and makes the best of the opportunities at its helm. As they become engrossed in a situation, the environment is better understood by them and then the chances for them to create a win-win situation are closely calculated. They practise boldness in the unknown situations and prudence in the case of familiar. The special insight and skills are used by an entrepreneur to win any kind of situation.
- **Independence:** An entrepreneur starts off his own venture because he doesn't like to work for others. They like to be independent and feel responsible for their own decisions.

- **Flexibility:** An entrepreneur is required to change the decision if the situation demands after weighing the pros and cons of the decision. They do not have any kind of hesitation to revise their decisions. Therefore, an entrepreneur has a flexible mindset.
- **Planner:** An entrepreneur is an able planner who plans the things to achieve the desired goals and objectives. They foresee future and then prepare accordingly to make it come true.
- **Interpersonal Skills:** An entrepreneur needs to deal with people of different types that come across him. He should be comfortable enough to deal with people of different nature and levels. An entrepreneur should be capable enough to make these people work for him, with him and help him to achieve the desired objectives and goals.
- **Motivator:** During the course of actions and activities, an entrepreneur may be required to influence people. This is required to make the people think in the way an entrepreneur does so that they (people) would act accordingly. Therefore, an entrepreneur should motivate people to act.
- **Stress Taker:** *Are you capable of working for long hours and tackling different problems at the same time?*: An entrepreneur may be required to involve a great deal of emotional and physical stress, being a protagonist of the entire enterprise. These traits are required to cope up with the changing situations and to take necessary and appropriate actions. Therefore, the capability to work for long hours and to be cool enough under any situation are a must to be a successful entrepreneur.
- **Orientation to Future:** An entrepreneur should not be obsessed with the past. They should be aware of the present and have a future orientation.

A person should make an inventory of the traits possessed by him to aspire to be an entrepreneur. The awareness about oneself will help in defining one's strength and weakness.

17.3 FUNCTIONS OF AN ENTREPRENEUR

The functions of an entrepreneur have surfaced in several theories. Each theory bestows one function or the other on an entrepreneur. According to Marshall, organization and management of a business venture are important functions of an entrepreneur. Risk taking was considered to be the most important function of an entrepreneur according to J.B. Say and Cantillon.

According to Prof. B.R. Knight, risk taking and control are conceived to be the important functions of an entrepreneur. An entrepreneur is required to perform one or more functions as the different theories suggest.

As a vital factor of production, an entrepreneur is required to perform the following functions:

- **Risk taking and uncertainty bearing:** An entrepreneur is required to take risk under the environment of uncertainty and unpredictable future. He should not only be ready to enjoy during the phases of profit if the venture succeeds but should also accept losses if the venture fails to succeed. Therefore, taking risk is one of the important entrepreneurial functions. There are two categories of risks: insurable and non-insurable. The changes in the preferences and tastes of the customer as well as the changes in the production methods and tools form the integral part of non-insurable risks, which are also regarded as the uncertainties. The levels of these uncertainties could be reduced by an entrepreneur using the skill sets and good judgmental qualities.
- **Taking business decisions:** An entrepreneur is required to take all the decisions regarding the business. He enters into a business venture once he is convinced that there are prospects of earning profit. A concrete plan is required to be produced which would help an entrepreneur to take decisions regarding the nature and type of product to be produced and the quality that needs to be associated with the product. He needs to decide on the production technique that could earn him a sizeable profit. Further, the decisions regarding the selection of a personnel and location of the production unit carry their own importance as well.
- **Managerial functions:** The managerial functions are vital elements for an entrepreneur. He should be able to arrange and manage the finances for meeting the needs of the business enterprise. The financial management will help him in arranging the required quantities of the raw materials, providing a proper infrastructure for the production of goods and services. Barring managing the finances, he is also required to assume the role of a personnel manager.
- **Innovation:** Innovation is by far one of the most important functions of an entrepreneur. Being innovative helps an entrepreneur to introduce the required improvements both in the quantity and quality of the production line. In doing so, the technical and economic feasibility is analyzed in the first prospect. The function of innovation injects the elements of dynamism into the economic system.

The nature and the type of an economic system dictate the manner in which the entrepreneurial functions are performed. In case of socialist economy, he assumes the role of a planner as opposed to being a king in a traditional society.

In the description of Arthur H. Cole, an entrepreneur is a decision maker. The analysis of Cole has attributed the following functions to an entrepreneur:

- To find out the objectives and goals to be achieved and if necessary to change the objectives according to the conditions required.
- The all-round development of an organization which includes maintaining relations with the employees as well as the subordinates in an efficient manner.
- To arrange and manage the finance required. To do so, a healthy relation is required to be maintained with the existing investors and all the other potential investors.

- To identify the required technological equipment and to requisite the same in an efficient manner. Revision of the new machinery at regular interval of time is equally important as well.
- To prepare a market for the produced goods and services. Devising new products in order to meet the changing demands and requirements of the economy is another vital function.
- To maintain healthy and good relations with the different public authorities and also with the society.

According to the present-day arbiters and analysts, an entrepreneur has following three main broad functions:

- **Innovation:** The main function of an entrepreneur is to commercialize the innovation. The invention of an inventor is given the shape required to meet the requirements of the society. An entrepreneur does things in a much better way. This may include the implementation of new methods of production, creation of new markets, besides establishment of a new venture.
- **Risk-taking and uncertainty-bearing:** Risk-taking ability of an entrepreneur makes him to take on new opportunities and tune them to the advantage of the industry. An entrepreneur should always be prepared for facing any kind of uncertainty associated with the plans of expansion and investment. A prospect of achieving higher quantum of profit is obvious with the increasing level of risk in the business. The fact is also corroborated by many modern writers and authors.
- **Organization and management:** An entrepreneur has the function of paramount importance to provide leadership to the established business venture. To have a complete control and management over a business is a vital function for an entrepreneur as recognized by Alfred Marshall. This requires an entrepreneur to control and manage the different input factors of production. Further, the decisions which are associated with the methods and products on a production line should also be managed by an entrepreneur. According to Marshall, as the business grows, the entrepreneur may appoint some subordinates to take decisions. However, the function of organization and management of production should be determined by him. The role of a leader should be adorned by him to take a final judgment related to the conduct of business.

At the later stages of the business venture, an entrepreneur may be required to perform many other activities. Some of these activities are as follows:

- The production should be diversified if needed to meet the changing demands of the market.
- The business could be expanded at the prospects of achieving higher goals.
- Problems related to labour and unions may be required to be tackled.
- Co-ordination with outside agencies.

As far as underdeveloped countries are concerned, Kilby has outlined the following wide range of the activities for an entrepreneur:

- Controlling and managing of the scarce resources.
- Maintain relations with the public bureaucracy regarding licensing, taxes, etc.
- Acquiring and overseeing assembly of the factory.
- Design and engineering from the industrial prospects.
- Marketing of product.
- Appropriate and efficient response to market competition.
- Management of finances and production line.

17.4 ROLE OF ENTREPRENEUR IN ECONOMIC GROWTH: ECONOMISTS' VIEW

An entrepreneur adorns the role of a director in an era of modern production. The complexity level of modern production era is much high and is directly linked to the economic development. The role of an entrepreneur is to take all necessary decisions regarding the production which he deems is required for the success of the business venture. The three main aspects of the role of entrepreneur in the economic development are discussed below:

- As already discussed that one of the key roles of an entrepreneur is to co-ordinate the input factors of production. This he does by assembling the different factors of production and combining them in the best possible manner to be made available to the production process. The co-ordination act involves the right selection of the factors, the analysis of right quantity of each factor to be employed, utilization of the best technical machinery and equipment, reduction of the waste produced, division of labour, etc.
- An entrepreneur performs the best under the environment of uncertainty. According to the analysis of Hawtrey, the risk bearing potential is one of the key functions of an entrepreneur and the conducted analysis also emphasizes that the volume of profit earned is directly proportional to the risks taken. Risks are generally based on the anticipation of demand. Prof. B.R. Knight opines that there are two types of risks: insurable and non-insurable. "Uncertainty" is another term that is synonymous to non-insurable risks. According to his opinion, the primary function of an entrepreneur that enables him to earn profit is the uncertainty bearing function. With the ever going complexities in modern production, this function has assumed great importance.
- An entrepreneur adorns the role of an innovator. He innovates ways to commercialize the inventions of the inventor.

The presence of discontinuous disturbance characterizes the process of economic development. These discontinuous disturbances come in the form of innovation as is opined by many economists. Modern economists have suggested the following five categories of innovation that can be undertaken by an entrepreneur:

- The introduction of new products and services or new quality of goods and services.
- The introduction of new tools and techniques of production.
- The creation of a new market for the produced goods and services.
- The conquest of a new source of supply of raw materials.
- Establishment of a new business enterprise.

The result of all the innovational activity is a greater output and hence greater income. The innovational activities lead to the increased efficiency of production and hence the productive efficiency of the economy is increased. The secret of economic development as analyzed by Schumpeter lies in raising productivity. Schumpeter also goes on to discuss the differences between economic development and economic growth. On the one hand the presence of more resources in the economy is the key to economic growth, while economic development occurs as a result of entrepreneurial activity and therefore economic development is an entirely different phenomenon.

The entrepreneur is the protagonist in the process of socio-economic development. He channelizes the economy's resources and productive lines by introduction of new factors and their combination. An entrepreneur can be distinguished from a producer in the sense that the latter chooses any one of the available methods whereas the entrepreneur introduces new methods of production. Further, an entrepreneur is neither a capitalist as the role of an entrepreneur is to divest and manage the funds to new production. The main objective of an entrepreneur is to establish an economic system to its dynamic best. Thus, entrepreneurial activity stimulates progress and forms the mainspring of economic development.

17.4.1 Importance of Entrepreneur in the Economic Development

The main objective of any economy is to achieve maximum economic development. The economic development of an economy has a direct relation to the human resources. However, the need of dynamic entrepreneurs alongside the human resources can also not be ignored. Irrespective of the richness and diversity in natural resources, a country will not be able to progress without the entrepreneurship qualities that lead to proper utilization of the natural resources. Many developing countries have begun to realize the importance of entrepreneurship. These countries have now initiated an attempt to motivate the industrial entrepreneurs.

An entrepreneur performs under the environment of risk and is a highly motivated individual who performs at his dynamic best under these circumstances. He seeks for new opportunities, seizes the new opportunities and manipulates these opportunities to the advantage of his business venture. The capturing of new opportunities leads to setting-up of new business ventures which henceforth bring economic transformation. They are therefore aptly called agents of change. By using the innovative ways and managerial skills, they not only meet the needs and requirements of an economy but also lead to the improvement of living standards. The society not only gets improved and new products but also there is reduction in the disparity in income levels. An economically advanced economy will be more powerful and confident of the self-image.

The instances on ability and innovation skills of entrepreneurs are plenty in history. The effort of entrepreneurs was well recognized during the 18th century in England, where many technological and scientific inventions took place and the entrepreneurs commercialized these inventions for the betterment of the society. It is therefore truly believed that the scientific discoveries would have not been put to use for the society in the absence of entrepreneurs. Therefore one of the key skills of any entrepreneur is the ability to innovate. The innovation skills have been utilized by entrepreneurs in developing new products or improving the quality of an existing product. All these have led to creation of more employment opportunities, income, i.e., socio-economic development of a society or economy.

The economic development of a country is dependent on the functions of entrepreneurs. They are agents to mobilize capital, search and exploit the natural resources, create a space for the produced products in the market. It is the entrepreneurial input that differentiates between prosperity and poverty among nations. For instance, the entrepreneurial inputs in the form of hardwork and the imaginative skills in a country like Japan, has led to her prosperity. The significance of entrepreneurship is clearly reflected in the economic progress of countries like USA and Western European nations. The small entrepreneurs in the newly industrializing countries occupy a central stage to economic development since they play a role of seed beds for the entrepreneurial and managerial talent. Thus, the scarcity of entrepreneurship input is the main inhibiting factor to accelerate the process of industrialization.

The contemporary economists also believe that an entrepreneur acts as a business leader who is capable enough to portend the future and thereby helps in fostering the economic growth as well as economic development. The importance of entrepreneurship input in the economic development is vital for an economy. It is not wrong to consider entrepreneurship as a panacea of the economic evils in a developing country. In fact, entrepreneurship is the dynamic need of a developing nation and sustains the process of economic development in the following ways:

- **Employment generation:** One of the acute problems of a nation is the growing unemployment and in particular the unemployment of educated population. The problems of only 5 to 10 per cent of the unemployed could be looked after through the available opportunities. As discussed, wage employment is self-saturating. Whenever vacancies are created in a department, these are filled and then there will not arise any vacancy for many years. Say for instance, there are 100 vacancies to be filled for a department, then 100 of these will be filled by the government and then there would be no vacancy for thirty years, or any people on these positions retire. If instead of getting employed, these people start their own ventures and not only create jobs for themselves but also create employment for others also. With the passage of time the business enterprise will grow in size and hence provide direct or indirect employment to many others. Thus, entrepreneurship is the panacea to fight the evil of unemployment.

- **National income:** The goods and services produced in a country and the exported products form the national income of an economy. The goods and services meet the demands of people within the economy and also the demand of exports. With the increasing standard of living and increasing population, the domestic demand increases. The domestic demand increases with ever increasing population and standard of living. The export demand also increases to meet the needs of growing import due to various reasons. The entrepreneurship inputs are required to meet these increasing demands of goods and services. In other words, entrepreneurship increases the national income.
- **Dispersal of economic power:** Power dominates the world affairs. Muscle power and economic power are the two main types of power. Economic power rules the modern world, whereas the muscle power has lost its relevance. The industrial and business activities result into economic power. The economic power can be concentrated in few hands as a result of industrial activities. The concentration in a few hands results in monopoly which is an evil in itself. However, this power can be dispersed amongst the population by developing and motivating a large section of population to tread the path of entrepreneurship. The harmful effects of a monopoly can be minimized by setting up of a large number of enterprises for the goods and services.

  Serious social and national implications can result if the wealth remains in the hands of a few families. This situation arises when the small business enterprises don't have enough competition due to lack of entrepreneurs and then these grow into big enterprises. The wealth will only be dispersed when there is no dearth of entrepreneurs in an economy. This dispersal of wealth promotes the real socialism and makes the economy healthy.
- **Balanced regional development:** The industrial growth and business growth lead to a large number of benefits, the development of different sectors of the economy which include health, education, road transport, entertainment, etc. A balanced regional development could be ensured with the rapid development of entrepreneurship. A rapid entrepreneurship avoids the concentration of development to only select few cities of a nation. The entrepreneurs will be forced to set up new businesses in smaller towns once there is large number of entrepreneurs in and around the city. Therefore, a rapid entrepreneurial expansion leads to development of backward regions also.

  The requirements of a large section of population will remain unsatisfied if a region has scarcity of entrepreneurs. The entrepreneurs from other places step in and set up enterprises to fulfil the pent up demand of the local people. These alien entrepreneurs do not invest the major part of the profits in the areas in which the unit is located. Usually, the profit is invested at a place where the entrepreneurs come from. Such entrepreneurs invest their profits in constructing their houses, etc., at the place of their origin. Thus, the backward areas do not get benefits of business or industrial profits. This drainage of wealth results in further deterioration of the area. The practice of siphoning the profits earned through entrepreneurial activities based on local resources by alien entrepreneurs has been compared with the blood sucking process practised by leeches, and termed as 'leech effect' by Dr. M.M.P. Akhori.

- **Harnessing locally available resources and entrepreneurship:** India is considered to be very rich in natural resources. In spite of more than four decades of planned development, a large number of states have remained economically backward. A few large-scale industries started by entrepreneurs from outside the state in economically backward areas may help as models of pioneering efforts, but ultimately the real strength of industrialization in backward areas depends upon the involvement of local entrepreneurship in such activities. Increased activities of local entrepreneurs will also result in making use of abundantly available local resources.
- **Reducing unrest and social tension amongst youth:** Many problems associated with youth unrest and social tension are rightly considered to be due to youth not being engaged in productive work. In the changing environment where we are faced with the problem of recession in wage employment opportunities, alternative to wage career is the only viable option. The country is required to divert the youth with latent entrepreneurial traits from wage careers to self-employment careers. Such alternate path through entrepreneurship could help the country in defusing social tension and unrest amongst youth.
- **Innovations in enterprises:** Business enterprises need to be innovative for their survival and better performance. It is believed that smaller firms have relatively higher necessity and capability to innovate. The smaller firms do not face the constraints imposed by large investments in the existing technology and thus they are both free and compelled to innovate. The National Science Foundation, an organization in USA found that small companies produce four times more innovations per research dollar than do bigger companies. Entrepreneurship development programmes are aimed at accelerating the pace of small firms' growth in India. Increased number of small firms are expected to result in more innovations and make the Indian industry compete in the international market.
- **Improvement in living standards:** Entrepreneurs set up industries which remove scarcity of essential commodities and introduce new products. Production of goods on mass scale and manufacture of handicrafts, etc., in the small-scale sector help to improve the standard of life of a common man. These offer goods at lower costs and increase variety in consumption.

- **Economic Independence:** Entrepreneurship is essential for national self reliance. Industrialists help to manufacture indigenous substitutes of hitherto imported products, thereby reducing dependence on foreign countries. Businessmen also export goods and services on a large-scale and thereby earn the foreign exchange for the country. Such import substitution and export promotion help to ensure the economic independence of the country without which political independence has little meaning.

18
Competing Theories of Entrepreneurship

18.1 INTRODUCTION

One of the key variables linking the social-cultural environment with the economic development is the entrepreneurship. The fact has been contended by a number of social scientists. Many economists have also shifted their focus to believe that the major determinant of the rate of economic growth is the growth of high-level manpower in the form of entrepreneur and not the rate of capital formation.

The word 'entrepreneur' appeared in the French language long before the emergence of the concept of entrepreneurial function. It was applied at first instance in the 16th century to the people who were part of the military expedition. Later on in 17th century, the term entrepreneur covered all the civil engineering activities which involved construction and fortification. The word was used in particular for the economic activities during the early 18th century.

Richard Cantillon identified the unique trait of performing under the environment of risk and uncertainty. According to Cantillon, an entrepreneur buys certain goods and services at some fixed price and later on sells the same goods and services at the uncertain prices. On analysis Cantillon found that it is a bearer of a type of risk defined as the non-insurable risk.

J.B. Say defines an entrepreneur as a person who is involved in coordinating, organizing and supervising the activities related to the business enterprise. He goes on to describe an entrepreneur as an agent who is involved in production of goods and services by continuous efforts in bringing and managing the different input factors of production. Say has defined important characteristics that an entrepreneur is required to possess: judgmental skills, perseverance, sound knowledge base and administrative capability. Besides these explicit factors, he has also defined three more implicit factors forming the crux of entrepreneurship:

- Moral qualities for the work.
- Should be able to organize and manage sufficient capital resources.
- Quality of superintendence and administration to overcome the uncertainty of business profits.

Both, Cantillon and Say, defined entrepreneurship in the most general terms, Cantillon extended his concept of entrepreneurship to every economic activity and regarded everybody as an entrepreneur. However, there was no obvious correlation of entrepreneurship with the general economic development.

According to Adam Smith, the main motive that motivates towards entrepreneurship is the profit. This sole motive will enable an entrepreneur to employ the capital resources in the productivity of goods and services. At the same time, profit also serves the purpose of savings which was identified by Smith with investments. Adam Smith opines capital formation as the main fundamental economic determinant of growth. The role of capital formation in the economic development has also been realized by Ricardo. According to him, there are two important factors governing the rate of capital accumulation:

- The ability to save
- The will to save.

Out of the two factors, the surpluses, i.e., the 'net income' determines the ability to save whereas the second factor of 'will to save' depends on the rate of profit. Therefore, the change in wage rates is one of the critical factors that affects the Ricardian profit since he considers the profit as a residual over and above wages.

The concept of entrepreneurship was treated in the same manner from Cantillon to Marshall. Accordingly, entrepreneurship was devised to be the function of the fourth factor of production. This was identified by different names however. The supply side was not considered for this factor of production and henceforth there was no supply curve. All the economists had considered entrepreneurship considering the stationary equilibrium and failed to recognize it as the main driving force to economic development.

18.2 THEORY OF ENTREPRENEURSHIP

18.2.1 Entrepreneurship: A Function of Innovation

It was in the year 1934 for the first time that Joseph A. Schumpeter regarded the humans as the agents for the process of economic development. A critical role of entrepreneurship was ascribed to the human agents in Schumpeter theory of economic development. Economic development was considered discrete technological change by him. The following five different types of events could be used to generalize the process of development.

- The introduction of a new product in the market.
- The introduction of new improved technology of production.
- The creation of a new market.
- The establishment of a new source of supply.
- The setting up of a new venture or organization in the country.

Some agency within the system is required to act as a catalyst that would deliberately and actively promote the cause of development since development is neither automatic nor spontaneous. Schumpeter called these agents as the initiators of the changes required for development and recognized them as 'entrepreneurs'.

An entrepreneur as described by Schumpeter is an agent having leadership quality to provide for the initial changes in the conditions of the economy. Thereafter, he should be able to cause dynamic changes in the economy which is discontinuous in nature. He is considered an innovator. By nature he is neither a technician, nor a financier. An entrepreneur is not solely motivated by the profit psychologically. According to Schumpeter, the element of interest and profit does not exist for a static society since both the elements arise from change which, in turn, is indicative of progress. Any creative response to any situation is Schumpeterian 'innovation'.

It was in the context of industrial revolution the Schumpeterian theory of economic development was conceived and therefore his theoretical explanations on the economic development are affected by the experiences of that period. The result of the innovations was profit that was available for reinvestment. As a result, using the surplus capital an entrepreneur was capable enough to invade the different economic fields and that too with spectacular success. As far as the scope of the Schumpeterian theory is concerned, it was modelled on big private entrepreneurship. Therefore, for the underdeveloped regions the applicability of the Schumpeterian theory is questioned on the basis of the following grounds:

- Whether, with only one characteristic of innovation can an underdeveloped nation or region of an economy lacking in basic infrastructure initiate an economic process and make itself sustainable.
- Is the available capital, which being small in magnitude, creating the conditions suitable for economic growth and progress? Further, will it be possible to create dynamic changes in the initiated economic process without wrenching the society or the economy.

According to A.H. Cole, entrepreneurship is the purposeful act carried out by highly motivated individuals or group of similar individuals, which is undertaken to initiate, maintain and canonize a profit oriented enterprise or organization for the production of required goods and services. The definition given by Cole and Schumpeter differs in respect to the range within which the term entrepreneurship could be applied.

18.2.2 Entrepreneurship: A Function of Group Level Pattern

The entrepreneurial characteristic at individual level was not accepted by Frank W. Young. According to him, groups of individuals with highly motivational characteristic behaviour qualifies as entrepreneurship group, as the groups with higher differentiation have the capacity to react. Young describes 'the capacity to react' using a term 'solidarity'. He defines it to be the degree of projection of a particular situation which is created, maintained and coherently presented. The term 'differentiation' on the other hand describes the diversity, as opposed to coherence. A unified situation is produced as a result of intensified internal communication which, in turn, is indicative of a higher degree of occupational and institutional diversity when compared to its acceptance. Despite there being difference in the family status and occupation, they find a way which allows for mutual understanding. This helps them to improve their symbolic position in the business enterprise established by them.

However, theory of Young and Schumpeterian finds similarity in the way they characterize an entrepreneur in the form of an innovator. The individual level of the entrepreneurship is recognized by him as the 'underside' of a group level pattern. He interprets that an entrepreneur does not work single-handedly and the entrepreneurial activity is produced as a result of combination of backgrounds of families, experiences and cultural values. The individual characteristics are due to the reflections of the different antecedent conditions. These constitute an independent factor mediating between the economic growth and structural factors.

The reactive sub-group which is incorporation of the society forms the basis of Young's theory. As per Young's theory the groups will become reactive when the following three conditions are met:

- Low status recognition is experienced by a group.
- The denial of access to important social networks.
- The better availability of the institutional resources to a group in comparison to the other groups in the society.

18.2.3 Entrepreneurship: A function of Managerial Skills and Leadership

According to Bert F. Hoselitz (1952), a person for being an entrepreneur must have additional skills than that arising due to motivation to amass wealth and earn profit. He is required to have managerial skills and more importantly the skills to lead the business enterprise or venture. These skills are critical to being a successful entrepreneur.

Hoselitz quotes from the history of French and German business establishments in order to strengthen his argument about being critical of managerial and leadership skills. The people from these industrial establishments had mechanical skills rather than the financial skills. For the underdeveloped countries, Hoselitz had identified three types of business leadership:

- The merchant moneylender type
- The managerial type
- The entrepreneur type

Out of the above three types, the functions that are predominantly market-oriented are exhibited by merchant/moneylender types, authoritarian orientation is exhibited by the managerial type, and the traits involving the above two orientations leading to product orientation are exhibited by the entrepreneur type business leadership.

Analysis of Hoselitz's into the development of entrepreneurship skills suggest the development of an individual with the personality that is involved and oriented towards productivity, working and creation. Such methods should be developed that lead to the maturation of the mentioned orientations. He further suggests a creative integration with the establishment of social institutions. These all will lead to the favourable environment for the establishment of independent enterprises or ventures.

Liquidity of wealth is another important trait an entrepreneur is required to possess according to the analysis of Hoselitz, besides having the desire to earn profit. An industrial entrepreneur produces his own commodity, the acceptability of which is uncertain which is opposed to a moneylender who has high chances of the acceptability of his deals. Therefore, the element of risk and the degree of associated uncertainty is much higher for an entrepreneur in comparison to those involved in lending profession.

According to Hoselitz, entrepreneurship can develop in a society when variety of choices are permitted in a society. Further, there is no rigidity from the different social processes and there is encouragement and motivation for the development of personalities interested in enterprise.

18.2.4 Entrepreneurship: An Organization Building Function

The most critical and crucial ability according to Frederick Harbison is the 'organization building' ability. Entrepreneurship according to Harbison means the skills to build a venture or a business organization. Harbison opines that an entrepreneur should have the ability to 'multiply himself' which means to delegate and disburse the responsibilities to other members. Harbison's entrepreneur is an organization builder as opposed to the innovator according to Schumpeter. He must have the potential to harness the new opportunities and ideas to the betterment of the organization. The analysis of Harbison's entrepreneur suggests that such a person may not be the one who has new ideas and the capital resources and the ability to try out new combinations but he may be simply a person with good leadership and administrative skills.

As far as the organization is concerned, Harbison lays more emphasis on the managerial and creativity skills for an entrepreneur. It can be realized from the analysis that Harbison's definition resembles very closely to that of Scumpeter's concept. However, the difference of opinion lies in the fact that Harbison considers the creation of new organization as being the element of innovation which will facilitate the economic use of other innovations. The absence of this skillset will lead to failure of implementation of other innovations and hence the economic development.

18.2.5 Entrepreneurship: A Function of High Achievement

The innovative traits for an entrepreneur are also ascribed by McClelland (1961), like Hoselitz. The role of an entrepreneur involves doing new things or the existing things in a new and better way. A person adopting traditional ways is not an entrepreneur. Further, the act of entrepreneurship involves decision making under the environment of risk and uncertainty. Therefore, if the actions involved are under insignificant uncertainty and applies or implements the known predictable results, then the act cannot be regarded to be that of entrepreneurship.

The two main characteristics of entrepreneurship have been identified by McClelland, like others. The first of the two is synonymous with the term 'innovation' and involves doing things in a new and better way. The second characteristic involves the decision making under uncertainty. The first characteristic is similar to that given by Schumpeter while the second is similar to that described by Cantillon. McClelland's major contribution lies in extending our understanding of causal sequence of entrepreneurial behaviour.

Weber's "Protestant ethic" which emphasizes the need for achievement as a driving psychological force is seen as the development for the McClelland's theory. However, Weber's explanation is implicit in nature while McClelland explicitly emphasized that the most relevant factor for explaining the economic behaviour is that of the need for achievement. This motive is defined as a tendency to service for success in situations involving an evaluation of one's performance in relation to some standard of excellence. Moderate risks would be undertaken by persons with high achievement. The behaviour of such people will not be traditional since they wouldn't be satisfied from the accomplished tasks. Further, they neither would behave as a gambler when the situation is such that probability of failure and dissatisfaction is more. The tasks that involve a great deal of imagination and mental manipulation associates with them a higher level of achievement. Non-routine tasks are examples of such tasks which involve initiative or inventiveness.

The profitability of an entrepreneur is explained in terms of need of achievement by McClelland. McClelland opines that money rewards influences to a great extent the person with low achievement in comparison to that with high achievement. A person will work hard for material gains and related incentives if the achievement levels are low, whereas on the other hand for a person with high achievements, profit is a measure of success and competency.

The inculcation of McClelland's attribute of achievement is similar to that oriented to child rearing practices. These emphasize on maternal warmth, lower degree of father dominance and self reliance training. Following is the causal sequence of entrepreneurial behaviour:

Ideological values → Family Socialisation → Need for Achievement → Entrepreneurial behaviour.

Following characteristics for an entrepreneur have been postulated by McClelland:

- Entrepreneurial Role Behaviour
    - (a) Moderate risk taking as a skill not chance decisiveness.
    - (b) Energetic and/or novel instrumental activities.
    - (c) Individual responsibility.
    - (d) Knowledge of results of decision—Money as a measure of results.
    - (e) Anticipated future possibilities.
    - (f) Organisational skills.
- Interest in entrepreneurial occupations as a function of their prestige and riskiness.
- Entrepreneurial status in various countries
    - (a) Contrasted with other occupational statuses.
    - (b) Differentiated by entrepreneurial success.

By assumption, the characteristic of achievement motive is a relatively stable and enduring trait of an individual. This implies that the change in achievement motive and related behaviour is not changed by the later events. But the Kakinada experiment shows that achievement orientation courses have shown significant improvement in many aspects of entrepreneurial performance. Therefore, achievement motive can be increased considerably by deliberate efforts.

18.2.6 Entrepreneurship: 'Input-Completing' and 'Gap-Filling' Function

Liebenstein (1968) defined two types of entrepreneurial activities: routine and new types. On one hand, a routine type entrepreneurship is associated with the managerial function of business; the new type is basically the Schumpeterian type.

Gap filling was identified as one of the most important characteristics by Liebenstien. The production function has been considered to be well defined in economic theory. However, there is no discussion about the individual who and in which discipline is required to have the production function. As far as the production function is concerned, there is existence of a larger gap in the economic theory. The deficiencies for the production function are a big concern for the economic theory. The gaps and deficiencies are made up by the entrepreneurial function. The gaps are inevitable given the vague nature of some of the inputs in the production function. The examples of such inputs are leadership, motivation, etc. An important entrepreneurial function referred to as input completing stems out as a result of the "gap-filling" activity. An entrepreneur is thus required to marshal all the inputs to realize final products.

Four main entrepreneurship characteristics have been identified by Leibenstein:

- The ability to connect different markets.
- The potential to make up the deficiencies present in the market.
- Input-completing and creation.
- The capability to expand time-binding input transforming entities (i.e., firms).

The two important factors governing the supply of entrepreneurship as stated by Liebenstein are the capacity of input-completing and the inadequate motivational state. Liebenstein also states the importance of investment criterion in the supply of entrepreneurship. According to Liebenstein, a lower profit investment may be fruitful in the longer run when compared to the higher investment profit. Although, it is not possible to find all the characteristics to make an entrepreneur, the training can do its bit to increase the supply of entrepreneurship.

18.2.7 Entrepreneurship: A Function of 'Status Withdrawal'

Everett Hagen (1962), defines the transition to the economic growth as the reflection of change in a society. Hagen searched the main cause of this transition. The transitions take place through generations and are gradual in character. The individuals of distinctive groups are the leaders to the economic growth and not by the individuals who are randomly distributed in the society. Hagen identified innovation as the fundamental characteristic of the economic growth.

The positions to authority of an individual as analyzed by Hagen in a traditional society, are not granted on the basis of the ability of an individual but is done so on the basis of his status. The authoritarian personality therefore characterizes the structure. On visualizing the characteristics of innovation, Hagen opines that innovation involves both arriving at a new concept and the transformation of the concept into material form. Therefore, Hagen also finds the creative individuals as the agents of economic growth.

A sequence related to the formation of authoritarian and creative personalities have been postulated by Hagen. The child-rearing practices have been identified as the main element responsible for shaping all the personalities. The forces required, disrupting the stability of a traditional society needs to be powerful in nature because of the higher degree of stability that can be ascribed to the traditional society. Hagen is of the opinion that disruptions of the kind are necessary to produce creative personalities from the traditional society. It is of course obvious that such changes may not occur in a generation but is a result that spans out several generations.

Experience of the so-called "withdrawal of social status" plays a crucial role according to Hagen's principal theme in the emergence of individuals or groups with creative personalities. Whenever a disruptive agent or a powerful force displaces a traditionally alike group from its previous status or when there is a change in attitude of any superior group towards subordinate group, the result is 'withdrawal of status respect'.

According to Hagen, four types of responses are created and following the suit four different types of personalities result from any withdrawal of status respect. These are:

- **Retreatist:** An individual who remains indifferent to his work and position while continuing to work in the society.
- **Ritualist:** An individual who is defensive in his behaviour and acts in a manner that is accepted to others in the society. He is not much concerned about improving his position in the society.

- **Reformist:** An individual of rebellion character and by virtue of character attempts to establish a new society.
- **Innovator:** An individual with the innovative personality and is therefore an entrepreneur.

As far as the analysis for growth is concerned, Schumpeter and Hagen have much in common. Further, the creative personality of an individual is also characterized by the McClelland's high need for achievement. Hagen's work is different from that of McClelland and other entrepreneurial economists in the sense that the work is based on the experiences accumulated from the backward areas of Asia and Latin America.

Since Hagen's analysis is based on the status withdrawal for the emergence of creative personality which is caused by disruptions which are hard to contemplate in a democratic setup, the analysis fails to give policy measures for backward countries which are striving for economic development.

18.2.8 Entrepreneurship: A Function of Social, Political, and Economic Structure

The theory of entrepreneurial supply has been put forth by Kunkel (1970). The model of entrepreneurship based on the behaviour has been elaborated by Kunkel. It has been repeatedly pointed out by the students of economic history that there is no equal distribution of entrepreneurship in the population of an economy. The talent pool has been provided by the minorities (ethnic, migrated, displaced). However, it is not obvious that all the entrepreneurial talent stems from the minorities. Hence Kunkel has argued that marginality doesn't guarantee entrepreneurship.

Four structures have been stated by John Kunkel on which the industrial entrepreneurship depends:

- **Limitation structure:** One of the most important deviant individual is the entrepreneur in the process of economic development. The social structure is the major determinant causing this deviance. The social structure is responsible for restricting the behavioural pattern of a segment of population. It is the society that limits some of the specific activities to members of particular subcultures which, in turn, affects the members of the society.
- **Demand structure:** On one hand the limitation structure is cultural and social in nature, the demand structure on the other hand is economic. With the changes in government policies and economic progress, the demand structure also changes. Therefore a demand structure is not static in nature. Material rewards can lead to improvements in the demand structure. The future social gains and its foundation rest on such material rewards. Therefore, the behaviour of people can be shaped in an entrepreneurial way by manipulating certain selected components.
- **Opportunity structure:** The opportunity structure is one of the key driving forces to increase the entrepreneurial activity. The opportunity structure comprises all the activities that are directly or indirectly associated with effective planning and

successful operation of the enterprise. This includes the availability of capital, technological and management skills, direct or indirect learning, etc.

- **Labour structure:** Kunkel argues that the labour supply is not identical to supply of other input factors of production. Therefore, Kunkel separates supply of the competent and willing labour from the opportunity structure. He further argues to state that labour is a function of several variables. The available means of livelihood, expectations of life are some of the factors determining the supply of factory labour.

According to Kunkel, the extent to which all these four structures are found in a society governs the supply of entrepreneurs in a society. Any inadequacy in perceiving these structures can result in discrepancy between the objective structures and the actual incidence of entrepreneurs. It is evident, however, that entrepreneurship depends on rather specific combinations of circumstances which are difficult to create and easy to destroy.

18.2.9 Entrepreneurship: A Function of Religious Beliefs

Max Weber had analyzed the impact of religion on enterprising culture. According to Weber, the set of attitudes consisting of money acquisition and the activities involved constitute the "spirit of capitalism". He has also demarcated to distinguish between "spirit of capitalism" and "adventurous spirit". The "spirit of capitalism" according to Max Weber is quite incompatible with giving free rein to impulse since it is subjected to a strict discipline. The cases where widely spread mental attitude being favourable to capitalism is absent; the "spirit of capitalism" according to Weber cannot generate itself. The kind of mental attitude is provided by "protestant ethic" according to Webber.

18.3 FEW ENTREPRENEURIAL DEVELOPMENT MODELS

There are certain models of entrepreneurship development and these can be categorized as follows:

- **Psychological models**: A significant lead has been given by McClelland (1961) in the identification of determinants of entrepreneurship. More importance was ascribed by him to achievement motivation and related it to child rearing practices. However, he changed his earlier proposition of relating the achievement motivation to the child rearing practices in his book with D.G. Winter. In the book he states that the ideological arousal which results for the need to achieve is the main determinant to the change in motivation. The training programme was found as the key policy measure for the achievement orientation. The training programme will lead to eagerness and willingness to exploit the new opportunities.

  The theory of social change by Everett Hagen lays emphasis on 'creative personality' being vital to the entrepreneurial behaviour. He identifies 'status withdrawal' as the determinant of 'creative personality'. The casual sequence of entrepreneurial has also been stated by Hagen; however there is no analysis of the policy variables for the development of entrepreneurship in his theory.

A behaviorist model was suggested and considered by John Kunkel (1965) for entrepreneurial behaviour. The key variable as stated by Kunkel in his model for entrepreneurial behaviour is the surrounding social structure. The social structure is in turn a function of manipulative social and economic incentives. So Kunkel's model identifies sociological variables as the determinants of entrepreneurial supply.

- **Sociological models:** The entrepreneurship theory of Frank W. Young is based on the inclusion of reactive sub-groups. The organization with better institutional resources gives rise and houses the entrepreneurial behaviour within the reactive sub-groups which otherwise experiences low status in a large society. The development of supporting institution in the society has been identified as a key determinant for entrepreneurship development.
- **Integrated models:** T.V. Rao (1975) suggested the following model for entrepreneurial development:

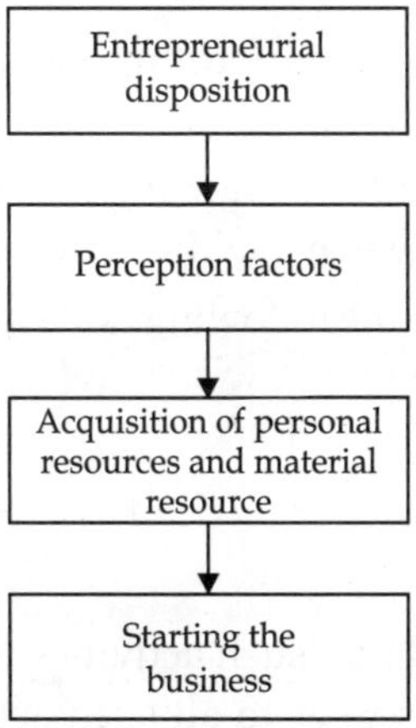

The following factors play a critical role in 'entrepreneurial disposition':

- Need for Motive: An entrepreneur will have the greatest possibility to achieve goals if the activities relating to the motive are performed dynamically.
- Long-term Involvement: There are certain activities that relate to achieving the short- and long-term goals. Therefore, in the view of achieving the goals and the target the activities demand a long term involvement.
- Resources: The resources, essential for the entry and success in the entrepreneurial activity, include personal, social and material resources.
- Socio-Political System: A system perceived as suitable for establishment and development of the enterprise.

The additive nature of all the above factors with their optimal character leads to entry point of entrepreneurship which, in turn, is responsible for the acquisition of material resources and initiation of the business venture.

Five stages to promote the small entrepreneurships have been described by B.S. Venkata Rao (1975):

- **Stimulation**: This stage includes creation of industrial atmosphere, policy statement emphasizing the role of small industry, wide publicity of industrial development programme, formation of special schemes and creation of support institutions. This stage is necessary to stimulate the interest in the backward regions in industrial activity and to create awareness.
- **Identification**: This stage is necessary to identify the prospective entrepreneurs. The prospective entrepreneurial force can be identified in rural artisans, factory workers, persons who have formal training in engineering and technology, and graduates in business administration and management.
- **Development:** This stage would include organization of motivation and managerial training programmes along with advice on technology, formulation of bankable project, location, etc.
- **Promotion:** This can be the job supporting institutions to provide developmental facilities, services, and incentives.
- **Follow-up:** This stage includes reviewing the policies and programmes of the government and seeking new ways with a view to make it more effective.

M.M.P. Akhori (1977) suggested the following cycle for the promotion and development of entrepreneurship:

- Stimulatory
- Support
- Sustaining activities

The stimulatory activity refers to all such activities that stimulate entrepreneurship in any society. The support activities refer to all such activities that help entrepreneurs in establishing and running their enterprises and the sustaining activities to those that help in continued efficient and profitable functioning of an enterprise.

K.L. Sharma (1978) described four stages of economic growth, namely,

- Entry into manufacturing
- Expansion of business
- Perceived stability in business
- Commitment to sustained growth.

The entrepreneurial growth is governed by three sets of entrepreneurial determinants:

- Need for achievement, motivation
- Socio-economic background of entrepreneur (family occupation, caste, religion and region)
- Political milieu.

The interaction of these stages of entrepreneurial growth and determinants of entrepreneurial growth, take place not in vacuum but with the existence of entrepreneurial prerequisites like material resources, entrepreneur's vision and confidence to run an industry and the general infrastructure available to the entrepreneur.

According to this model and empirical analysis, K.L. Sharma suggests that family occupation is more effective for entry into manufacturing and that political factors make positive contribution in the expansion of a unit and these factors are more important at the third stage, i.e., perception of business stability.

19
Government Policy Towards Small-Scale Industries' Structure

19.1 INTRODUCTION

Rapid industrialization and the different parameters of a welfare state were the two key considerations in the post-independence era for a government. Synchronization and the harmonization of these two considerations were important for a government in the post-independence era. The overall strategy involved the economic growth and development with a view to social justice. A mutually complimentary role was assigned to the different segments of the industry—large, medium and small. The important objective to facilitate an integrated and harmonious growth of industrial sector was kept in the view while assigning the complimentary role. The development of small-scale industries was considered essential by the Indian economy in the context of major problems of poverty and unemployment. This was essential because of the capability of Indian economy to contribute to decentralization, to promote entrepreneurship and the optimum use of talents and local resources.

19.2 INDUSTRIAL POLICY RESOLUTIONS IN INDIA

The central government since independence has announced a series of industrial policy resolutions. These resolutions were aimed at promoting industrial growth. Another important aspect that the government kept in view was that of the identification of the pattern of the state intervention and assistance. The small-scale industries were realized to be the most suitable for the utilization of the natural resources by the Industrial Policy Resolution, 1948. Also, the local self-sufficiency to produce goods was one of the key aspects for the small-scale industries. In 1956, the central government initiated to support the cottage, village and small industries. This was taken in a view to build the competitive strength of small and village industries. The roles of the different small-scale industries in providing the employment opportunities, mobilizing the capital resources and local skills, etc., were underlined in the 1956 Resolution.

The emphasis on the dispersion of the cottage and small-scale industries in the rural areas was made in the Industrial Policy Statement, 1977. In order to provide services to the different small industries under one roof, the concept of District Industries Centers was also mooted. The Industrial Policy Statement of 1980 laid emphasis on the creation of nuclear plants. The emphasis for enhancing the contribution of small-scale industries (SSI) in the generation of employment, overall exports, etc., was outlined in the Industrial Policy Statement of 1990.

The stress on strengthening and promotion of small and village industries was announced in the Industrial Policy measures announced in 1991. The role of the state government and the other financial institutions was realized in affecting the changes in the equity participation and investments limit through the Integrated Infrastructure Development scheme for the small-scale industries. The scheme also mooted the pro-active role for the NGO sector. Different support measures to protect the interests of the small-scale industries while promoting their rapid development have been initiated in the form of different policies on modernization, reservations, marketing assistance, etc.

The necessity to provide for the structural and fundamental changes in the policy framework stems out due to the competitive and the liberalized economic environment. The changes play a vital role in the development of the economy. The changing economic scenario has led to the shift of focus from 'protection' to 'promotion'. A number of steps have been taken in this regard for strengthening of this sector. These changes include partial de-reservation, facilitating foreign participation, marketing assistance, export promotion; incentives for quality improvements, etc.

The key points highlighting the Small-Scale Industries Policy of August 1991 were as follows:

- There was increment of investment limit from two lakhs to five lakhs. This limit on investment has now been increased to 25 lakh.
- In order to support small-scale industries and aid them in export promotion, nodal agencies had been recognized in the form of Small Industries Development Organization (SIDO).
- For further augmentation of the export activities, an export development centre was set up in SIDO. The small units were served through the network of field officers.
- To improve the quality and the competitiveness of the produced goods and services, a technology development cell (TDC) was set up in SIDO.
- The handloom sector contributed about 30% of the textile production in the country. Keeping this in view and hence the local needs, the schemes on handloom sector were redesigned. The policies of government were important for sustaining the employment in the rural areas and improve the quality of life for the employed weavers.
- To promote marketing and consumption of items on mass scale and under a common brand, National Small Industries Corporation (NSIC) was set up.
- There was widening of the national equity fund scheme in order to cover the projects up to 10 lakhs.

- To cover the projects up to 20 lakhs with working capital margin up to 10 lakhs, the single window loan scheme was also enlarged.
- The equity support to the tune of 24% of the total investment was provided to the small-scale units from the different large-scale and medium enterprises, public undertakings and foreign investments.

A number of promotional innovative schemes have been introduced confirming the socio-economic development. The schemes are operated either separately or jointly by the development banks. Soft loan scheme, risk capital assistance, seed capital assistance are some of the promotional innovative schemes. In addition, different schemes relating to the subsidy for new and small entrepreneurs are operated by IFCI. Recently, four subsidy schemes and eight consultancy schemes have been introduced to benefit the entrepreneurs.

Even in the changing liberalized environment, the SSI sector has proved its mettle. However, with the dynamic economical scenario, new opportunities and challenges are thrown to this sector. Therefore, it becomes important to provide for sustenance through suitable measures to boost up this sector. The efforts made in this direction will help in converting new opportunities and challenges to scale new heights.

A new ministry of Small-scale Industries and Agro and Rural Industries was setup on 14th of October 1999, to solve the different problems faced by the SSI sector. This functions under the Independent Charge of a Minister of State. The ministry had announced an "Agenda of Millennium" in order to orient the perspective to the development strategy. The announcement laid much emphasis on improving the supply of credit, providing better infrastructural facilities, technology upgradation, and evolution of new policy framework.

The agenda clearly stated the role to be played by the information technology, hi-tech industries, and sunrise industries. All the possible steps to meet the requirements of the different industries were also stipulated by the agenda. Further, a study group was constituted in 1999 to solve the problems of small enterprises.

19.3 INCENTIVES AND SUBSIDIES

Bounties and concessions are included in the term "incentive". A single lump sum given to industry by the government is known as 'subsidy'. The industries of national interest are eligible candidates to receive 'subsidy'. The financial benefits or the bonuses, given by the government so that the industry is able to compete with other units of the nation or the foreign market, are referred to as 'bounty'. The proportion in which this is given depends on the output. On the one hand, subsidy is given keeping in view the interest of the nation, while bounty on the other hand confers benefits on a particular industry. Following advantages are offered by the subsidies and the incentives:

- They are the driving force attracting the prospective.
- A motivation for entrepreneurs for entering the manufacturing line.
- Entrepreneurs feel encouraged to start business in backward areas.
- The government by providing subsidies and incentives:
  - brings industrial development uniformly in all regions,
  - leads to the development of new entrepreneurs, and
  - encourages the entrepreneurs to face competition.

19.4 SCHEMES FOR INCENTIVES

The different schemes to the development of the entrepreneurial activities have been offered by central and state governments including union territories. These are as follows:

- **Incentives for development of industries in backward areas:** A number of concessions and facilities for the industries in the backward areas have been announced by the government of India. These have ensured a balanced regional development. More than 200 districts declared as backward have been identified eligible for receiving the subsidies. A brief discussion of the programme of assistance for setting up industries in the selected backward area/district is indicated below.
- **Concessional finance**: The financial assistance to the new and existing projects, which are part of the expansion scheme, is given by all the financial institutions such as Industrial Credit and Investment Corporation of India, etc. The financial assistance is extended irrespective of the location of the projects. The financial assistance given by the financial institutions are in the form of concessions which are in the form of low interest rates, reduced underwriting commission for shares and debentures, reduced commitment charges, longer amortization and increased initial moratorium period.

  Some of the financial institutions also adopt a flexible attitude in extending the financial assistance which is judged with respect to the promoter's contribution, margin requirements, etc.
- **Capital investment subsidy:** Capital investment subsidy is calculated on the capital investment. It is calculated on the amount of capital invested in the industrial units located in the backward districts. The grant may be from 10% to 20% of the invested capital. The capital investment subsidy is given by the central government.

  Around 100 districts from the identified backward districts by the Planning Commission, qualified for receiving the central investment subsidy. The salient features of the scheme are given below:

- **Quantum of subsidy:** The reimbursement to the tune of 10% on the investment made on fixed capital investment with the ceiling of 15 lakhs was originally announced in 1971. Land, building, plant and machinery comprises the fixed capital investment. The percentage of reimbursement was increased to 15% from 1973 onwards, however the ceiling being at 15 lakhs.
- **Eligibility:** All the industrial units making investments after 1973 in land, building and plant and machinery and located in the identified backward areas were eligible to claim subsidies. The existing industrial units which took to expansion and diversification were also eligible to claim the subsidies.
- **Procedure for claiming subsidy:** To administer the scheme of investment subsidy, nominations of the disbursing agencies has been done by the state governments/ union territory administrations. Some of the agencies that have been nominated include State Financial Corporation; financial institutions such as IDBI, IFCI, and ICICI. In order to claim the subsidy each of the industrial unit has to get itself registered with the Director of Industries. The recommendations regarding the disbursement of the subsidy to the desirous is made by the disbursing agencies to the state level committee appointed in each state/union territory.

• **Tax holiday to new industrial undertakings set up in backward states and union territories:** Deductions under section 80-IA of the Income Tax Act 1961, is allowed on the profits earned from the business enterprise or a ship or hotel business. The deductions allowed is 30% of the profits earned in the assessment period, i.e., the year in which the industrial undertaking begins to function, or the ship is first to use or the year in which the hotel starts to function. This is allowed for nine succeeding years. Similarly, in case of co-operative society, the deduction allowed is to the tune of 30% and is allowed for the succeeding years. Whereas in case of non-corporate assesses, the deductions are at the rate of 25%. The deductions are as high as 50% for the hotels set up in a hilly or a rural area as has been identified by the central government.

The Finance Bill has proposed the dispersal of industrialization in the regionally backward areas and territories. This provided substantial thrust for the setting up of the industries in the backward areas of the states and union territories. It was also proposed in the Eighth Schedule of the Income Tax Act to provide deductions to the tune of 100% for the new industrial undertakings that started to manufacture after 1993. The deductions were envisaged under section 80-IA. The deductions were allowed for the first five assessment periods the beginning year being the year in which the industrial undertaking begins production or manufacturing. After the five years of deductions, the deductions were fixed at the rate of 30 per cent in the case of companies and for the non-corporate assesses, the deductions were fixed at 25 per cent.

The list of states and union territories that have been identified as industrially backward are the ones in which all the districts are industrially backward. This was in accordance to the backward area Notification S.No. 165 dated 19.02.1986. The list of these states and union territories include Arunachal Pradesh, Goa, Assam, Jammu and Kashmir, Himachal Pradesh, Manipur, Mizoram, Meghalaya, Sikim, Nagaland, Tripura, Andaman and Nicobar Islands, Daman & Diu, Dadra & Nagar Haveli, Pondicherry and Lakshadweep.

- **Subsidized consultancy services to small entrepreneurs:** The technical consultancy organizations (TCOs) provide technical consultancy services at low cost to the small entrepreneurs willing to set up rural, cottage, tiny or small-scale units. The small entrepreneurs who propose to expand/modernize/diversify their units can also seek technical consultancy from the TCOs. The TCOs are sponsored by different financial institutions at national and state levels. The entrepreneurs need to pay only 20% of the fees charged by TCO for preparation of feasibility studies, market studies, project reports, and diagnostic studies and any other special studies and applications for seeking financial assistance from the financial institutions. In case the assignment is related to the renewable energy resources, IFCI subsidizes 18% or rupees 5000 of the entire balance, whichever is lower. 100% of the fees charged by the TCO or rupees 6000, whichever is less, is subsidized by TCO in case of physically handicapped or scheduled caste/tribe entrepreneurs. The report prepared by the TCO will be confiscated by the TCO and then can be entitled to other entrepreneur in case an entrepreneur fails to set up project within a year from the date of completion of consultancy assignments. An entrepreneur may be eligible for receiving subsidy in case he proposes to set up the second project also. However, for more than two projects, an entrepreneur will not be entitled to receive the subsidy.
- **Subsidy for market studies:** TCO provides for the cheaper market studies for the new entrepreneurs (locally based or non-resident Indians) entering the field of medium and/or medium large industry for the first time in the country. IFCI subsidizes the cost by up to 75% or rupees 15000, whichever is lower, for the preparation of market studies by TCO. However, the subsidy will be made available only to the TCO with which one or more financial institutions or development agencies at the state or all India level are associated as shareholders(s) or member(s) of board of management.
- **Adoption of indigenous technology:** The subsidies for the interest payment to IFCI due to the operation of project during the first three years of its inception, is also provided to the promoters involved in the exploitation of indigenous technology for the project. The upper limit for the subsidy is rupees 5 lakh a year. However, the amount can be as high as rupees 25 lakh for a period of five years in appropriate cases. On making the payment of first installment of interest to IFCI, the stipulated amount of subsidy will be reimbursed. The projects set up from the loan by IFCI as well as based on indigenous technology are only eligible for the subsidy. Further, the

indigenous technology should have been acquired from the institutions recognized by the government of India. These institutions include government laboratories, universities, and public sector companies to name a few. The acquired technology should have been exploited on a commercial scale and the certificate for the same should be acquired from the concerned institution. The project must be of national priority.

- **Special facilities for import of raw materials:** The concessions are provided for the raw materials as envisaged in the Import Policy of 1978-79 to the industrial setup in backward areas or that setup by graduates/diploma holders or by ex-servicemen. The projects belonging to scheduled castes or scheduled tribes, the ceiling to the subsidies is kept at rupees 5 lakh. They will also be eligible for preferential treatment in the matter of canalized items.
- **Transport subsidy:** The subsidy to the extent of 50% is envisaged in the transport subsidy scheme, 1971 for the transport of raw materials from the selected areas to the industrial setup and also for the transport of finished goods to the selected areas from the industrial setup. The states covered under this scheme are Jammu and Kashmir, Uttar Pradesh, Himachal Pradesh, Assam, Manipur, Meghalaya, Nagaland, Arunachal Pradesh, Mizoram, Andaman and Nicobar Islands, Lakshadweep.

  The highlights of the above scheme are:

  - The subsidy is given to the transport of raw materials and the finished goods to and from the industrial units in these above mentioned areas.
  - For the internal movement of raw materials in the finished goods in the states of Jammu and Kashmir and the states in the north-eastern region will not be entitled to receive the transport subsidy.
  - The transport subsidy will however be given to the transport of raw material and finished goods between Siliguri and the industrial units located in the north-eastern region. The cost is calculated from Siliguri to the nearest railway station that is nearer to the industrial unit.
  - For the movement of goods by road, the freight charges will be determined on the basis of the rates fixed by the concerned state government or the actual freight paid, whichever is less.
  - The transportation charges will also include the charges incurred in loading and unloading of goods.
  - The new industrial units in the above-mentioned areas will be eligible for transport subsidy to the extent of 50%.
  - The subsidy of 50% is also given to the diversified and expanded existing industrial units.
  - The system for the registration units for the transport subsidy will be laid down by the Directorates of Industries in the states/union territories.

- **Incentives available to SSI Units in Backward/Rural Industries Project Areas:** The backward areas are entitled to certain facilities and incentives. These are enumerated below:
  - The subsidy to an extent of 15% of the invested capital with ceiling of rupees 15 lakh is provided to the industrial units in the backward districts.
  - Liberalized policy towards allotment of factory or factory sheds in the industrial estates.
  - For the tax paid from the sales made by the SSI in other states, interest-free loans are available for a period of up to 7 years. However, the loan amount in a given year should not exceed 8% of the capital invested.
  - Loans for the acquisition of fixed assets are given by the State Financial Corporations. For limited companies and registered societies, the loan amount is up to rupees 30 lakhs whereas for others this is rupees 15 lakhs. The loan is given for a longer period and at liberalized margin of interest rates.
  - For setting up of medium and large units, there is participation in the preference shares of the limited companies by the central/state government directly or through its subsidiary concern. In certain situations, possibilities to set up joint ventures are exploited for setting up of joint ventures with the private sector.
  - Following tax exemptions are given to the SSI in the backward areas and to the other industries with capital investment of up to rupees 1 lakh in plant and machinery:
    - The exemption for the payment of electricity duty for a period of seven years is given to the new units established in the districts.
    - The property tax is also exempted for the new units.
    - The new units lying in the limits of municipal corporations are exempted to pay octroi subjected to a maximum period of three years.
    - In order to ensure the quality products, the SSI units can seek assistance from the different testing laboratories, export inspection councils and other institutions set up by the state governments and the central government.
    - To further extend the assistance to help the SSI to build modern techniques of manufacturing a network of industrial development centers and advanced level workshops have been set up by the states.
- **Seed capital assistance:** The first generation or the technical entrepreneurs face a hurdle in the resources required to meet the minimum promoter's contribution. Different financial institutions have come up with their own schemes on the seed capital. However, the industrial units, both existing and new, in the backward areas are not eligible for this scheme. On the fulfilment of conditions, the maximum amount, which can be sanctioned, is to the extent of Rs. 5 lakh per project.

- **Objectives of the scheme:** The main objective is to aid the first generation talent having the traits of entrepreneurship but lacking capital resources to start the business venture. For meeting the risk associated with the capital investment, the scheme envisages to provide for assistance at a nominal service charge. Through its various policies, a wider dispersal of ownership and control of industrial undertakings is promoted.
- **Agencies for operating the scheme:** Agencies of notified SIDCs and SFCs are mainly responsible for operating the scheme.
- **Eligibility criteria:** An entrepreneur should be qualified both technically and professionally to be eligible for the scheme. Further, he should possess the required experience and skills to run the business or the trade. The categories of entrepreneurs that are eligible for assistance are as under:
  - New generation entrepreneurs who have their businesses falling in the small-scale sector and the seed capital required is more than Rs 4 lakh.
  - The entrepreneurs falling under the category of small-scale enterprises and wish to undertake diversification or modernization.
  - The existing entrepreneurs who propose to shift from small-scale to medium sector.
  - The new entrepreneurs who are willing to set up their business in the medium sector for the first time.
  - Entrepreneurs in the medium sector and willing to expand or diversify their business.
  - The existing entrepreneurs who run out of the capital because of the factors beyond their control and therefore seek additional seed capital.
  - The entrepreneurs who wish to take over an existing unit which has been closed and was a part of the public/private partnership.
- **Amounts and mode of assistance:** The ceiling to the assistance amount in the form of seed capital should not exceed beyond Rs. 15 lakh. The gap in the equity required for the venture and also the shortfall of the promoters' contribution forms the basis of determining the amount of seed capital to be granted as assistance. The quantum of assistance is also decided on the basis of equity norm which for the medium scale units is 1.5:1 and for the SSI is 2:1.

  In case of the proprietary concerns, the assistance is in the form of soft loans. However, it is in the form of subscription to 1% cumulative redeemable preference shares or soft loans in case of public limited companies.

  The soft loan would be interest free which will carry a service charge of 1% per annum. However, IDBI may have option to charge the interest on soft loans at a different rate. There is no commitment charge. The repayment period depends upon repaying capacity of the unit with an initial moratorium period not exceeding 5 years. No security except the personal guarantee of the promoter is stipulated.

- **Taxation benefits:** Taxation benefits available to small-scale industries are explained below:
  - **Tax holiday:** A tax exemption under Section 80J of the Income Tax Act is given to the new small-scale industries or the companies. The percentage is fixed at 6% on the profits earned by the new small-scale industries whereas it is to the extent of 7.5% for companies. The profit is calculated from the income earned on the sale of units manufactured in the assessment year. The tax holiday is available for a period of 5 years from the initiation of the manufacturing unit.
  - **Depreciation allowance:** Deductions on the depreciation of machinery and plant, buildings and land are given to small-scale industries as per Section 32 of the Income Tax Act. The ceiling on the deductions from the actual cost of machinery and plant is fixed at Rs. 20 lakh. The reducing balance forms the basis of calculation of the depreciation amount. Irrespective of the number of days the asset has been used, an industry is eligible to depreciation deduction for a year.
  - **Development rebate:** An amount known as the development rebate is given to the small industries for the machinery and plant that is used only for the product which doesn't include the office appliances and the transport vehicle. The rebate is in addition to the normal depreciation and is allowed under Section 33 and is specified as below:
    - It is 35% of the actual cost of the machinery if it were installed before 1st April. However, the rate is 25% of the actual cost if the machinery is installed after 31st March 1970.
    - The development rebate is given at a specified rate for the machinery that was installed after 31st March 1967, and the cost incurred is due to the research related to the business. Such machines are therefore asset to the unit conducting the research.
  - **Rehabilitation allowance:** The rehabilitation allowance is given to the small-scale units, whose business has been disturbed by the following. This is allowed as per Section 33B.
    - Civil disturbance or the disturbance arising due to riots.
    - Hurricanes, floods, earthquakes, cyclones, or other natural disasters.
    - Fire or explosion which occurred accidentally.
    - Attack by an enemy.

    The deductions, by the way of rehabilitation, are equivalent to 60% of the amount of the deduction allowance on the unit.
  - **Publication of books:** For the small industries the publication of books, not including magazines, journals, pamphlets, brochures and the other similar publications, the deductions equivalent to the 20% of the profit earned can be claimed under Section 80 of the Act.

- **Tax benefits for amalgamation of sick units:** One of the major concerns is the presence of sickness in the large or small industry. This is a widespread problem of concern. An amount of more than Rs. 2000 crore has been estimated to be aggregated because of the sick enterprises and industries. The government policy has been to provide for concessions to the healthy units to take over the sick units in public interest.

- **Incentive to the small-scale/ancillary units acquiring ISO 9000 certificate:** For the small-scale industries acquiring ISO-9000 certification or its equivalent, a scheme proposed to give incentive was announced by the government of India in 1994. The scheme provided for the reimbursement to the tune of 75% of the cost subjected to a maximum limit of Rs. 75000.

  The norms to claim for the reimbursement have been reviewed and simplified. According to the revised procedural norms, in place of certified copies of various receipts of payments, a certificate from a chartered accountant certifying the various expenses incurred towards assessment fee, audit fee and other related expenses for obtaining the ISO-9000 certification can be submitted. The simplification and the revision will not only accelerate the process of reimbursement but also reduce the documentation work to a great extent.

- **Credit Linked Capital Subsidy Scheme for Technology Upgradation of SSIs-Guidelines:**
  - **Title:** The scheme is called the "Credit linked Capital subsidy Scheme for Technology Upgradation of the Small-scale Industries".
  - **Purpose:** The SSIs are entitled for the 12 per cent subsidy for the projects proposed for upgradation. The SSI must produce specified products.
  - **Scope of the scheme:** The scheme covers the following products to avail the benefits of the capital subsidy:
    - Leather and Leather Products including Footwear and Garments
    - Food Processing
    - Drugs and Pharmaceuticals
    - Information Technology (Hardware)
    - Auto Parts and Components
    - Glass and Ceramic items including Tiles
    - Electronic Industry particularly relating to Design and Measuring
    - Dyes and Intermediates
    - Tyres
    - Toys
    - Hand Tools
    - Foundries—Ferrous and Cast Iron
    - Bicycle Parts.

- **Type of unit to be covered**
  - » The SSI units propose for the upgradation without the expansion of their units. Such SSIs must be registered with the State Directorate of Industries. Further, there should be no proposal for the expansion of their units.
  - » The new SSIs are also entitled to receive the subsidy. However, besides being registered with the State Directorate of Industries, these should have approval from the Technical Advisory Committee for the proven technology that they are likely to establish within their units.
- **Definition of technology upgradation**
  - » The inclusion of the state-of-the-art technology or may be the near state-of-the-art technologies is considered the technology upgradation. Technology upgradation is a significant move for the small-scale sector since majority of the product manufacturing takes place in the Indian small-scale sector. The move of technology upgradation leads to a higher productivity, improvement in the quality of the products, manufacturing under improved environment. Besides these, there is improved quality of packaging, anti-pollution measures and conservation of energy from the use of the machinery.
  - » Replacement of existing equipment/technology with the same equipment technology will not qualify for this scheme, nor would the scheme be applicable to units upgrading with second hand machinery.
- **Duration of the scheme:** The duration, for which the scheme was operated, was from the year 2000 to the year 2005. On reaching the ceiling of lending of up to Rs. 600 crore, the scheme ceased to operate.
- **Nodal agency:** The nodal agency maintaining the scheme was the Small Industries Development Bank of India (SIDBI).
- **Cap on the amount of subsidy**
  - » The financial assistance by the banks/SIDBI for technology upgradation will be need-based.
  - » Value of plant & machinery being acquired under the scheme will be determined by its purchase price.
  - » Capital subsidy under this scheme will not be admissible for loan amount exceeding the limits indicated above.
- **Working capital requirement:** The availability of the working capital was a requisite for the success of the scheme. Therefore, commercial banks were required to have the adequate working capital.
- **Other conditions for loans**
  - » The lending agencies were to decide the security amount of the promoter, security, debt-equity ratio, etc.

» The SSIs opting for the credit linked capital subsidy are not entitled to receive any other subsidy benefits such as interest subsidy or any other scheme of the central government.

» One of the main requirements of sanction of assistance under the Technology Upgradation Scheme will be the availability of competent management to the unit concerned to carry out the upgradation and to manage the operation of the unit efficiently. Towards this end, the lending agencies may stipulate conditions as may be considered necessary.

- **Monitoring of the scheme: constitution of a governing board**

  The Scheme will be monitored by a Governing Board. The Secretary (SSI&ARI) will be the Chairperson of the Board and the Development Commissioner (SSI) will be its Member Secretary. The Governing Board shall consist of representatives of Banking Division (Ministry of Finance), Planning Commissioner, Department of Science and Technology, Council of Scientific & Industrial Research. Indian Council for Agricultural Research, SIDBI, some selected public sector banks and some selected small-scale industries associations as members. The governing Board will monitor and review the functioning of the scheme and will meet at least twice a year.

Announced in 1991 it laid special thrust on promotion and strengthening of small, tiny and village industries.

Besides, effecting changes in investment limits, equity participation, etc., a new scheme of Integrated Infrastructure Development for SSIs with the participation of state governments and financial institutions was initiated and a proactive role for NGO sector was mooted. In order to protect their interest and facilitate their rapid development, the government in pursuance of its policies, initiates a number of support measures from time to time which include policy of reservation, revision of investment ceilings, modernization, technology up gradation, marketing assistance, etc.

The emerging economic scenario in the changed liberalized and competitive economic environment has necessitated structural and fundamental changes in the policy framework. Accordingly, there has been a shift in focus from 'protection' to 'promotion'. In the post-reform period, a number of steps including partial de-reservation, change in investment limits, facilitating foreign participation, establishment of growth centres, export promotion, marketing assistance and incentives for quality improvement, etc., have been taken by the Government for strengthening of this sector.

In order to enable the government to place more focused attention on the problems of the SSI sector, a new Ministry of Small-scale Industries and Agro and Rural Industries was created on 14th October 1999, under the Independent Charge of a Minister of State. Knowing of the crucial role of small enterprises, and the problems being faced by them, the Planning Commission, in 1999, constituted a Study Group. The Study Group submitted its report on 13th July 2000.

SECTION VI
INSPECTION AND STATISTICAL QUALITY CONTROL

20
Defining Quality

20.1 IMPLICATIONS OF QUALITY

The American Society for Quality defines quality as "the totality of features and characteristics of a product or service that bears on its ability to satisfy stated or implied needs." There are several other definitions for the term quality from different perspectives. Some of the definitions for quality are user based. The definition as proposed from such a perspective believes that the quality lies in the eyes of the beholder. Many people from the marketing field like this definition and so do different customers from different backgrounds. For them quality is a measure of performance, features and other improvements. Higher the qualities better the performance and the same applies to the features and improvements. On the other hand, the definition for quality is manufacturing based for the production managers. The production manager believes that quality means conforming to standards. Another approach to the definition of quality is product-based. They view quality as a precise and measurable variable.

Research should be used as a basis to first identify the characteristics that connote the term quality (a user based quality approach). These identified characteristics are then translated into specific product attributes (a productbased approach to quality). The manufacturing processes are then organized accordingly ensuring that the products are made to the specifications and with precision. It is therefore often believed that a process that ignores any one of these steps will not fulfill the definition of a quality product.

Figure 20.1 depicts a continuous quality improvement process.

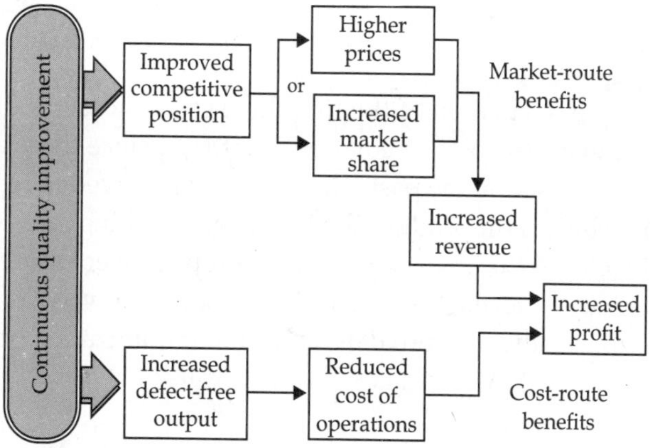

Fig. 20.1: Continuous quality improvement.

20.2 COST OF QUALITY

The cost of quality (COQ) may be defined as the cost associated with doing things wrongly. Four major costs are associated with the cost of quality. These are:

- Prevention cost: The cost which takes care to reduce the number of defective parts and services produced by a manufacturing unit.
- Appraisal cost: The cost for analysis and evaluation of the manufactured goods and services. The costs include the payment made against testing of products, the payments incurred to laboratory and the technicians facilitating the testing process.
- Internal failure: The cost that is due to the production of goods and services before delivery to customer. The example includes that of reworking, scrap and downtime.
- External costs: The costs that result after the delivery of goods and services to the customer. Example includes that of returned goods, cost to the society, liabilities, etc.

Figure 20.2 shows the traditional view of the quality cost.

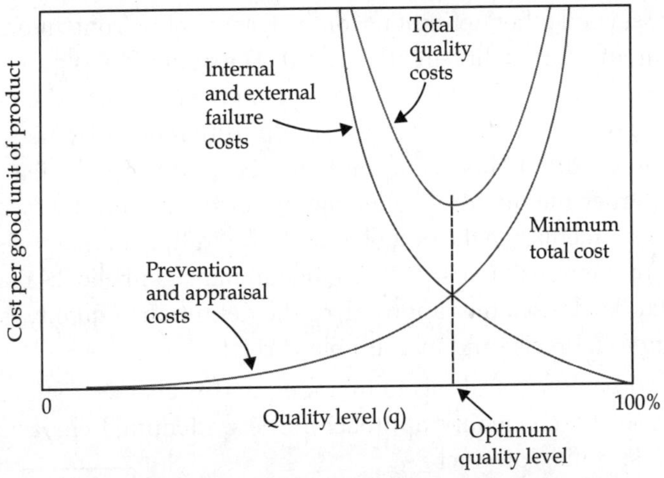

Fig. 20.2: Quality cost—a traditional perspective.

The calculation of the first three costs is easy as these costs can be quantified, whereas the external costs calculation is difficult since these are hard to quantify. There are many instances from the past where the cost involved in repairing is far more than the cost of the machine or the product. For instance, the calling back of more than three million dishwashers by GE. In this instance the cost of repairs were more than the cost of machine. Therefore, it was believed that the cost of poor quality is consistently overestimated. Figure 20.3 depicts how the zero defects lead to minimization of cost quality.

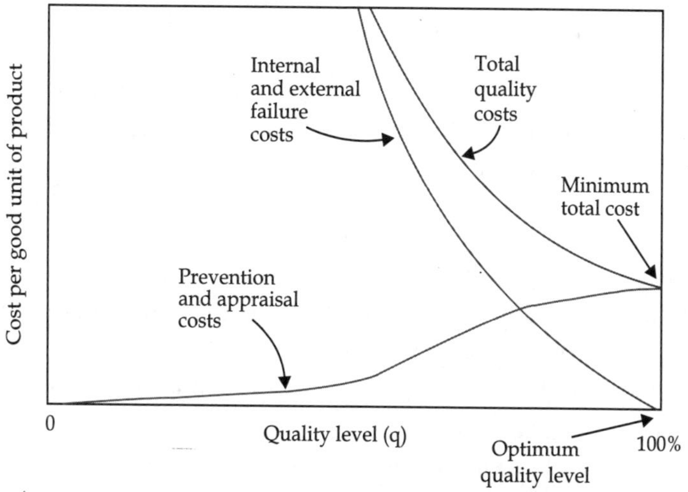

Fig. 20.3: Quality cost minimized at zero defects.

It is believed by the observers of quality management that, on balance, the cost of quality products is just a fraction of the benefits. According to them, the failure to work aggressively on the quality of product by the manufacturing unit makes these units the real losers. For instance, according to Philip Crosby, quality is free and states that "What costs money are the unquality things – all the actions that involve not doing it right the first time."

Table 20.1: Summary of the philosophies and contributions of other prominent personalities.

Leader	Philosophy/Contribution
W. Edwards Deming	According to Deming, it is the management to accept the responsibility for building good systems. The quality of products and services produced by the employee cannot exceed the quality that the process is capable of producing.
Joseph M. Juran	Juran, a pioneer to teach the Japanese on improving the quality, believed in the commitment, involvement and support of the top management in the quality effort. He defines quality as fitness for use.
Armand Feigenbaum	He laid out forty steps to the process of quality management in his 1961 book on Total Quality Control. He believed quality as the total field that integrates the process of the company and not as a set of tools. He is the pioneer of the concept of cross-functional teamwork through which the people have learnt to work and learn from each other.

20.3 ETHICS AND QUALITY MANAGEMENT

One of the major concerns for the managers is to deliver safe, healthy and quality products to the customers. Higher costs may result owing to the production of products that are of poor quality because of the inadequacy of design and production process. This not only results in higher costs but also leads to injuries, lawsuits and increased government regulations.

An ethical conduct must dictate the responsible action from the firm on believing that it has produced, delivered and introduced a questionable product. In majority of instances, this may lead to recall of the goods and services from the market by the manufacturing unit. For example, in case of Jhonson & Jhonson, for Tylenol; Perrier for sparkling water; etc. It is the manufacturing unit to accept the responsibility of poor quality product.

There are number of stakeholders involved in the production and marketing of poor quality products and services. These include employers, customers, distributors, suppliers and creditors. Therefore, as a part of ethical conduct it is the responsibility of the organization to identify the stakeholder for the poor quality products and services.

Core values need to be developed so that these become guidelines for everyone from the CEO to the production and assembly line employees.

20.4 INTERNATIONAL QUALITY STANDARDS

International standards lead to promotion of trade and cooperation. It allows a customer to purchase products and services from different manufacturers with a belief that the product will perform equally well. A common approach to managing quality and environment can be adopted on the basis of the international standards. Figure 20.4 shows how the ISO standards are implemented to ensure a better quality product to the end user.

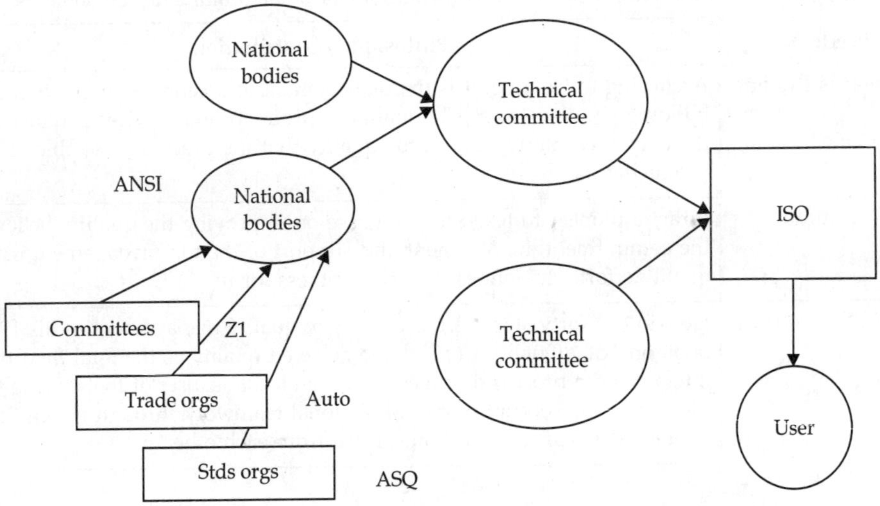

Fig. 20.4: The functioning of international organization for standards.

ISO 9000: is one of the quality standards with international recognition. A series of quality assurance standards in the form of ISO 9000 were published in 1987 by a total of 91 member nations. The focus of the standards lies in establishing quality management procedures, through leadership, work instructions, detailed documentation and record keeping. These standards have nothing to do with the quality of the product but deal with standards to be followed.

The organizations are required to undergo a 9-18 month process involving the documentation of quality procedures, ongoing series of audits of their products and services, an on-site assessment. A general ISO 9000 consensus process is shown in Fig. 20.5.

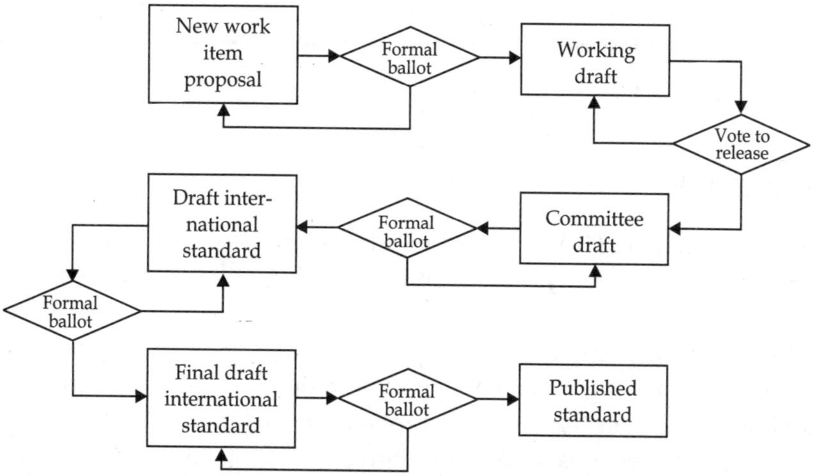

Fig. 20.5: ISO 9000 consensus process.

ISO 14000

It is another standard which proves the continuing international focus to ensure quality of products and services. The core elements that constitute the ISO 14000 standard are:

- Environmental management
- Auditing
- Performance evaluation
- Labeling
- Life cycle assessment

The new standard has certain advantages:

- Positive public image and reduced exposure to liability
- Good systematic approach to pollution prevention through the minimization of ecological impact of products and services
- Reduction in need for complete compliance.

The standard is achieving great attention as it is concerned with the environmental impacts of activities systematically.

21
Total Quality Management

21.1 INTRODUCTION

Total Quality Management (TQM) refers to the total emphasis on the quality of goods and services and encompasses the entire organization. TQM ensures that the management is committed to quality of goods and services through its companywide drive emphasizing on the excellence in all aspects. Each of the decisions taken by the managers is taken to deal with identifying and meeting the customers' expectations. Meeting the expectations of the customers is dependent on the level of emphasis given on TQM which is essential in ensuring that the firm remains to be competitive enough to compete against the world leaders. Six concepts to implement the TQM process are discussed in the subsequent sections of the chapter.

21.2 CONTINUOUS IMPROVEMENT

A never ending process for the successful implementation of the TQM is essential. The process should cover a wide range of people, equipment, procedures and materials. The underlying philosophy is that improvements can be made in each of the different aspects of a product. The main objective is to achieve perfection, which in reality is never achieved but always sought.

Plan-Do-Check-Act

A version of continuous improvement in the form of a circular model known as PDCA was developed by Walter Shewhart. This is shown in Fig. 21.1. This concept of continuous improvement was then later taken to Japan by Deming. The circular model of PDCA is indicative of the circular nature of the continuous improvement.

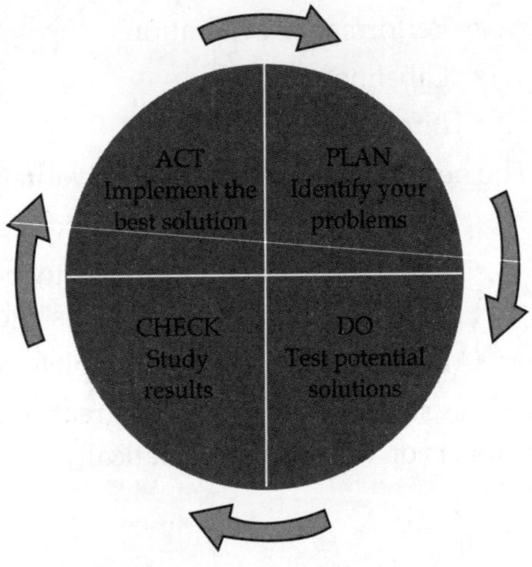

Fig. 21.1: PDCA process.

The term "Kaizen" is used by the Japanese to describe the continuous process of improvement which is setting goals and then adopting methods to achieve the goals. In the US context, the terms TQM or zero defects are used to describe this continuous process of improvement. Irrespective of the context in which the concept is used, managers are the protagonists in building a work culture that endorses the practice of continuous improvement.

21.3 SIX-SIGMA

The term SIX-SIGMA was popularized by Motorola, General Electric and Honeywell. There are two different perspectives to it and hence two different meanings in TQM. From the statistical point of view it describes a product, service or process that has extremely high level of capability (99.9997%). For instance if an airport has around 1 million passengers through it with checked baggage, then a Six Sigma programme will ensure that only 3.4 passengers will complaint for their misplaced luggage. While on the other hand, for Three Sigma programme in place, there would be around 2700 passengers complaining for their misplaced luggage every month. This is because Three Sigma provides an accuracy of nearly 99.37%.

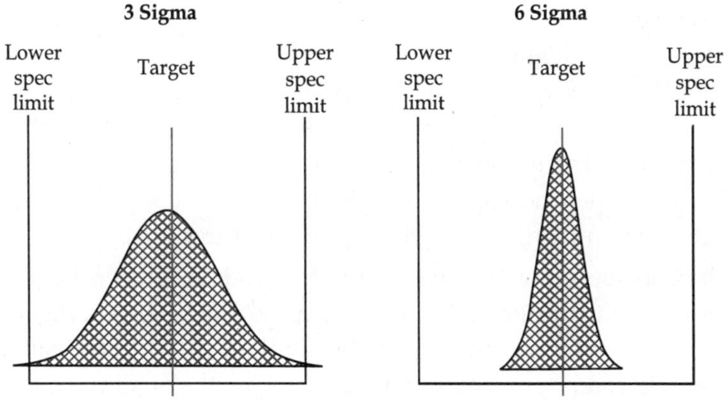

Fig. 21.2.: Difference between 3 Sigma and 6 Sigma.

According to the second definition of TQM, Six Sigma is defined as a programme to reduce the defects in product or service. This will, in turn, help to reduce cost, time and enhance the level of customer satisfaction. Six Sigma is a comprehensive system—a strategy, set of tools and a discipline which aims to set and achieve business objectives. Six Sigma is a strategy as it leads to the customer satisfaction. Further, due to it being following the footsteps of DMAIC which is a formal Six Sigma improvement model, the comprehensive system is a discipline. The improvement model consists of five steps:

- The first step is to define the purpose of the project, its scope and hence the expected outputs. On the basis of the definition, the information is collected which is also in line with the customers' definition of quality.

- Measuring of the process and collection of data is the second step.
- Analysis of the data to ensure repeatability and reproducibility.
- Modification and redesigning of the existing procedures and processes to make improvement.
- The last but not the least step is to control the process to make sure that the performance level is maintained as expected.

Six Sigma is a cluster of tools that includes check sheets, scatter diagrams, Pareto charts, cause and effect diagrams, histograms, statistical process control, etc.

According to the head of the programme at Praxair, implementation of the Six Sigma is a big commitment. The commitment is required especially from the top management who has the responsibility of formulating the plan, communicating of the firms' objectives and establish themselves as an example for others to follow.

21.4 EMPLOYMENT EMPOWERMENT

Involving employees in each and every step of the production process is employee empowerment. It has been observed that around 85% of the quality problems are related to the material and processes and hence the role of employee performance is insignificant. Therefore, the main objective for an organization is to design processes and equipment that produce the desired quality of the products. The personnel with a high degree of understanding of the processes will be the suitable candidates to help in achieving the desired objective of efficient design of processes and the related activities. The fact is further corroborated by the observation that the TQM programme is likely to succeed much more effectively when the responsibilities were delegated to the shop-floor employees in comparison to when implemented with "top-down" directives.

Whenever there is aberration in the quality of a product, the workers cannot be held responsible. It is the faulty design of the product, or the improper training to the employee handling the processes or the system responsible for the product was wrong. It is believed that an employee will rarely cause a problem that will on the other hand help to solve the problem.

There are different techniques to building employee empowerment. These include the following:

- Building network of communication that includes the employee.
- Development of open and supportive supervisors.
- Transfer of responsibility to production employees from managers and staff.
- Building of high morale within the organization.
- Creation of teams and quality circles and other such formal organization structures.

Variety of issues can be addressed through team building. The main focus of such teams is quality and hence these are usually referred to as quality circles. Therefore, a quality circle is a group of employees who meet regularly to solve the work related problems.

Training is given to the members of the team which includes training on group planning, statistical quality control and problem solving. No financial reward is given to the employees; however they tend to receive recognition from the firm. A facilitator is usually chosen from the team to facilitate the training to other team members and help run the different meetings smoothly.

21.5 BENCHMARKING

Another ingredient to a TQM programme is benchmarking. It involves the selection of standard products, services, practices and costs that represent the best performances of the activities and processes similar to the ones under consideration. The key is to set a target and then set a certain benchmark against which the comparison of the performance can be evaluated. The different steps to benchmarking are as follows:

- Identification of the activities to be benchmarked.
- Formation of a benchmark team.
- Identification of partners for benchmarking.
- Collection and analysis of information related to benchmarking.
- Actions to match or exceed the benchmark.

There are certain measures to benchmarking that include the following:

- Cost per unit or per order
- Percentage of defects
- Service response time
- Customer satisfaction rates
- Customer retention rates

In an ideal situation in a particular organization, leaders in the area in which the study is being conducted, are selected as a benchmark to compare oneself against them. The company may not be part of the industry. In fact it's best to look outside the industry in order to set world-class standards.

Benchmarks often take the form of best practices found in other firms or in other divisions. Some of the best practices to resolve customer complaints are tabulated below:

Table 21.1: Best practices.

Best practice	**Justification**
Make it easy for the clients to complaint	It is free market research.
Quick response to complaints	It leads to addition of customers and increasing level of loyalty.
The complaints to be resolved in the first contact	It leads to reduction of cost.
Computers to be used for managing complaints	It helps in discovering trends, sharing them and then aligning one's services accordingly.
Best to be recruited for customer service jobs	It should be part of formal training and career advancements.

21.6 JUST-IN-TIME (JIT)

The continuous improvement and problem solving in an enforced manner are the main philosophies underlying the concept of just-in-time. The main objective of designing the JIT concept is to ensure the delivery of goods and services as and when required. JIT is related to quality in three important ways:

- **JIT cuts the cost of quality:** This is a result of scrap, rework, damage and inventory. The costs associated which of these is directly related to the inventory on hand. The costs are lower with lower inventory on hand with JIT. JIT on one hand exposes the bad quality, inventory hides the same.
- **JIT improves quality:** As JIT shrinks lead time, it also keeps evidence of the fresh errors and hence limits the number of potential sources of error. An early warning system for the quality problems is often created by the JIT.
- **Easier to employ JIT:** Better quality means less inventory and hence better and easier to employ the JIT. The main purpose of keeping the inventory lies in ensuring protection against poor quality production. The existence of better quality ensures less inventory and hence JIT allows for reduced cost.

21.7 TAGUCHI CONCEPTS

Most of the problems are a result of poor quality product and the poor design of the processes that goes into product building. The two main concepts for improving the quality have been provided by Genichi Taguchi. These are discussed below:

- **Quality robustness:** The products that are manufactured under the adverse manufacturing and environmental conditions are known as the quality robust products. The main focus of Genichi Taguchi was to remove the main effects of the adverse conditions instead of removing the causes. This is because he believes that removing the effects is cost efficient in respect to the removing of the causes. This ensures that small variation in materials and processes doesn't destroy the product quality.
- **Quality loss function (QLF):** This leads to the identification of the costs that are connected with the poor quality of the product. It also depicts the manner in which the cost increases as the product moves away from the expectations of the customers. The costs besides considering customer satisfaction also takes into account service costs, repair costs, and the costs to society. Figure 21.3 shows the quality loss function curve:

The losses due to poor performance of the product which is directly to the society are included in the loss function. The desirability of the product increases with the decreasing cost. The severity of the loss increases as the product deviates from the targeted value.

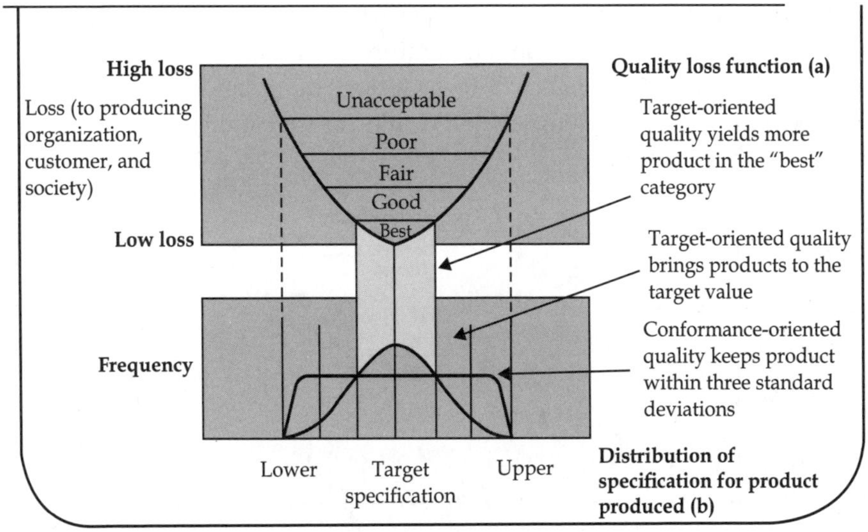

Fig. 21.3: Target-oriented quality.

21.8 TOOLS OF TQM

This section discusses the different TQM tools.

Check sheets: A kind of form that is designed to record data. The recording of data clearly depicts the pattern and hence helps in proper analysis. The facts derived through the data can be used in making subsequent analysis. Figure 21.4 shows an example of check sheet.

Motor Assembly Check Sheet

Name of data recorder: Lester B. Rapp
Location: Rochester, New York
Data Collection dates: 1/17 - 1/23

Defect types/ event occurence	Sunday	Monday	Tuesday	Wednesday	Thursday	Friday	Saturday	Total
Supplied parts rusted		|||||||||	|||||	||||	||			20
Misaligned weld			|||			||		5
Improper text procedure								0
Wrong part issued					||				3
Film on parts								0
Voids in casting				||||	||			6
Incorrect dimensions						||		2
Adhesive failure								0
Masking insufficient									1
Spray failure			|||||					5
Total		10	13	10	5	4		

Fig. 21.4: Check sheet.

Scatter diagram: It shows the relationship between two variables. The relationship between the sales of a ice-cream with the noon temperature is an example of scatter diagram. The data points on the scatter diagram will form a close tight band if the two variables are closely related. However, a random relation results for unrelated items. Figure 21.5 shows an example of scatter diagram.

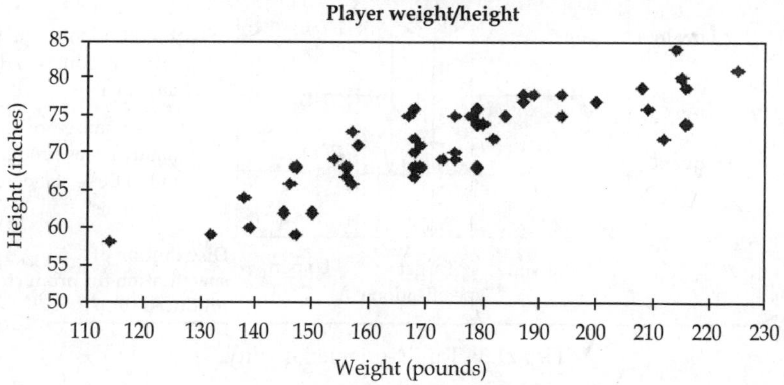

Fig. 21.5: An example of scatter plot.

Cause and effect diagram: It is one of the tools for identification of quality issues and inspection points. This is also referred to as **Ishikawa diagram** or the **fishbone diagram.** Initially, the operations manager starts with four categories: material, manpower, machinery and methods. The causes associated with the individual categories are tied in the form of separate bones to the respective category. Figure 21.6 shows a fish bone diagram below.

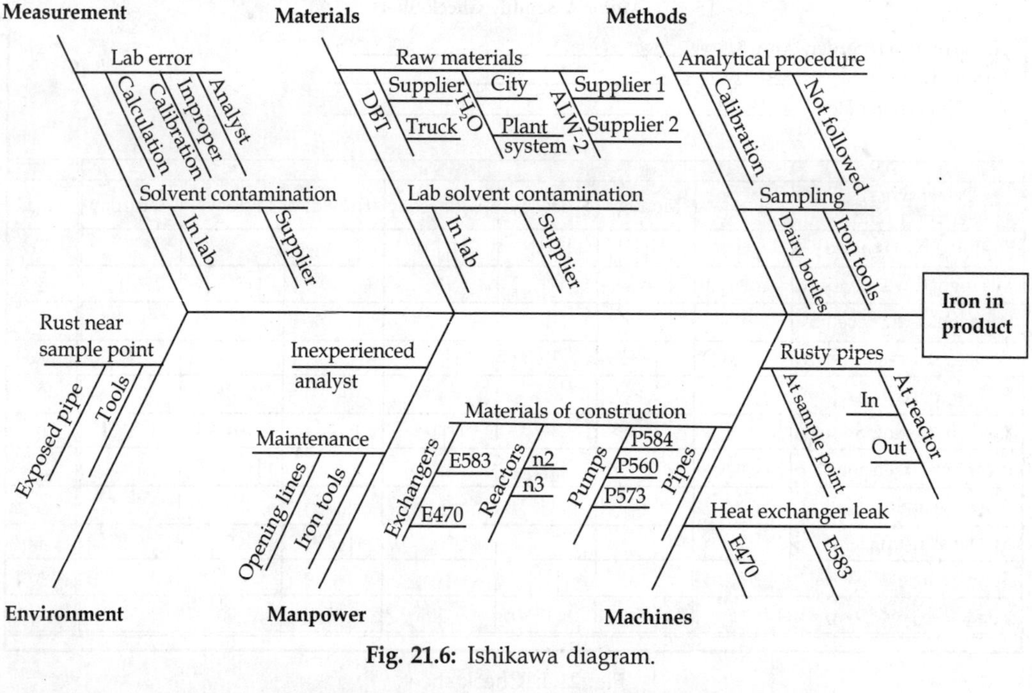

Fig. 21.6: Ishikawa diagram.

Pareto charts: These are the methods to organize errors, defects or problems to help solving on problem solving efforts. Vilfredo Pareto is the pioneer of the Pareto charts. The Pareto analysis clearly indicates the problems which may yield the greatest payoff. Figure 21.7 is an example of Pareto chart.

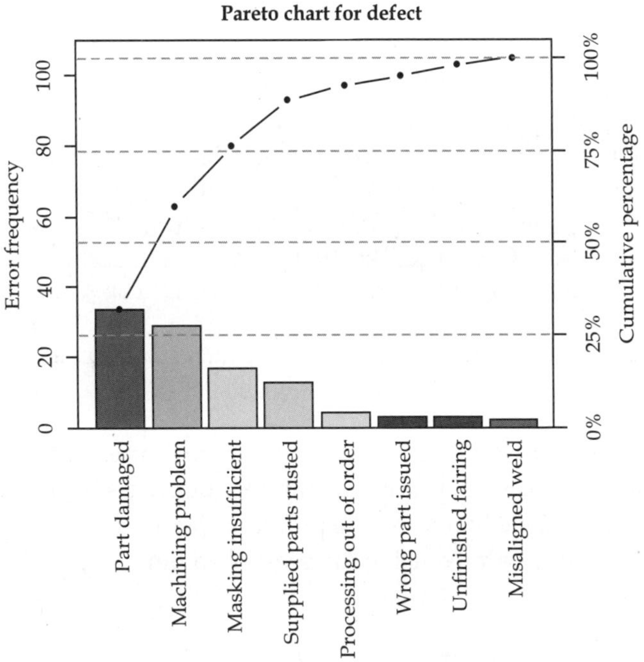

Fig. 21.7: Pareto chart for defects.

Flowcharts: A flowchart makes use of annotated and interconnected boxes to depict a process or a system. It's one of the valuable tools for the explanation of processes. One such example is shown in Fig. 21.8.

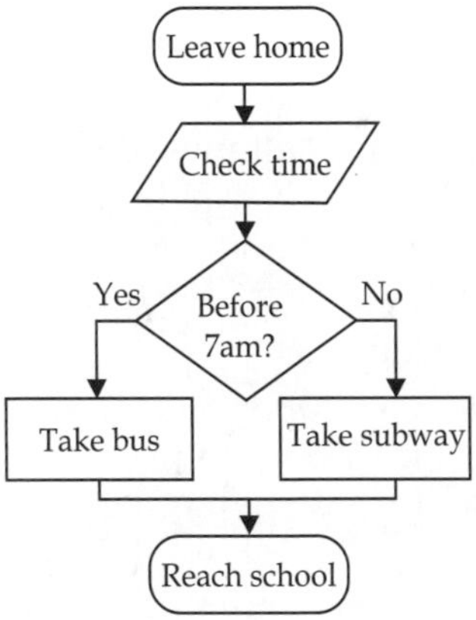

Fig. 21.8: Example of a flowchart.

Histograms: It shows the range of values of a measurement and frequency with which each value occurs. They depict the most frequently occurring readings as well as the variations in measurements. An example of the histogram is shown in Fig. 21.8.

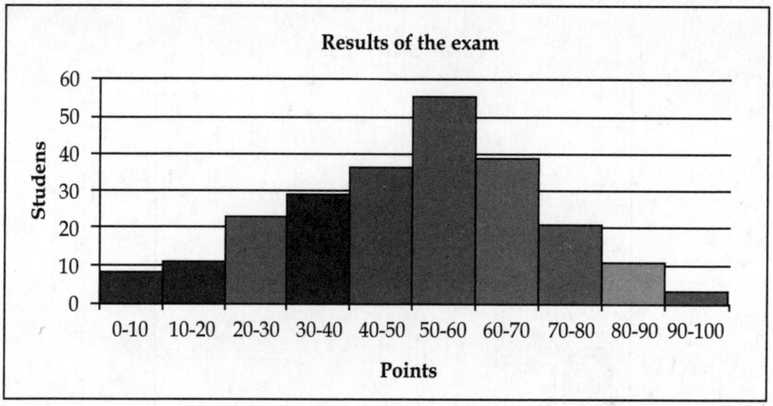

Fig. 21.9: A histogram.

Statistical process control: Monitors standards, makes measurement, and takes corrective actions as goods and services are produced. Samples of process outputs are examined if they are within the acceptable limits and the process is permitted to continue. The process is however terminated if they fall outside the prescribed limits.

22
The Role of Inspection

22.1 INTRODUCTION

A control mechanism is required to make sure that the system is producing at the expected quality level. The processes that have little variation from the set standards or the benchmarks are considered to be the best. One of the main tasks of an operation manager is to design such processes and to verify that they are performing as expected. The process of verification is known as inspection which includes measurement, touching, tasting, testing or weighing of the product. The main objective of inspection lies in detecting a bad process immediately. Inspection doesn't correct defects or deficiencies in the product, nor does it increase the product value but is expensive to be performed.

22.2 WHEN AND WHERE TO INSPECT?

The type of process dictates the decision on when and where to perform inspection. Inspection can take place at any one of the following points:

- At the supplier's plant while the supplier is producing.
- At the location where the goods are dispatched by the supplier.
- Before the performance of irreversible or costly processes.
- During the step-by-step production processes.
- On completion of the production and services.
- Before the product is delivered to the customer.
- At the point of customer contacts.

The different TQM tools aid in taking the decisions regarding "when and where to inspect". However, inspection is not a substitute of robust product produced by well trained employees in a good process. For example, say a firm conducts an experiment in which 100 defective items were added to a lot of perfect items. This lot was then subjected to 100% inspection. In the first phase of inspection, 68 pieces were found to be defective by the inspectors. The other 30 defective products were found in the next three phases. However, the remaining two defects were never found. Thus, there is variability in the inspection process. This is because of many factors such as the involvement of human resource which gets tired, bored, etc. Another factor is the equipment which itself has variability. Inspectors cannot guarantee 100% perfection. Therefore it is better to consider employee empowerment, good processes and better solution rather than going for inspection.

The above fact can be explained through the example of Velcro Industries. As in many other organizations, the role of producing quality goods and services was considered to be for the quality people. The inspection process was based on random sampling, i.e., a part was thrown out on being inspected bad. The organization decided to invest more money in training and paid more attention towards operators, measurement methods, machine repair and design and responsibilities. Over the time as defects declined, Velcro was able to pull half its quality control people out of process.

22.3 SOURCE INSPECTION

The best inspection can be thought of as no inspection at all. This kind of inspection is done at the source. This involves doing the jobs in a proper and systematic manner with the operator ensuring that this is done in the way expected. This may be called source inspection. The concept of source inspection is consistent with that of employee empowerment, where individual employee self-checks his own work. The main idea is that each process, supplier and employee treats the subsequent step as a customer, ensuring perfect product to the next customer. Checklists and other control mechanisms may be used to provide an aid to the source inspection, for instance a fail-safe device also known as *poka-yoke*, a term of the Japanese context.

A *poka-yoke* is a foolproof technique or device that ensures perfect products are produced every time. Such devices help in avoiding errors and provide best products by providing a quick feedback to the problems. For instance, the French fry scoops and the bags for the French fries are the poka-yokes. Checklists are another kind of poka-yokes. Thus the main idea of poka-yokes and source inspection is to ensure 100% good product or services.

22.4 SERVICE INDUSTRY INSPECTION

Inspection points are provided at wide range of locations in case of service-oriented organizations. This is illustrated in Table 22.1. It is the sole responsibility of the operation manager to decide on the places where the inspections are justified and may use the different tools of TQM to arrive at such decisions and making these judgments.

Table 22.1: Service oriented inspection.

Organisation	What is Inspeccted?	Standard
ABC Hotel	Reception desk Room Minibar	Use customer's name All lights working, etc. Restocked and charges accurately posted to bill
X hospital	Billing Pharmacy Nurses	Accurate, timely and correct format Prescription accuracy Charts immediately updated

22.5 INSPECTION OF ATTRIBUTES VERSUS VARIABLES

There are certain quality characteristics that can be measured for making an inspection. These quality characteristics may be either attributes or variables. Attribute inspection on one hand classifies the item as good or bad but doesn't define its degree of failure. For example, if a light bulb burns or not. On the other hand, a variable inspection measures dimensions such as weight, speed, size and makes decision whether a product falls within the acceptable limit. For example, if a piece of wire is to be 0.01 inch in diameter, then a micrometer can be used to see if the wire is close enough to pass inspection.

23
Statistical Quality Control

23.1 INTRODUCTION

The Statistical Process Control (SPC) is a process that monitors the standards by analyzing and therefore taking the corrective action as the product or a service is produced by the organization. SPC is the application of statistical techniques to the control of processes. It is a widely used process by the different organizations in the different parts of the world that helps the organizations to keep a track of the products and services meeting the required standards and the benchmarking. The processes responsible for the manufacturing of the products and services have certain degree of variability associated with them. The different variations can be grouped into two main categories: natural and assignable. A technique and tool to separate these two categories of variations is a control chart.

SPC process is mainly used for measuring the performance of a process. When the only source of error is natural, then a process is said to be operating in statistical control. A process is brought into the statistical control, by eliminating the assignable causes of variation. Once the process is in statistical control, its performance is predictable and therefore its ability to meet the customer expectations can be assessed. One of the main objectives of the process control is to provide a statistical signal when the assignable causes of variations are present. The signal will accelerate to help in eliminating the variable causes of error.

23.2 BASIC DEFINITIONS

Natural variations: The natural variations are inevitable and affect almost every production process. These are the sources for the other kinds of variations for a process under statistical control. Natural variations behave like a constant system of chance causes. Although the individual values are all different, as a group they form a pattern that can be described as distribution. The following two parameters characterize the normal distribution:

- Standard deviation, σ which is the measure of dispersion
- Mean, μ, which is a measure of central tendency (average value)

The process is said to be in control, as long as the output parameters are within the specified limit. The natural variations under such cases are said to be tolerated.

Assignable variations: Such variations can be traced to specific reasons. The factors such as machine wear, fatigued or untrained workers, maladjusted equipment, are all the potential sources of assignable variations.

The two tasks for the operation manager are clearly distinguishable through the natural and assignable variations. The first of these is to ensure that a process is performing under statistical control with only natural variations. The second task is to identify the assignable variations and eliminate them to ensure that the process remains to be under control.

Samples: The average of small samples is used by the statistical control because of the presence of natural and assignable variations. The individual parts are not considered as they tend to be too erratic to make trends quickly visible.

Below discussion shows the detailed steps in determining the process variations. The horizontal scale can be any physical parameter such as weight, length, etc. The frequency is represented on a vertical scale.

(a) The different boxes of cereals, say five are taken off the machine line and are weighted. Thus the variation lies in the weight of the cereal boxes. Figure 23.1 shows the arrangement of the number of cereal boxes with a particular weight.

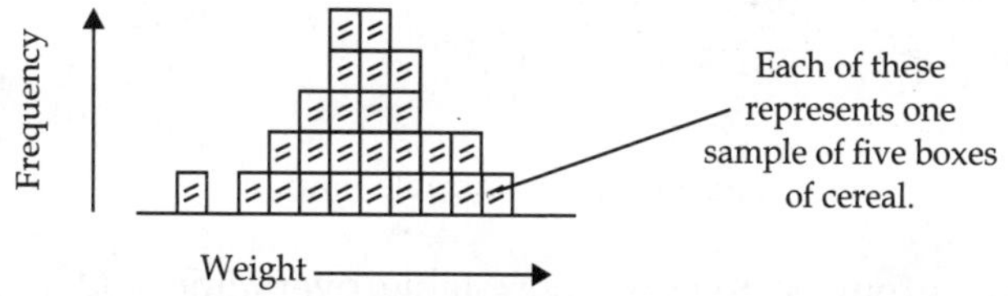

Fig. 23.1: Arrangement of cereal boxes with different weights.

(b) A pattern known as distribution is formed after enough sample means are taken from a stable process. Figure 23.2 shows the distribution below.

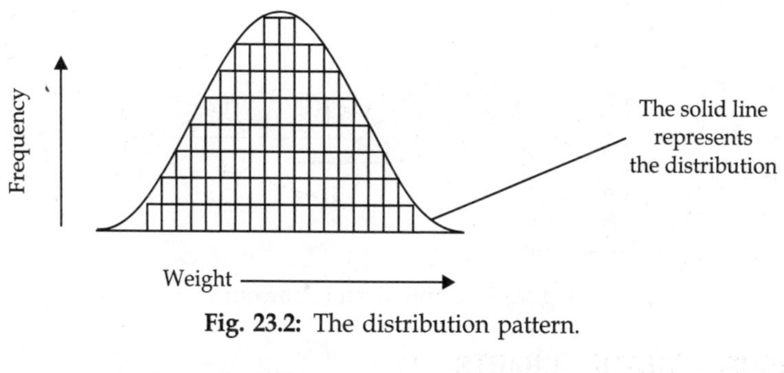

Fig. 23.2: The distribution pattern.

(c) There are a number of different types of distributions, including the normal distribution. The distributions differ in terms of central tendency, shape and standard deviation or variance as shown in Fig. 23.3 below.

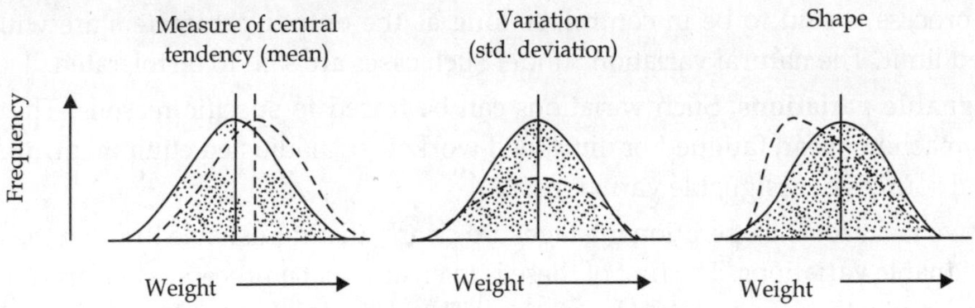

Fig. 23.3: The different forms of distributions.

(d) The output of a process will form a distribution that is stable over a time and predictable. This also signifies that there are only normal variations. The same is depicted in Fig. 23.4 below.

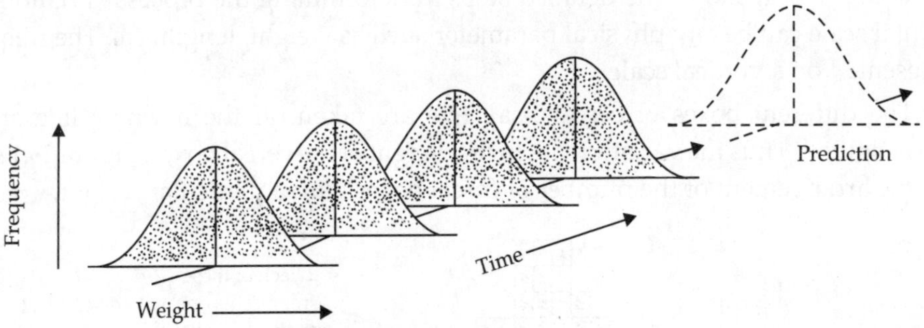

Fig. 23.4: A predictable output.

(e) The process output is however not stable over time and is not predictable if assignable causes of variations are present. The samples will yield unexpected distributions that vary by central tendency, standard deviation and shape.

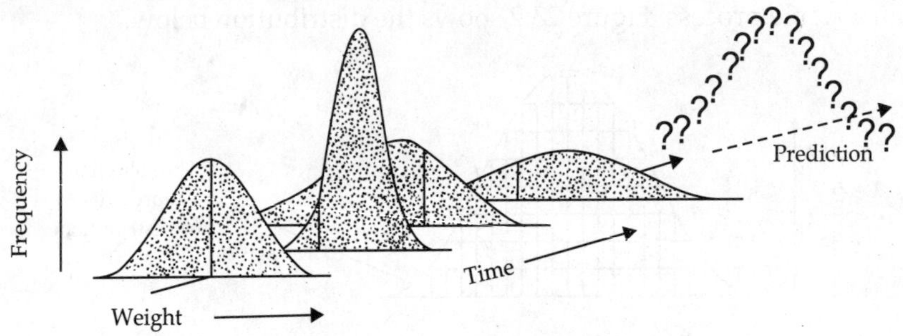

Fig. 23.5: Unpredictable outcome.

23.3 TECHNIQUE – CONTROL CHARTS

Figure 23.6 shows the process of building a control chart. The figure delineates the three different types of distributions that are derived as a result of three different types of processes. Small samples are plotted and then the characteristics are examined to see if the resulting data is within the control limits. The main purpose of the control charts lies in distinguishing between the natural and assignable variations.

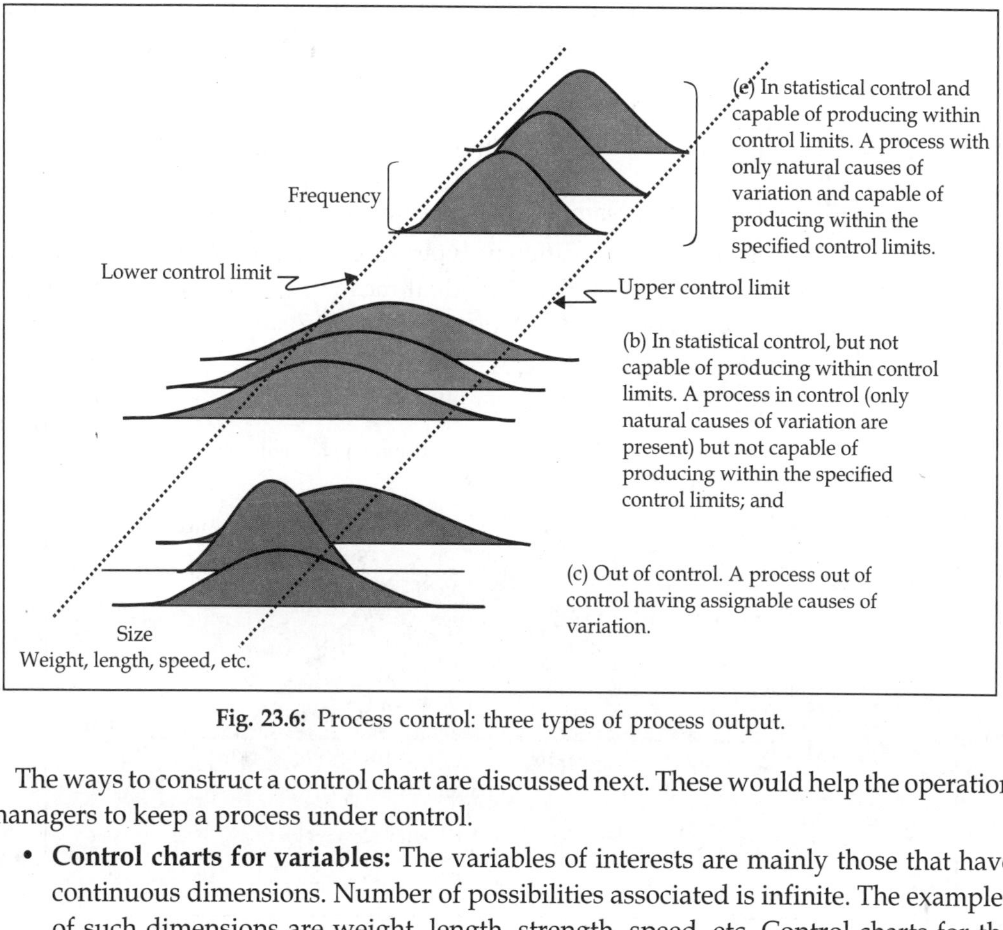

Fig. 23.6: Process control: three types of process output.

The ways to construct a control chart are discussed next. These would help the operation managers to keep a process under control.

- **Control charts for variables:** The variables of interests are mainly those that have continuous dimensions. Number of possibilities associated is infinite. The examples of such dimensions are weight, length, strength, speed, etc. Control charts for the mean $\overline{x}$ or x-bar, and the range R are used to monitor the processes that have continuous dimensions. The changes in the central tendency of a process are indicated by the $\overline{x}$ chart. Such changes may occur due to the factors such as tool wear, a second shift with a different method used, new materials and gradual increase in ambient temperature. A gain or loss in dispersion is reflected by the R chart. Such changes may arise due to loose tools, sloppiness on the part of an operator, worn bearings and an erratic flow of lubricants to the machine. The variables are monitored by the two charts simultaneously.
  - **The central limit theorem:** Central limit is the theoretical foundation of $\overline{x}$ charts. According to the theorem, the distribution of $\overline{x}$'s obtained will follow a normal curve irrespective of the distribution of the population. This is the case as the

number of samples increases. However, the distributions of the averages will roughly follow normal curve even if the sample size is small. The theorem states the following:

$\bar{\bar{x}} = \mu$ the mean of distribution of $\bar{x}$'s equals the mean of the overall population and,

$\sigma_{\bar{x}} = \frac{\sigma}{\sqrt{n}}$, where $\sigma = \sqrt{\frac{\sum_{i=1}^{n}(x_i - \bar{x})^2}{n-1}}$ is the population standard deviation, $\sigma_{\bar{x}}$ is the standard deviation of the sampling distribution, n is the sample size.

Figure 23.7 shows the three different types of possible population distribution each being characterized by the individual mean and standard deviation. The resulting distribution obtained is depicted in Fig. 23.7.

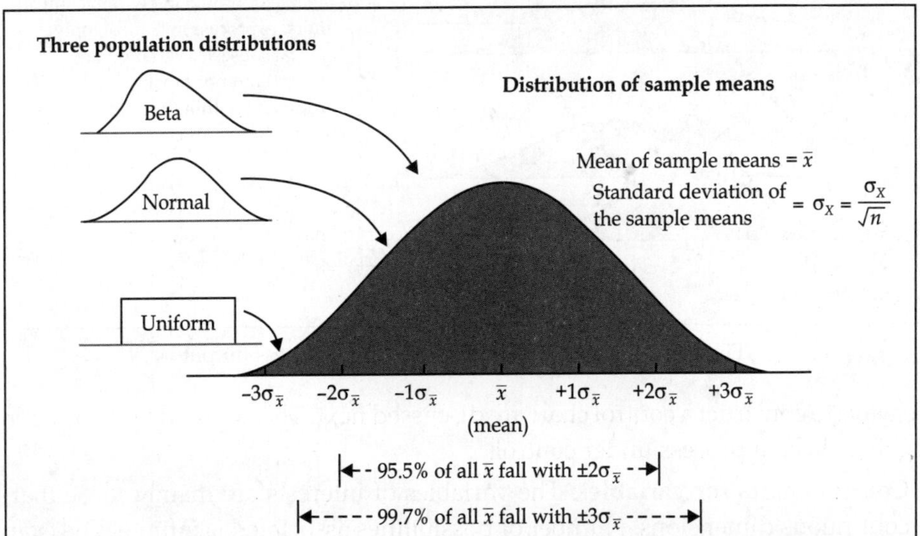

Fig. 23.7: The relationship between population and sampling distributions.

- **Setting mean chart limits:** The upper and lower control limits can be set using the following equations:

  Upper control limit (UCL) = $\bar{\bar{x}} + z\sigma_{\bar{x}}$

  Lower control limit (UCL) = $\bar{\bar{x}} - z\sigma_{\bar{x}}$

where, z is the number of normal standard deviation.

- **Setting range chart limits (R-Charts):** The operations managers are also interested in process dispersion or range. The theory behind the control charts for ranges is the same as that for process average control charts. The following equations are used to set upper and lower control limits for the ranges:

$UCL_R = D_4 \overline{R}$

$LCL_R = D_3 \overline{R}$

where, D_3 and D_4 are the constants.

- **Using mean and range charts**

  Following steps are generally followed in using a $\overline{x}$ and R chart:

  - Collect 20 to 25 samples, often $n = 4$ or $n = 5$ for a stable process.
  - Compute the overall means ($\overline{\overline{x}}$ and $\overline{R}$), set appropriate control limits, usually at the 99.73% level, and calculate the preliminary upper and lower control limits. Use the desired mean μ instead of $\overline{\overline{x}}$ to calculate the limits.
  - Graph the sample means and ranges on their respective control charts and determine whether they fall outside the acceptable limits.
  - Investigate the points and patterns that signify that the process is out of control.
  - Collect additional samples if required.

- **Control charts for attributes:** The control charts such as $\overline{\overline{x}}$ and $\overline{R}$ charts do not apply for cases where sampling of attributes is involved. These are typically classified as defective and non-defective. Measuring defectives usually involves counting them. Whereas variables are usually measured for length or weight. There are basically two categories of attribute control charts:
  - **p-charts**: measuring the percentage of defectives in a sample
  - **c-charts:** counts the number of defects.

  The formula for upper and lower limits for a p-chart can be calculated using the following equations:

  $(UCL)_p = \overline{p} + z\sigma_{\hat{p}}$

  $(LCL)_p = \overline{p} - z\sigma_{\hat{p}}$

  where, $\overline{p}$ = mean fraction defective in the samples

  Z = number of standard deviations

  $\sigma_{\hat{p}}$ is the standard deviation of the sampling distribution and is given by $\sigma_{\hat{p}} = \sqrt{\overline{p}(1-\overline{p})/n}$

SECTION VII
PRODUCTION PLANNING AND CONTROL

24
Production, Planning and Control

24.1 INTRODUCTION

The knowledge of production, planning and control is necessary to help the future executives to gain an insight into the methods, techniques, plans that are essential and vital to operate an enterprise or an industry effectively and efficiently.

The production of the goods and services is the main objective of the manufacturing organization. Hence for the entire business operation, production is the centre or nucleus. The preplanning, production and control (PPC) functions take care of the manufacturing activities. The key function of PPC is to plan the manufacturing process in such a way that the routing and dispatching of the leads to smooth movement of materials, enhanced performance of the machinery and efficient performance of the worker. PPC ensures the quantity, quality of the produced goods and services.

Planning and control are interrelated managerial functions and are often regarded as one function. Planning is the function that involves preparation before production or any other related operation while control is the function that is carried out post-production or manufacturing process. The constraints are identified while planning sets the objectives, goals, targets and therefore forms the basis of carrying out the production activities. Control on the other hand is the assessment activity that involves the assessment of performance which is done on the basis of some standards that have been established through different studies. The actual performance is compared with the established standards and therefore any aberrations are analyzed.

Planning is a vital activity that is required to be carried out to anticipate the difficulties that could arise while converting the raw materials into useful goods and services. This makes the production an organized activity since it decides on how the production needs to be carried out in order to be an economical activity.

The planning operation is followed by the control. The control activities provide a tool to the management to take all possible steps in order to keep a track of the activities that go into production of goods and services. Control sees that the activities that are involved are going as per the plan and ensures that these are being carried out according to the standards set. Thus the two activities of control and planning together ensure that the products of right quality and in right quantities are produced.

Therefore, planning the production activities in advance and then controlling the activities to match the set standards is what defines the term PPC. The principle of PPC lies in the statement "first plan your work, and then work your plan". The departments like the personnel department, manpower planning, costing departments and other departments are part of the process of PPC.

24.2 PREPLANNING, PLANNING AND CONTROL

Activities of preplanning, production and control are performed in their respective time-frames. They occur one after the other in a sequential manner. Before the commencement of production and manufacturing activities, the task of preplanning is completed. The planning activity is preceded by the preplanning activity which is completed immediately before the production begins. Control is exercised during the performance of different production activities.

Preplanning

The preplanning is related to the development of proper work layout and installation of the necessary tools. It involves different activities of an organization. Preplanning involves forecasting, the design of the products to be produced, design of jigs and tools, selection of a suitable machine for carrying out the production. Therefore, preplanning draws attention as to what is to be manufactured and how it should be made.

The manufacturing process can turn out to be uneconomical if the task of preplanning is omitted. The probable errors in cost can be omitted given that preplanning is carried out in a proper manner as it is intended to be. Setting up new plants for manufacturing with least errors is only possible with preplanning.

Planning

The place of production and manufacturing of the product is decided through the planning element of the PPC. The planning activity decides on the sequence of operations and the time schedule of the different manufacturing activities.

The guidelines and the procedures for planning of the materials and their supplies, loading of the machines and deliveries of the goods and services are planned through the planning element of the PPC. To carry out the different functions properly, the statistical data related to the cost can be obtained from the preplanning stage of the PPC.

Control

To ensure that the planned activities of production and manufacturing are carried out in accordance with the standards, control stage of PPC is an essential element. The plan is executed at the right time through the control mechanism in place. The control mechanism then takes care of the unforeseen circumstances that may arise during the performance of the activity. The evaluation of the performance of job with the set standards is a feedback mechanism which is again set in place by the control element of the PPC. Material control, utilization of the machine, control of the labour force, cost and quality control are some of the disciplines which circumscribe the total control mechanism.

24.3 PROJECT PLANNING/PREPLANNING

The success of a project and the efficiencies with which the related activities are carried out are critical to an organization. Therefore, planning is done at the start of any project and should be taken up with great care. During the planning phase, each and every minute detail is required to be worked out and should be considered carefully. Planning of a project consists of the following steps:

- **Market survey:** The suitability of the business to produce the required goods and services is a critical factor in deciding the success of an organization. Market survey is a commercial survey that provides the required information in this regard and therefore aids in forecasting the project.
- **Project capacity:** The amount of capital that would be required to produce a particular type of product decides the capacity of the project. The information on project capacity is crucial to know the amount that would be required for the production and the way in which the financial resources need to be arranged. Following factors should be taken into account while deciding the capacity of the project:
    - o The market demand of a particular product.
    - o The availability of land, water and other related resources.
    - o Nature of product.
    - o The capacity in which the investment can be made.
- **Selection of site:** Some of the critical aspects while selecting the site should be considered. These factors cover the technical, commercial and financial aspects of the project. The two important stages of selection of the site for setting up of the manufacturing unit are:
    - o General location of the factory.
    - o Selection of exact site.
- **Plant layout:** The layout of the production system is another important factor that needs to be considered in the planning phase. The key is to optimize the arrangement of different machines and systems.
- **Design and drawing:** Detailed drawing of the products and goods to be manufactured is necessary so that any doubt in relation to the product can be averted. The detailed specification of the raw materials and also that of the machine that is required to be used for the product manufacturing is equally critical.
- **Material requirement:** Engineering drawing is used to prepare the list of materials that would be required for manufacturing. The list is referred to as "Bill of materials".

- **Operation planning:** In order to minimize the wastage of material, time and money, a proper method of manufacturing is required to be selected. The operation planning takes care of the selection of suitable production method. By doing this, the fatigue involved during the manufacturing process can also be eliminated. Time study and work study are used to determine the time that would be required for a particular job and the optimized motion that needs to be taken by the operative to perform an activity.
- **Machine loading:** The time taken by the machine to perform an element of a job should be analyzed via time study to decide the number of machines required to be installed in a manufacturing unit. This is also necessary to determine the optimized utilization of the machine and therefore the machine programme needs to be prepared carefully and accordingly.
- **Sub-contract consideration:** The manufacturing of each and every part required in assembling the product is difficult due to the requirement of specialized machines. Therefore, the decision to sub-contract the manufacturing of a product or to buy from other vendors needs to be considered judiciously. The decision in this regard is taken by the planning department after analyzing the merits and demerits.
- **Equipment requirement:** The idea of the capital requirement for the purchase of the different tools, machines required could be determined through cost data of the equipment required to be purchased.
- **Organizational layout and staff requirement:** The staff in required quantity is selected by considering the organizational layout of organization which, in turn, depends on the nature of work and the type of industry.
- **Material handling:** The material handling problems must be studied before the erection of the factory building and plant layout.
- **Budgeting:** The market trends and the past experience aid in preplanning and forecasting the capital investment required in the future period.
- **Cost calculation:** The expenses that have been incurred on a product during its period of manufacturing gives the total cost of a product.
- **Procurement of finance:** The lock capital required is managed through partners and shareholders whereas the working capital is arranged through shares, loans and banks.
- **Critical report on feasibility:** Analysis of feasibility of the project is one of the critical parts of this phase. This can be obtained from the rate of return on the invested capital.

24.4 PLANNING

For attaining the objective, or to fulfill a need under the circumstances that are restrictive in nature, an intelligent anticipation in the form of planning exercise is essential. Therefore planning provides a support structure to achieve the objective. The role of planning doesn't analyse the nature of the objective, i.e., the objective is good or bad, right or wrong and henceforth. The nature of the objective is decided before carrying out the planning exercise.

The nature and the type of objective, the circumstances and the skills and techniques of the planner dictate the accuracy of the planning exercise. The lack of resources is another critical factor determining the crucial role that is played by the planning exercise.

Planning of the production activities occurs at the aggregate level. The planning takes into account a specific duration of time to take decisions, this time frame may vary from as short as a month or quarter of a month and may be as long as six months or even a year. In the majority of situations, it is considered to be six months or a year.

Determination of the production rate is the main problem of aggregate planning. The planning should be able to decide on the rate such that it satisfies the anticipated output requirements and at the same time minimizes cost associated with the inventories, fluctuation of work and the related decision variables.

There are three distinct types of production planning:

- Project planning.
- Progressive or continuous planning.
- Lot or batch planning.

24.5 CONCEPTS OF PRODUCTION PLANNING AND SCHEDULING

Production planning plays a crucial role in determining the policies, the procedures and the facilities that would be required for the production of the product that meets the market requirements. The planning of production circumscribes the determination of capacity and product determination. The former is decided on the basis of the quantity of the product to be manufactured while the latter leads to the type of product to be manufactured which is futuristic. The planning exercise takes care of the manpower with the requisite skills and the financial resources. The exercise also ensures the other inputs such as machinery and raw materials besides the aforementioned inputs. Therefore, the main objective of the planning lies in keeping a check that everything is available on time and therefore the production schedule is met as decided.

Planning exercise must take into account the different limiting factors that circumscribe the manufacturing system. These factors include market price, availability of funds, expected delivery requirements, process time, the storage requirements and other inherent product restrictions.

As opposed to planning, the exercise of scheduling is more specific and is less future oriented. The current conditions relating to the availability of machinery, material and manpower are accepted by the scheduling exercise which then goes on to utilize these facilities in an optimized approach to achieve the immediate product objective. The desired end result that has been already analyzed is the initiation step for the scheduling exercise. The scheduling provides a blueprint for accomplishing the task to achieve the desired product objective. The blueprint lays down the specific operations that are needed to be completed to accomplish the required objective. Further, it specifies the start and end times and other related details for the different operations. Often the more specific a schedule is, the better it can be used as a production control device.

The blueprints as suggested by the scheduling and planning stage will lose its value until and unless these are accompanied by a feedback. The feedback provides the necessary information on how well the plans are executed. The feedback measures provide the necessary inputs related to the aberrations and deviations that arise and therefore suggest the corrective measures in early stages and certain preventive measures for the future. The key managerial tools and the valuable information on future planning are also suggestive of the proper feedback mechanism.

Production control circumscribes the important skill of inventory control. Inventory control involves both the cost and the use of certain techniques and concepts to minimize the wastage of raw materials and to ensure the availability of the same as and when required. Therefore, inventory control is complex in nature. The production plans as well as the customer delivery are affected by the availability of the inventory.

The situations as that of the long lead times truly recognize the need for production planning. The capability of the company to expand itself in the situation of changing market requirements is restricted because of the rare availability of the skilled workforce for the imported equipment, or the availability of the raw materials. Therefore, a careful planning with the effective feedback mechanism is a must to avert the restrictions.

24.6 PRODUCTION

The stage involving the transformation of ideas in the form of design to the working system is the implementation stage of the project. Different departments of the organization are involved during the implementation stage of the project. The activities are carried distinctly under the supervision of different departments. Further, controls to critical schedules are taken care by the departments.

Production is one such department that takes care of the objective of producing goods and services as per the market requirements. The production department organizes labour, capital materials and other related resources with an objective to meet the changing market requirements. The production system occurs in a wide variety of disciplines such as factories, hospitals, banks, stores, etc. Irrespective of the discipline, all the production systems produce output on the basis of certain inputs.

For the production of goods and services, the production system takes inputs from the different subsystems of the organization to transform them into outputs. The inputs may be service inputs, for instance maintenance, supervision, design, etc., and may be control inputs such as that of measurement, data processing, forecasting, order and sales information.

The three main factors determining the place of production planning and control in an organization are as below:

- The quantity in which the required product needs to be manufactured.
- The regularity of the manufacturing process.
- The capacity of plant being indicative of the size of the manufacturing unit.
- The nature and the type of product manufactured.

There are several ways in which classification of industry can be made. The classification can be based on the availability of labour in different geographical locations, the factors relating to the investment policy and so on.

24.7 OBJECTIVES OF PRODUCTION PLANNING

- The determination of the capacity for the different manufacturing units.
- Planning systematically the production related activities so that the activities can be well coordinated to meet the sales requirements.
- The smooth and steady transformation of the received orders from the sales department into the orders of work department.
- To organize and arrange for the manufacturing requirements in order to meet the production schedule on time. Ways should be adopted to ensure the availability of different resources in the right quality and quantity.
- In order to obtain fine balance between the different activities, coordination between the departments is another important function of PPC.
- Ensure the utilization of the plant to its fullest capacity.
- To motivate labour for the right and more earnings.
- To encourage the staff to enhance their performance for their duties.

24.8 CONTROL

The principles that apply to production control, budgetary control, managerial controls and cost control are similar for the different control mechanisms. The cycle of events that comprises the control mechanism is action, feedback, evaluation and adjustment. All these events take the form of closed loop circuit because of their continuous and dynamic nature. The seven essential steps in the establishment and application of operating controls are discussed as below:

- **Operation:** First step in the control cycle. There are certain faults that are obvious while performing a job or task. Such faults can be corrected easily. There are other faults that can be concealed deceptively and therefore proper procedural steps need to adopted to correct the faults of such nature.
- **Measurement:** Measurement is the second step and is required to measure what is being done. For instance, measurement of variation of physical, chemical,

dimensional, electrical and other related properties. This is done for the field of quality control. In the case of production, control measurement of operations is done to determine the time required for their performance. Further, it also leads to identification of the capacity of the machine or equipment with which the work is performed. The measurement in case of electronic and mechanical operations is done in terms of milliseconds.

- **Capability studies:** The accurate projection of the action that is required to be taken can be done through the utilization of different statistical techniques. The process quality needs to be figured out for determining the scrap and other losses.
- **Objectives:** On the analysis of what can be done, the narrowing down of the actions should be done keeping in view the capabilities. This decision then leads to plans for using excess capabilities on other plans to increase capabilities either for quality or quantity so that the objective can be met.
- **Evaluation:** The feedback information is compared with the created blueprint. The information is compared with the set plans and objectives.
- **Adjustment:** Adjustment is the last step in production control. The adjustment process is often complicated in nature since it requires increasing or decreasing of quantities which are based on the past operation. The quality of a product is maintained within limits through the quality control measures.
- **Feedback & flexibility:** The information that has been gathered from the different operations and actions and then compared with the set plans and objectives, thus serving as the basis of future performance is termed feedback. Feedback is similar to knowing how close one has hit the target. If one knows about the target then the next shot could be adjusted to come closer to the set target. Therefore, feedback is the vital control.

  Feedback and flexibility are the two key elements leading to the successful plant implementation. Therefore, information must be supplied in time to adjust against any aberrations or anomaly that exists in the process being carried out. The manufacturing unit must be flexible enough to shift if necessary. This is only possible if benchmarks and standards are set in the planned period.

  Target or goal say is to double the production within two years. This shouldn't be confused with the plan. In order to achieve the goals, a concrete plan must indicate how well can this be done. Care is taken by the plan in place as to when the different steps will begin and be completed. Further, the assumptions underlying the plan and goal must also be stated. During the implementation of the plan, frequent checks are necessary to be carried out to determine whether the things are proceeding as per the schedule or not. Frequent checks should be made on the ordering of the machinery, the training of the workers, behaviour of the market, etc. The cause behind any aberrations must be analyzed. It is only after the analysis, one can decide on the different adjustments that are required to be made.

24.9 FUNCTIONS OF PPC

The production of product in the required quantity and of the required quality by employing the most economical method leads to the highest efficiency in production. To achieve the goal of highest efficiency, PPC tools are used to coordinate all the manufacturing activities. Therefore, the key function of PPC is to coordinate all the manufacturing activities that are related to production or manufacturing.

- **Materials:** The availability of different raw materials and standard finished parts must be ensured in time while starting the operation within time.
- **Methods:** The different methods of production and manufacturing must be analyzed to select and opt for the best method according to the environment and the given set of circumstances. This function determines the sequence in which the different operations need to be carried out. Further, it also determines the division of product into assemblies and sub-assemblies. These then can be modified in accordance with the limitation of the existing layout and work flow.
- **Machines and equipment:** The methods used for production and manufacturing should be identified on the basis of the available machinery and the equipment. Further, it should be coupled with the detailed study of equipment replacement policy. The managerial responsibilities for equipment consider the maintenance policy and the procedures and schedules for carrying out the different functions. The design of the tools and the work layout are also critical functions of the PPC.
- **Routing:** Routing is the specification of the sequence of operations and different processes that must be followed in manufacturing a particular lot. Therefore, routing determines that operations will be performed on the product and also lays down the steps that are required to be followed sequentially to accomplish the finished product. The different operations with their paths are estimated along with the proper class of machines and personnel required for carrying out the different operations.

  The relative cost, purchasing policies, availability of equipment, skilled personnel are some of the factors that aid in deciding as to what components are needed to be manufactured and what are required to be purchased.

  - **An analysis of article to determine what materials are needed:** The drawing and specifications, the quality standards, product application determines as to what materials are needed. More often this depicts the additional material required.
  - **Determination of manufacturing operation and the sequence**: The appropriate methods of production and their proper sequence to manufacture the product are established in this section. These are made on the route and operations sheets.
  - **Determination of lot sheet:** The determination of the optimum lot size depends primarily on the manufacturing involved and it should be such that the cost involved in the setup and that involved in carrying the inventory for the article to be manufactured is optimum. The lot size is the sum of customer's order and

the allowance of stock required to be kept to take care of any unwanted circumstances.

- **Determination of scrap factor:** The scrap or the wastage of material that is encountered in the course of manufacturing is the critical factor determining the cost of production. Establishment of the standard scrap factors is indicative of the best manufacturing practices.
- **Analysis of cost article:** It includes cost accounting department for cost estimation of product.

The different factors that affect the routing procedure are:

- Manufacturing type employed.
- Availability of plant equipment and its component parts.
- Characteristics of physical plant equipment and its component parts.
- Human elements.

- **Estimating:** The time required to perform an operation can be worked out using the detailed operation sheet that carries the data related to the feeds, speed and the use of auxiliary attachment methods. In the absence of the operation sheet and hence the estimation process, the chances of wide operation times and therefore large fluctuations are inevitable. This can have a damaging effect on the system as a whole.
- **Loading & scheduling:** The performance capabilities and the capacities of the machines are the determining factors for the machine loading. Machine loading ensures the smooth flow of work and the appropriate feeds and speeds utilization. Besides these functions, it also analyzes the process capacities ensuring the proper coordination of the different operations with varying flow rates along the production lines.

The detail and the time period are the two major points on the basis of which one can distinguish between planning and scheduling. Planning has objective that spans over years where the objectives for scheduling span over a week or in most cases it may be weeks. Say for instance, the objective of doubling the production of units spanning over two years is planning whereas, the schedule will be to produce 200 units in week one, 300 units in week two and so on.

Therefore, scheduling determines the quantity of units to be produced during the next few weeks. The scheduling process leads to the specification of the type of product that a machine will be manufacturing, the quantities of each product to be produced and the start and end time of the production. The other related activities such as maintenance, movement of goods and even the staff meetings are also circumscribed by the scheduling process. In essence, a schedule is a detailed statement of how, when and where specific resources are going to the employed to produce specified output or results.

The schedule stage is integral part of the control system. For instance, in the field of finance, budget is used as a schedule for the usage of the funds. On the other hand, budget is also integral to the control system that is used for monitoring expenditure. Therefore, a schedule provides for the sequential path in which the different activities need to be performed which should accompany the sensitive controls and the response time which is rapid in nature.

The process of scheduling depends on the nature of operation of the activity which can be either very simple or very complex. The scheduling is simple, for instance in case of cottage industry where a worker may be asked to produce a given number of carvings or may be square meters of fabric per week. Therefore, the scheduling involves only the count made each week.

- **Decision rules:** The lower or the middle management takes care of the process of scheduling. Consequently, the schedulers, of themselves, are actually not in position to relate their activities to the overall company goals and objective.

  Yet the function of schedulers is important to achieve the scheduling process. In process to meet such ends, it becomes necessary to tie the two levels of management together through certain decision rules. To be fairly specific is one of the important characteristics for the decision rules for scheduling. The schedulers not only link the scheduling functions with the attainment of total organizational goals but they also ensure the consistency in the scheduling process. This helps in ensuring that the people can be interchanged if required. This also ensures that uniformity is maintained throughout the organization for the interpretation of the schedule and hence there is a proper understanding of the process. They also make it possible to place much of the scheduling detail work on computers.

  The forms that the decision rules can take depend on the circumstances under which they are required. Competitive conditions, internal cost structures, the nature of the product, capacity consideration, etc., will all have their effect.

  Examples of possible decision rules include the following:

  - The longest job should be scheduled first.
  - The order in which the jobs are received is another rule for scheduling the jobs.
  - The jobs with the earliest delivery dates should be scheduled first.
  - The jobs requiring the production capacity that have the greatest idle capacity should be scheduled first.

Besides the above mentioned, there are umpteen number of rules. The different decision rules are not only applicable to the production operations but also to the other processes that require scheduling.

Depending upon the situations existing in a company, specific set of decision rules after experimentation could be developed by the companies. The decision rules could be experimented upon a part of project before their introduction into the system. The experimentation before implementation is really useful to avoid any future disruptions of the production. However, there is caution to designing the rules that shouldn't be generalized for different circumstances.

The decision rules must be consequently a guideline and should be flexible to consider for any deviation when necessary. However, a thorough explanation of any deviation is required to be produced which could be sensible on the part of scheduler. The rules should not be changed by the scheduler if these provide benefits to the firm as a whole. If the rules tend to maximize the profit, then these should be continued by the organization. The implementation of the decision rules should be accompanied with the feedback.

A point often overlooked is that if decision rules for scheduling are not formally and explicitly established, they usually evolve through default. Each person involved in the scheduling process will usually have his own method, perhaps one that makers sense only themselves, but still a method. Sometimes this may be the best alternative for a firm (e.g., the potential cost saving does not justify taking the time to establish a formal procedure).

However, this should be explicitly determined. Otherwise, an organization may be looking towards a major opportunity for improvement and enhanced efficiency.

- **Dispatching:** It is an important mechanism of production control. Meaning of this term is sending to destination or starting something on its way. When applied to production control, it means the assignment of work to different machines or workplaces which involve insurance of order and production form in order of their priority as determined by scheduling. In dispatching, translated into reality or physical work which has been termed planned scheduling.

  Duties of dispatching:

  - Assignment of work to different machines of workplace men.
  - Movement of material from stores to the first process and from process.
  - Issue of tool orders, instructing the tool department to collect and make ready jigs and fixtures, in advance of time, at which the operation will commence.
  - Issue of time ticket, drawing, instruction cards and other necessary information presented performing the work.
  - Issue of inspection order after each operation to determine the result in the number of pieces "good" and the "bad" and cause of spoilage.
  - Issue of more orders and collection of time tickets, drawings, instruction cards for all completed operations.
  - Recording time of beginning and completing of jobs and calculating duration of, forwarding complete records to production department and time card pay roll department.
  - Recording and reporting idle time of machine and operation.
- **Dispatching procedure:** Manner in which schedule or orders are issued depends upon whether the dispatching is decentralized or centralized. The manufacturing schedules or work orders in blanket fashion to the foreman or dispatch clerk within department occurs in decentralized dispatching. It is the duty of a foreman or clerk to dispatch the orders of material to each machine and operator.

In centralized dispatching, orders are dispatched from central dispatching division to machine or work station. Capacity and characteristic of each machine is recorded in central dispatching station. Regardless of type of dispatching it is customary for department inform to the starting dates, progress of each order by means of wall chart visible index file or one of the several types of department dispatching boards.

Dispatching rule:

- **Simple rule:**
  - **Earliest due date:** Run the job with the earliest due date, results in good date performance.
  - **First come first served:** Run the job which arrived in the waiting line first. Result at low variance of manufacturing cycle time.
  - **Shortest processing time:** Run the job which has the shortest set up plus machining for the current work centre.
- **Combination rule:**
  - Minimum stock: Slack equals calendar time remaining minus processing time remaining or slack equals date minus present time minus set up and machining time for all remaining operations.
  - Critical ratio: The critical ratio made to order work is a slack type rule. Critical equals 0 to due date minus present time divided by number of days required to complete the job order.

- **Expediting:** Follow-up regulates the progress of materials and parts through the production process. This closely interrelated with activities of dispatcher to whom is delegated the scheduling responsibility.

  Follow-up is that novel tool which acts as a regulator of material and component parts when they are travelling on the path of performance as laid down by sheets and

  schedule charts. It serves as a catalytic agent to fuse the various separated and unrelated production activities into the unified whole that means progress.

  - **Type:**
    - **Materials:** To follow up purchased materials is responsibility of purchasing department. This can be accomplished most simply by filling one copy of requisition in a daily follow-up file or in ticket file according to the date of materials due to be received.
    - **Work in progress:** This follows up the work by checking the process and recording the production that has been accomplished by production line. This is then compared with preplanned schedules. It is the duty of follow-up men or expediters to advise the foreman about the best sequence in which the orders can be run so that the required part in which order is to be fabricated and brought together at right time and place for the completion of finished product.

- » **Assembly and erection:** Responsibility for assembly and erection of products in assembly manufacturing is almost invariably rested. When all the parts are available, the follow-up man permits assembly of products. In case of large complicated product, this is very necessary.

- **Inspection:** Another major control is inspection. Its finding and criticism are of importance both in execution of current programme and planning stage of fibre undertaking when the limitations of the processor, method and manpower are known. These limitations can form a basis for future investigations in evaluating the improving production methods.
- **Evaluating:** Perhaps the most neglected, but an essential link between control and forwarding is that of evaluating. The essential task of dispatching and evaluating are concerned with the immediate issue of production and with measures that will be as certain fulfilment target.

  Valuable information is gathered limited in nature and provision is made so that all the accumulated information can be properly digested and analyzed data may be irretrievably lost. Thus here the evaluating function comes in to provide a feedback mechanism on the longer term basis so that the past experience can be evaluated with the view to improving utilization of method and facilities. This is the integral part of control function.

SECTION VIII
LOCATION SELECTION AND PLANT LAYOUT

25
Plant Location

25.1 INTRODUCTION

When the Nano was launched by Ratan Tata of Tata Sons, there was widespread jubilation and anticipation of where the factory was going to come up. Various state governments offered attractive concessions to the Tatas urging them to set up the facility in their State. West Bengal was selected to house the Nano plant and work began at Singur. Not only the Tatas, but even their joint venture partners invested crores of rupees to set up their respective facilities.

However, the location option proved to be wrong. Barely months before commercial production were to start, there were agitations by the locals at Singur against the project. The situation worsened and the Tatas were forced to abandon their project at Singur and relocate to Sanand, Gujarat. So what went wrong? Without going into the reasons vis-à-vis the Tatas project, in this unit you will learn about the factors that must be taken into consideration when selecting a location for setting up a factory. You will also learn about layout plan and its various aspects.

25.2 DEFINITION AND OBJECTIVES OF PLANT

Before we look into the process of location decision let us first define the term 'location'. *Facility location is the selection of suitable location or site where the factory or facility will be installed, and from where it will function.*

There are two fundamental objectives to a facility location exercise. These are:

- Minimizing cost
- Maximizing revenue

Whatever may be the nature of the firm these objectives will govern the location decision. The planning for 'where' to locate should start from 'what' are the organization's objectives, priorities, goals, strategies, etc., and what it is doing to achieve them in the socio- economic-technical-legal environment. Unless the objectives and priorities have been clearly understood, the decision regarding the location cannot be correct.

25.3 IMPORTANCE OF FACILITY LOCATION

Why is facility location so important? What could happen if the selection of location was wrong? We have read in the beginning that the Nano project faced losses even before commercial production had begun. Moreover, the car was to have started commercial production in December 2008. This could not happen.

So let us see what all can happen to a facility which is operating in an improper/incorrect location.

- The company may have to close down its operations and liquidate its assets. In that case:
  - Locating buyers for used equipment will be difficult.
  - Price received for used equipment will be a fraction of the original investment.
- The company may relocate its facility, just like the Tatas have done. But this will involve:
  - Huge expenditure in shifting machinery, equipment, manpower, etc.
  - Time and added costs for taking new land lease/outright purchase registration, etc.
  - If the company continues its operation at the wrong location:
    - » It may accumulate losses.
    - » Competitors with better locations will have an edge.
    - » The company will lose market share/customer goodwill.
- Location facility is an issue for consideration either for starting a new facility or for starting additional facility.
- Additional or multiple facilities can be desired due to the following reasons:
  - Separate facilities for different products/services, e.g., Videocon has different plants for its different products such as washing machines, TVs, refrigerators, microwave ovens, etc.
  - Separate facilities to serve different geographical areas, e.g., LPG filling plants across the country to serve different locations.
  - Separate facilities for different processes, e.g., separate facilities to make pizza base.

25.4 FACTORS AFFECTING LOCATION DECISION

In this section, you will learn about the various factors that affect decisions regarding choice of location. These factors are explained below.

- **Proximity to customers (markets):** When the plant is located near the customers/markets, the cost of transportation is low. This reduces the product cost. Most small ancillary units are located near big automotive factories. The OEMs (original equipment manufacturers) are the institutional customers of small parts, components, or sub-assemblies from these ancillary units. The Maruti Joint Venture Complex at Gurgaon near the Maruti Suzuki car factory is a good example of how proximity to the customer reduces the transportation cost of auto ancillary units, which supply parts, components, sub-assemblies, etc., for making the Maruti car. Proximity to markets also allows companies to meet sudden spurt in demand, thus providing an advantage over competitors who are located at far-off places. That is why we find hospitals, schools, post offices, banks, insurance companies, etc., located in high population zones so that they are able to serve a large number of customers.

- **Proximity to raw materials:** Why are the integrated steel plants of SAIL located in Bihar, West Bengal and Orissa? This is because of the large presence of iron ore, coal, dolomite and limestone mines in these regions, which are the basic raw materials for steel making. Proximity to the source of raw materials is an important consideration for facility location, especially if the raw materials are bulky, and huge shipping costs will be incurred in transporting them. Where it becomes absolutely necessary to transport them, it is found that cost of the material is equal to the shipping cost thus making the raw materials more costly at the point where they are used.
- **Good transportation facilities:** Good transportation facilities are necessary for movement of goods and people. Regions near metro cities have these facilities, as they have a good network of rail, air, water, and road transportation.
- **Availability of power:** Uninterrupted power supply is a basic requirement of most industries. Companies have to set up their own DG sets or have captive power plants if they are located in areas with power problems. This increases the cost of the product, besides additional problems of running the DG sets, captive power plants, etc.
- **Basic amenities:** The location site should have certain basic facilities like sewage system, piped water supply, security, etc., that are managed by the local municipality. Roads up to the factory premises are always desirable. If these basic amenities are provided, it will be easier for the employees and they will be willing to work in that factory. Availability of housing facilities, schools, colleges, banks, post office, hospitals, etc., are added advantages for locating a facility in an area.
- **Government policies:** Relaxed taxation policies, excise duty exemption and various other promotional efforts attract industrial activities in a region. Pondicherry and Daman and Diu are declared 'no sales tax regions' and we find that many companies have their offices/warehouses located there. Many state governments promote industrial activities in their regions by creating Industry Development Zones, Special Economic Zones, etc. The governments of Karnataka, Andhra Pradesh, Tamil Nadu and UP have created software development parks, where facilities such as high-speed Internet, servers, etc., are provided to software companies at subsidized rates. Agriculture gets maximum subsidies from the central as well as many state governments. Various processing plants of agricultural and horticultural products

located in these states can avail of these advantages. Before locating a facility at a particular site, the government policies of that region must be considered.

- **Environmental and community considerations:** Many state governments have strict environmental policies, which have to be followed by the industries operating there. States such as Uttaranchal do not give permission to such industries which release toxic effluents. Opposition from the community regarding the construction of a plant in their region can disrupt the whole project. The Sardar Sarovar Dam project is an example where opposition from the locals interrupted the construction of the dam over the Narmada. In the Chipko Movement, started by S.L. Bahuguna, the locals embraced a tree each, and did not allow the officials to cut the trees and thereby eliminate the forest. After the Union Carbide factory disaster in Bhopal some decades ago, every new factory faces close scrutiny on the environmental front in the area.
- **Proximity to subcontractors:** Small ancillary units manufacturing small components/ sub-assemblies are important for any new factory. Ancillary units and joint ventures set up their facilities near the OEM. The advantage to the ancillaries is that it will reduce their component cost. The OEMs too benefit if they set up their facilities near these ancillaries. Maruti Suzuki set up its second facility at Manesar near Gurgaon (where their first facility is located) so that it could take advantage of the suppliers present at the Maruti Joint Venture Complex at Gurgaon.
- **Availability of cheap land:** Land is the basic necessity for the construction of a new plant. Many big companies set up their facilities in backward areas because of availability of low-priced land.
- **Low construction costs:** Construction costs of a plant may be low at a particular place due to cheap labour available there. The construction material may also be cheaper at another place. Such places are preferred for locating a plant.
- **Availability of cheap, skilled and efficient labour:** Many companies locate their facilities at places where there is cheap, skilled and efficient labour. Many companies are locating their branches in South India because the people here are more disciplined, efficient and skilled.

25.5 LOCATING FOREIGN OPERATIONS FACILITIES

Globalization has made consumers expect the best products at the lowest prices irrespective of where they are produced. So while considering the location of a facility in a foreign country, in addition to all the factors listed above, the following additional factors should also be considered.

- **Trade barriers:** The Import Export Policy of the government of India imposes some restrictions on the import of certain goods. For some goods import duties are levied, which make these products expensive in the local market. In such situations, foreign companies overcome these trade barriers by producing the goods in that country locally.

- **Local customers:** If a foreign company has a large customer base in a country, it may be beneficial for it to start operations locally in that country. This way the company can serve the customers better and take advantage of their brand loyalty.
- **Incentives:** To increase the inflow of Foreign Direct Investment, certain countries provide industrial infrastructure, insurance, tax exemptions/reductions, interest-free/subsidized loans, etc., to foreign companies that are willing to establish operations facilities in their region.
- **Share prices and goodwill:** The market value of the firm may soar as international operations are deemed prestigious by investors.
- **Operations in competitor's home:** Initiating operations at the competitor's home country may at times force the competitor to concentrate more on the home turf and wind up or downsize its international operations.

26
Location Decision and Layout

26.1 THE LOCATION DECISION PROCESS

Let us now learn the various steps in the planning of location. The process of deciding on the facility location begins by listing the various location options. Then the advantages and disadvantages of each location are identified. These are then compared with the list of factors that are necessary for that particular industry, e.g., the essential parameters, or the factors that would be of advantage to that particular industry, etc. Then each option is screened using various models and the locations are rated according to these models. Based on the outcome of this exercise, the most suitable location is chosen. Various methods/models are used nowadays to determine the most suitable location. We will learn two important methods here.

- **Techniques of factor rating and location rating:** This is the simplest method for arriving at the best location. In this method, two types of ratings are given:
  - Every factor that is relevant to the industry is given a rating between 1 and 5. These factors are relevant to the industry, irrespective of the location. This is called **factor rating.**
  - Every factor that has been listed in (1), is given a relative rating between 1 and 5 for each of the locations proposed to be selected. This is called **location rating.** We will learn how to use these two ratings to arrive at the best location, by means of an example.

Example 1: M/s Indiana Leathers has identified three locations, Kanpur, Noida and Lucknow, to set up a leather goods manufacturing facility. The factor ratings and locations ratings have been given. Arrive at the best location using the Factor and Location Rating methods.

Factor	Factor rating	Location rating		
		Kanpur	Noida	Lucknow
Proximity to market	3	4	6	3
Proximity to raw material	5	10	5	4
Transportation facility	4	9	10	5

Basic amenities	2	6	7	6
Acceptance of leather factory by locals	4	8	3	7
Availability of cheap land	3	7	2	8
Low construction costs	1	5	1	6
Easy availability of cheap and skilled labour	3	3	8	4

Factor ratings are 1 to 5 – 5 being the highest and location ratings are 1 to 10 – 10 being the highest

Solution: For each location find the product of factor and location ratings. Add them up for each location. The location having the highest product will be the best location.

Product of factor and location ratings

Factor	Kanpur	Noida	Lucknow
1	12	18	9
2	50	25	20
3	36	40	20
4	12	14	12
5	32	12	28
6	21	6	24
7	5	1	6
8	9	24	12
Total	177	140	131

The highest score is for Kanpur. So it is the best location.

Break-Even Analysis Method

This method is based on the concept of break-even analysis. We know that there are two elements of cost, i.e., fixed cost and variable cost. Fixed cost includes capital expenditure, land, building, manufacturing and equipment. This is irrespective of the volume of production and will be incurred even if there is no production. Variable cost includes raw material, labour, etc., which are directly involved in the production process and are proportional to the volume of production. Total cost is the sum total of fixed cost and variable cost. When the volume of production of a product is low, the component of its fixed cost is high and variable cost is low. As the volume of production increases, the variable cost component increases while the fixed cost component reduces, till a point is reached beyond which variable cost again begins to increase. This point is called the **break-even point** at which the total cost is the lowest. This volume of production is called **break-even volume.**

A company wants a low break-even volume so that it can recover its costs soon. A location which gives the least break-even volume is preferred. Let us understand this by an example.

Example 2: M/s Vignesh Steels intends to set up a rolling mill to roll different grades of high carbon steels. Potential locations selected by the company are Alipore, Bhatinda and Calicut. The cost structures for each of these locations are shown below. The product is expected to sell at Rs. 130 per kg.

(a) Find the most economical location for an expected volume of 6000 kg per year.

(b) Expected profit at that location.

(c) For what output is the range in each location best?

	FC	VC/kg
Alipore	150,000	75.00
Bhatinda	200,000	50.00
Calicut	400,000	25.00

Solution: Find the variable cost for producing 6000 kg. Then add the fixed cost and variable cost to arrive at the total cost.

	FC	VC/ Ton	VC for 6000 kg	TC (FC + VC)
Alipore	150,000	75.00	450000	600,000
Bhatinda	200,000	50.00	300000	500,000
Calicut	400,000	25.00	150000	550,000

The place having the least total cost for the volume of 6000 kg is the best location. In this example, it is Bhatinda.

(b) Selling Price = 130 × 6000 = 780000

Profit = Selling Price –Total cost = 780,000 – 500,000 = 280,000/year

(c) Make a table for outputs 1000, 2000, 3000, 4000, 5000, 6000, 7000, 8000 units/year for each location.

For example, for Alipore, FC = Rs 150,000.

Qty	1000	2000	3000	4000	5000	6000	7000	8000
VC	75000	15000	225000	300000	375000	450000	525000	600000

For Alipore, break-even is reached at 2000 T production. Why? You can also draw the graph with quantity on X-axis and cost on Y-axis. The point where the lines of fixed cost and variable cost meet is the break-even point.

Similarly, calculate/draw for the other locations.

26.2 LOCATION DECISION FOR WAREHOUSES

Warehousing plays a crucial role in the total distribution design. Suppose a firm does not own any warehouses. If its factory is located far from its suppliers of raw materials, the inbound transportation costs will be very high. Also longer delivery times increase the chances of material shortages for production.

If the factory is located far from its retail stores, then transportation costs incurred in shipping from the plant to the retail stores (outbound transportation costs) are very high. The delivery times increase the chance of out-of-stock situations, which reduces the level of customer service.

In both the situations, the presence of warehouses, both close to the markets as well as close to the factory, can provide quick and efficient functioning of the factory as well as delivery to retail stores.

Suppose the firm owns several manufacturing plants, which produce a variety of products. In the absence of a warehouse, the company's distribution system would look like this:

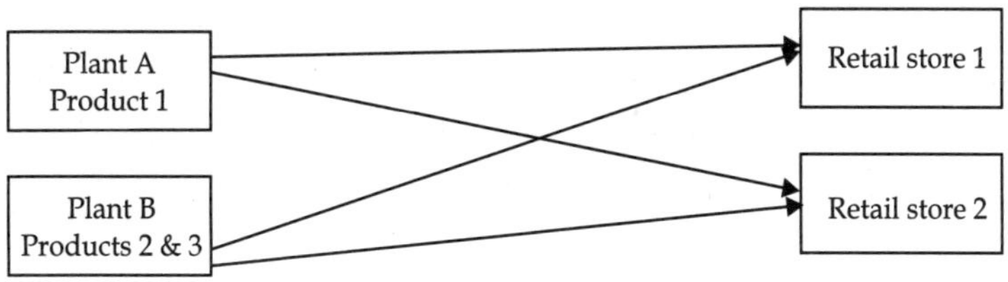

Fig. 26.1

Rather than ship small quantities of each product directly from the plants to retail stores, a warehouse can be used for consolidation of orders, as shown below. The economic advantage of such a system is that it is often cheaper to ship in truckload or wagonload quantities than in small quantities. Productivity is increased, since transport vehicles are used more efficiently and unit costs are reduced.

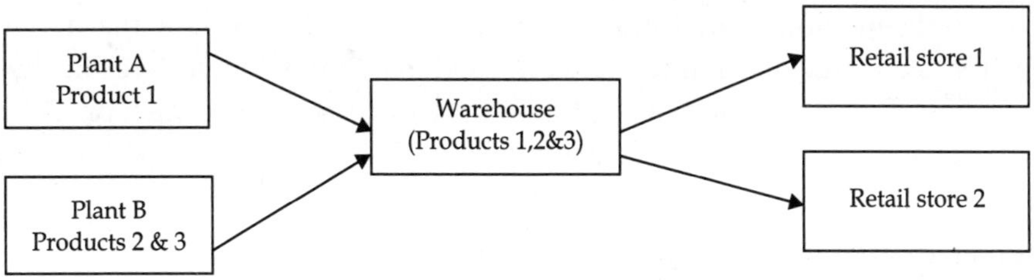

Fig. 26.2

The level of customer service also varies with the number of distribution centres. Many different productivity measures can be used to evaluate customer service. Common among these are:

- The average order processing time (the time between the receipt of an order at the warehouse and its shipment)
- The percentage of shipments delivered within 'x' days of order receipt
- The percentage of orders that are accurately filled
- The number of damaged items

- The managers responsible for location decisions must therefore make decisions depending to a large extent on the overall goals and objectives of the firm and their customer service policies.

26.3 NEED FOR LAYOUT PLANNING

Once the facility location has been decided and land has been acquired, a sketch or plan is made to decide where each department/section, entrance and exit gates, restrooms, storage areas, etc., will be located. In the subsequent sections, we will see how this type of planning is done.

26.4 DEFINITION OF LAYOUT PLANNING

We can define layout as, *'The physical location of the various departments/units of a facility within the premises of the facility.'* The departments must be located based on some consideration. The common considerations are:

- Logical sequence of processing operation
- Direction of material flow and material handling
- Aesthetic considerations
- Government regulations
- Special requirements

The entrance and exit gates are usually critical in the layout planning of facilities.

26.5 OBJECTIVES OF A PLANT LAYOUT

Plant layout is the method to plan and arrange materials and facilities so that a steady flow of production is ensured at minimum cost. A good plant layout always results in comfort and satisfaction of workmen and this automatically increases the production. A bad plant layout leads to accidents and unnecessary problems.

A good plant layout is designed to achieve the following objectives:

- Economic handling of materials and finished goods
- Fast and efficient quality production
- Enhanced utilization of available space
- Flexibility in change of plant design and possibility of expansion at a later date
- Improvement in work conditions leading to higher productivity
- Unidirectional/systematic flow of production operation
- Reduction in waiting time
- Reduction in manufacturing cost

26.6 ADVANTAGES OF A GOOD PLANT LAYOUT

A good plant layout results in better production and lower costs. The advantages of a good plant layout are as follows:

- **Well-organized workspace:** A good plant layout means well-organized workspace with adequate facilities provided for the machines as well as for the workmen. Proper arrangement of machines and tools eliminates congestion. The materials required are stored in their appropriate places. Workmen are also distributed to their respective departments.
- **Better working conditions:** A good plant layout results in labour satisfaction due to improved and clean working conditions. Motivation level increases when lighting and other aesthetics are improved. Safety of workmen is another important factor. A good plant layout ensures that the machines are properly placed, with adequate space in between so that there is no congestion and no danger of the workmen getting injured. This provides safety to the workmen and creates a good environment for work.
- **Minimization of material handling costs:** A good plant layout minimizes material handling costs. The machinery and equipment are placed in such a manner that there is no difficulty in transferring materials between workstations. The provision of adequate material handling systems will ensure that there is minimal labour cost, labour fatigue, etc.
- **Minimization in damage and spoilage of material:** In a good plant layout, materials are handled properly which results in good quality of production. There is minimum damage and spoilage of materials. Minimizing waste also leads to increase in profits.
- **Flexibility in changing production conditions:** A good layout provides adequate space for future expansion, laying additional workstations, etc. The advantage is that in future if the market conditions change, the firm can easily put up new machinery, etc., without having to dismantle the existing ones and with minimum hindrance to the daily schedule or work.

26.7 TYPES OF LAYOUT

There are four basic types of layout.

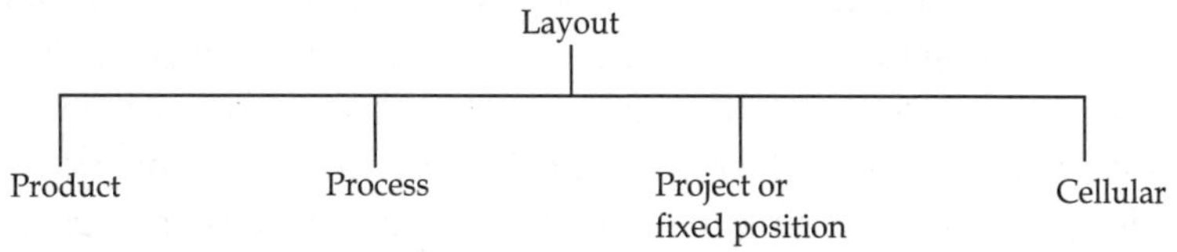

Fig. 26.3: Types of layout.

- **Product layout:** The placement of the equipment/machinery and materials in the order in which they are to be used for producing the product is called the **product layout** or **line layout**. This type of layout is found in industries where assembling of materials and parts takes place, such as the automobile industry. In such industries, the process starts with feeding in the raw materials and ends with the final product. The flow diagram of a Line Layout can be seen in Fig. 26.4.

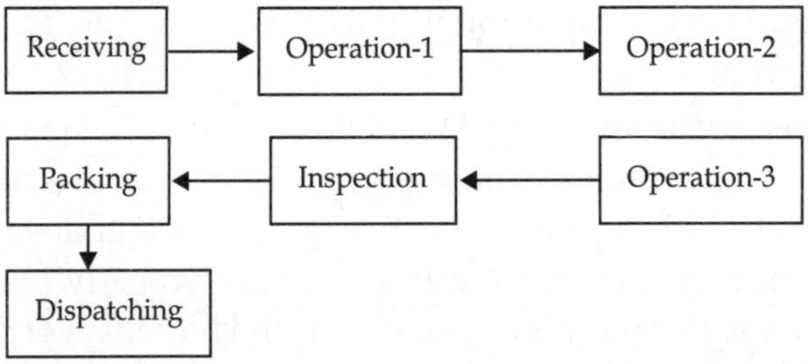

Fig. 26.4: Flow diagram of a product/line layout.

Advantages of product layout

- There is less work in process since output of one stage is automatically the input of next stage.
- Material handling is less since the process is automatic.
- Labour costs are less, as there is division of labour.
- Quality control is easier to implement.
- Easy and accurate scheduling of materials is possible.
- Production control is simpler due to less product variety.

Disadvantages of product layout

- It is not easy to change the product - this will involve change in the layout and this is expensive and time consuming. This layout is not flexible.
- If even one machine breaks down, the entire line will stop.
- Expansion of work area or insertion of any machine in between other machines is not possible or is very difficult.

- **Process layout:** The layout in which all the equipment/machines performing similar tasks are grouped together is called the **process layout** or **functional layout**; for example, the milling machines can be grouped together to form one department and the grinding machines can be grouped together to form another department. Depending on their processing requirements, parts are moved in different sequences among departments. Dividing the whole workplace into small units helps in faster production and better utilization of the workplace. The process layout can give a higher variety of products; for example, in a garment plant the stitching machines are kept in one place, pressing machines such as irons in another, knitting machines in another and so on.

Stores	Grinding	Foundry
Receiving	Planning production control	Despatch
Milling	Casting	Welding

Fig. 26.5: The process layout.

Advantages of process layout

- Flexibility in adapting to changing volumes, and changing varieties.
- Helps workmen learn more skills as job rotation enriches their skills.
- Problem in one machine does not affect other machines and production need not stop.
- In case of future expansion or increase in varieties, the existing setup need not be pulled out.

Disadvantages of process layout

- Space requirement increases when the work volume increases.
- Mechanization of material handling is not possible or is very costly.
- High work in progress inventory as jobs have to queue up for each operation.
- Difficulty in scheduling work, as different jobs have different operation sequences.
- High level of supervision is required. Production planning and control is more difficult.

- **Project layout:** The layout in which the production operation is performed in a fixed position is called the **project layout** or **fixed position layout**; for example, aeroplane and ship building industries use this type of layout. While making a rocket (the real ones, not fire crackers) the workmen/scientists, machines and tools and raw materials are moved to the place of construction of the rocket. Building bridges, roads, the Metro rail, etc., are all projects.

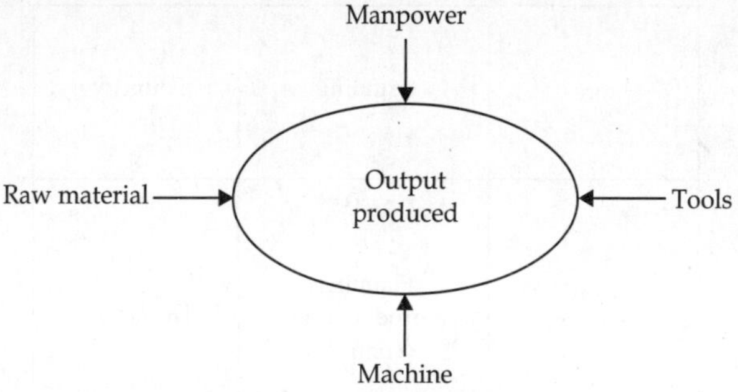

Fig. 26.6: A project layout.

Advantages of project layout

- It minimizes movement of machines and equipment.
- Continuity in production allows several activities to take place simultaneously.

Disadvantages of project layout

- Skilled and versatile workers are required. The necessary combination of skills may be difficult to find. Suitable workers would have to be paid attractive salaries.
- Once the project is over, the equipment/materials will have to be moved. Not only is this an expensive proposition but equipment utilization is also low since equipment is kept idle during the time that it is being shifted.
- **Group layout:** This layout is a combination of the layouts we have studied so far and is more commonly seen in the industry today. **Group technology,** or **cellular manufacturing** has the advantages of both process layout as well as line layout.

  In group technology, parts are grouped into families. The layout consists of groups of different machines (called cells) that are necessary for the production of families or parts.

Advantages of group technology

- The design of new products is good.
- Production control is simpler than in process layout or project layout, since scheduling of machines is less complex and fewer tools and materials are required.
- Material handling costs are fewer than in process layout.
- There are savings in setup time which leads to increase in production.

26.8 LAYOUT PLANNING FOR STORAGE AND WAREHOUSING

The design and layout of a warehouse is slightly different from that of a production unit. A warehouse is used for storing raw materials and supplies, tools and equipment and semi-finished and finished goods. Warehouses are often located at a distance away from actual production or customer locations.

A warehouse should focus on achieving high productivity in day-to-day activities of material management. These productivity objectives are:

- Maximum utilization of space.
- Efficient stock location and identification.
- Conservation of time, labour, and equipment.
- Rapid and easy transfer to and from storage.

Meeting these goals depends on a variety of factors, such as the size and shape of the physical facility, type of material handling equipment that is available, placement and arrangement of stock, and the nature and usage of items.

Small firms provide storage space within their own production facilities or in an adjacent warehouse. Larger corporations, particularly multi-plant companies and pure distribution system such as grocery chains or retail department stores, use cubic footage to the maximum. Pallets or portable platforms are used to take advantage of vertical stacking capabilities. They are moved easily by forklift trucks and other handling equipment. Other storage methods are used for small items or those that are used infrequently. Racks, shelves, and bins are used for small items and they are usually picked by hand.

The arrangement of items in storage depends on a variety of factors. These are:

- Items subject to deterioration, such as foodstuffs, medical supplies, iron or paints must be protected from dampness, insects, or extreme temperatures.
- Valuable items need special storage locations with security provisions.
- Hazardous materials require special attention and location.
- The size, weight, and shape of items affect storage and handling. For example, fragile items cannot be stacked very high, and heavy or bulky items are best stored near the shipping area to reduce handling needs.
- Produce turnover also affects storage and handling. Fast moving items need to be handled quickly, while slow movers can be stored in locations that require slower handling.

26.9 METHODOLOGY OF LAYOUT PLANNING

- **Line or product layout:** This is easier to plan since the machines have to be arranged or laid out as per the sequence of operations involved in converting the raw material into finished goods. The problem in line layout is not of how to sequence or relatively position the work areas, but how to group the work elements in such a manner that there is very little idle time between the work centers.
- **Process layout:** The problem in process layout is one of arranging the different work areas in such a way that the material movement costs are kept to a minimum. It is assumed that the other relevant costs of layout will also be reduced on account of this optimizing procedure.

The material handling costs between two work areas (departments) = {distance between the two work areas} × {Load handled between the two departments during a unit period of time}. (Here, **load** means the total number of units of different products any department processes.)

The sum of these products, for all the combinations of departments, should be kept minimum for an optimal plant layout. This can be expressed as follows:

$$\text{Minimize } \Sigma D_{ij} \times L_{ij}\, I_{ij}$$

where, D_{ij} is the distance between departments i and j, and L_{ij} is the number of loads per unit time moved (handled) between departments i and j.

The starting point in such a mathematical optimization procedure for the process layout is gathering data on the number of loads per unit time moved between different combinations of the work areas. This data is called 'load summary' and is presented in matrix fashion.

- **Closeness rating:** Closeness ratings indicate the relative degree of desirability of having one department situated near another. These are very effective tools, especially in service facility layout planning; for example, in an MBA institution, it is advantageous to have the library and computer centre as close as possible to the lecture theatres. The boys' and girls' hostel should be as far apart as possible. The girls' hostel is usually located near the teachers' residential premises.

The closeness rating can be indicated as shown below.

Closeness rating	Importance
Absolutely necessary	1
Highly important	2
Important	3
Slightly important	4
Unimportant	5
Undesirable	6

Example 3: Indiana Hospital has made the following matrix to show the closeness ratings of the various departments for its proposed new building. The matrix shows that the closeness rating between departments D_1 and D_2 is 2, departments D_1 and D_3 is 4, D_6 and D_1 as 5, and so on.

Make a layout for the hospital building keeping in view the closeness ratings.

	D_1	D_2	D_3	D_4	D_5	D_6	D_7	D_8	D_9
D_1									
D_2	2								
D_3	4	6							
D_4	1	5	1						
D_5	4	4	5	4					

D_6	5	4	3	4	6				
D_7	4	5	5	5	2	5			
D_8	5	6	3	1	4	5	3		
D_9	1	4	3	6	5	4	3	1	

Solution:

Step-1: Make a list of department pairs with ratings 1. This is necessary.

$D_1 - D_4$

$D_3 - D_4$

$D_1 - D_9$

$D_4 - D_8$

$D_8 - D_9$

Make a list of department pairs with ratings 6. This is undesirable.

$D_2 - D_3$

$D_5 - D_6$

$D_2 - D_8$

$D_4 - D_9$

Step-2: Now make a network of departments having the rating 1, with the department occurring most frequently (D4) at the centre.

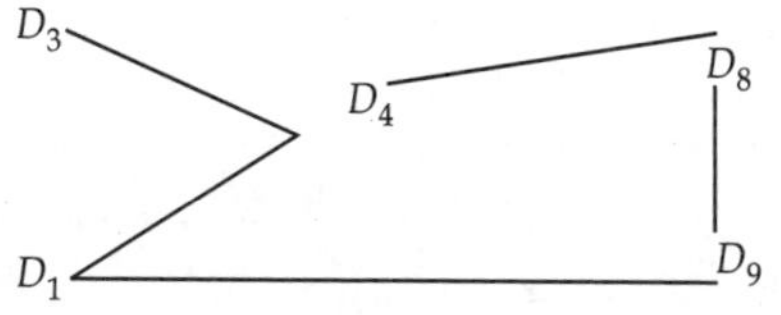

Fig. 26.7

Similarly, make a network of departments having the rating 6, with the department occurring most frequently (D2) at the centre.

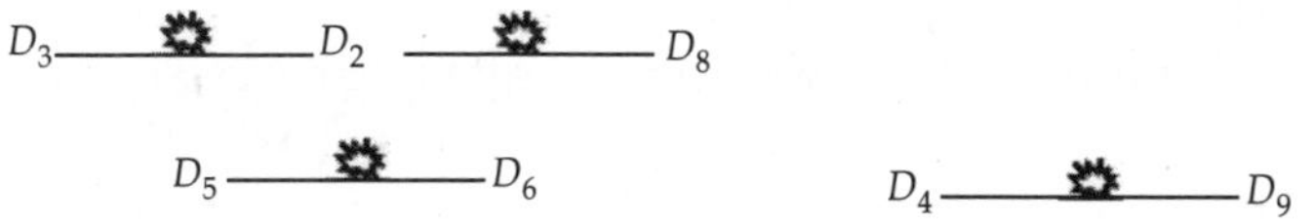

D_2	D_4	D_3
D_6	D_1	D_8
D_7	D_9	D_5

Fig. 26.8

Now, keeping in view the above combinations, place the departments in the nine cells as shown above. This placement satisfies all the conditions of not only departments with ratings 1 and 6 but also of those with other ratings. While making the placements, we have to consider only ratings 1 and 6; the other ratings are automatically satisfied.

Closeness ratings require a trial and error method for placement of departments. The assignment method is more useful and commonly used in industry. Several computer software such as ALDEP (automated layout design programmes) and CORELAP (computerized relationship layout planning) are based on the closeness ratings method. Another software, CRAFT (computerized relative allocation of facilities), is based on the load distance analysis method which is explained below.

- **Load distance analysis:** In this method, two or more layouts can be compared to find out which one minimizes the total load-distance value of the product manufactured. Let us understand this technique by means of the following example.

Example 4: The figures shown below display two layout options of a facility: Layout A and Layout B. The distance between any two adjacent departments is 10 m. No diagonal movement is possible, e.g., if a load has to be moved from Department 7 to Department 5 in Layout A, it can be done either through Departments 8, 9, and 6 or through Departments 3, 1 and 2 by travelling a distance of 40 m. The table below shows the department processing sequence of various products and their quantity produced per month. Calculate which layout is better in terms of lower total load-distance value.

LAYOUT A

1	2	5
3	4	6
7	8	9

LAYOUT B

5	3	4
9	6	1
2	7	8

		Distance	
Product	**Processing sequence**	**Layout A**	**Layout B**
V	5-7-2-9	40 + 30 + 30 = 100	30 + 10 + 10 = 50
W	4-3-8-1-5	10 + 20 + 30 + 20 = 80	10 + 30 + 10 + 30 = 80
X	3-9-4-1	30 + 20 + 20 = 70	20 + 30 + 10 = 60

Now multiply the load, i.e., quantity per month with the distance calculated.

Solution: Find the total distance travelled by a product while getting processed, according to the given sequence.

		Qty × Distance	
Product	**Qty**	**Layout A**	**Layout B**
V	3000	3,00,000	1,50,000
W	4000	3,20,000	3,20,000
X	2000	1,40,000	1,20,000
		7,60,000	5,90,000

The total load distance of Layout B is less than Layout A. Hence, Layout B is a better option.

SECTION IX
JOB EVALUATION AND WAGES

27

Job Evaluation

27.1 INTRODUCTION

A person is required to be given the compensation for the job being performed by him/her. This should come into effect once a person is placed in the right place. A systematic relationship among the base compensation rates for the different performed jobs within an organization must be established to ensure that each and every worker is entitled to equal payment. The base rates established for compensation should also be consistent to ensure the aforementioned objective. The process of establishing such compensations for the different jobs performed in an organization is known as job evaluation.

To ensure that an equitable wage structure is established in an organization, different jobs in an organization are required to be evaluated and their worth needs to be established so that the compensation could be given on the basis of ascribed values. The equal wage structure ensures that cordial relations are maintained between the employee and the employers. The task to evaluate the different jobs and hence to form the compensation rates is cumbersome and requires a lot of efforts. Hence the efforts involved in plotting the intricacies for the job evaluation needs to be appreciated. This lesson, is a first step, dedicated to discuss the various aspects of job evolution.

27.2 CONCEPT AND RELATED TERMINOLOGIES OF JOB EVALUATION

In order to facilitate for the efficient communication, certain technical terminologies are used in the field of job evaluation study. The technical terms are listed below with their explanation that provides a better understanding of the different allied terms. Further, the terms that are often confused with the job evaluation have also been discussed below: (Fig. 27.1)

- **Position:** The group of tasks assigned to an individual is termed 'position'. The number of positions is thus equivalent to the number of personnel in an organization.
- **Job:** According to Edwin B. Flippo, a job is a group of similar group of positions. The positions should be similar on the basis of the kind and level of the work. There may be circumstances in which there exists only one position in a job because of

non-existence of other similar positions. For example, since there exists only one human resource manager in an organization, the job will constitute only the human resource manager at the position.

- **Job analysis:** The process involving the study and collection of information for a specific job is known as job analysis. The information and the study should be made for the operations and the responsibilities comprising a job. The job analysis results into job descriptions and job specifications.
- **Motion study:** The motion study too involves the study of job or in other words this is one of the ways of studying a job. The objective of motion study lies in establishing the easiest, effective and economical method of performing a job. Therefore motion study is a part of the job design function.
- **Job description:** Job description is a factual statement of duties and responsibilities relating to a specific job. The job description describes the jobs to be done, the manner and the way in which a job is to be performed and the reason for performing the job. A job description provides for the appropriateness and authorized contents of a job.
- **Job specification:** A job specification carries a factual statement relating to the minimum qualities that an operator is required to possess to perform a job in an efficient manner. Thus the qualities required for the acceptable performance of job by a personnel is carried by a proper job description.

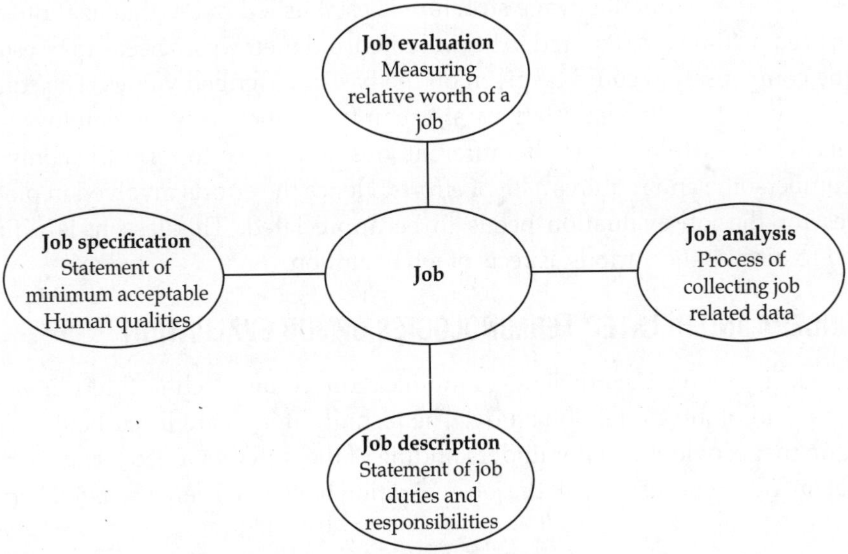

Fig. 27.1: Different technical terms.

- **Job evaluation:** A large amount of the collected data are analyzed and scrutinized to provide an overall judgment of merit or worth. Thus, according to Wigley, evaluation can be referred as a data reduction process to a judgment. Job evaluation comprises of systematic steps to compare the different jobs on the basis of their worth and merit. The orderly and systematic process determines the worth of a job to determine the rate of pay. Thus, there is a distinction between job analysis and job evaluation. The job analysis provides the preliminary data required for making job evaluation. The objective of job evaluation lies to determine the ratings for different jobs in an organization. Job evaluation establishes the value or the worth of different jobs in a job hierarchy and therefore provides for the basis of comparison of different jobs through the relative intrinsic values of jobs within an organization. The definitions for job evaluation as given by different prominent authors are described below.

Scott, Clothier and Priegel define job evaluation as "the operation of evaluating a particular job in relation to other jobs either within or outside the organization".

Dale Yoder described job evaluation as "a practice which seeks to provide a degree of objectivity in measuring the comparative value of jobs within an organization and among similar organizations".

Arthur A. Sloane described job evaluation as "any formalized system that attempts to determine the relative worth of different jobs in the organization so that jobs of greater value can be rewarded by greater pay".

According to the International Labour Organization (ILO), "job evaluation is an attempt to determine and compare the demands which the normal performance of a particular job makes on normal workers, without taking into account the individual abilities or performance of the workers concerned".

The British Institute of Management defines job evaluation as "the process of analysis and assessment of jobs to ascertain reliably their negative worth using the assessment as the basis for a balanced wage structure".

Wendell French defines job evaluation as "a process of determining the relative worth of the various jobs within the organization, so that differential wages may be paid to jobs of different worth. The relative worth of a job means relative value produced. The variables which are assumed to be related to value produced are such factors as responsibility, skill, effort and working conditions".

27.3 OBJECTIVES OF JOB EVALUATION

Ensuring an equitable remuneration in accordance with the relative merit or worth of a job is the main objective of job evaluation. The establishment of relative intrinsic values for different jobs in a given organization is the main objective of the majority of the systems of job evaluation. The different job evaluation systems in place determine the relative worth of a job as established on agreed logical basis. A number of factors play the role of deciding factor in describing and assessing the value of all jobs in an organization. However, the relative importance of these factors varies from job to job.

The different objectives as put in a systematic manner are listed below:

- A systematic and orderly process is established that determines the relative worth of different jobs in an organization.
- Equitable wage and remuneration are ensured for a job in an organization. Further, a reasonable wage differential between the different jobs is established in a hierarchical organization.
- A fair rate of pay is established for a job which is equitable to other jobs in the plant, industry or an organization.
- Wage inequalities if existing are eliminated.
- Incentives and different bonus plans could be established on the basis of the outcomes of the job evaluation.
- It provides a fair basis for the consideration of promotion and transfer for all the employees within the organization.
- The career planning of the different employees could be made using the job evaluation as a benchmark.

27.4 PRINCIPLES OF JOB EVALUATION

There are certain principles to job evaluation. A person involved in making job evaluation is required to keep these principles in mind before making any evaluation. The principles not only aid the job evaluator to evaluate the job properly but also provides clarity for the process of job evaluation to the different employees of the organization. The different principles for job evaluation according to Kress are as follows:

- The evaluation should be done both for the job and the performer of the job. The rating of each one of the elements of the job must be done on the basis of the requirement of the job, i.e., what it demands to get it done.
- The number of elements of a job must be few and should be explainable in terms. The elements for rating purposes should fulfill the necessary requisites for every job.
- There should be proper definition to each and every element of the job and should be selected properly.
- Participation of foreman in the ratings of the job should be motivated. This will lead to better coordination amongst the operators from different departments.
- The participation of different employees will ensure maximum co-operation to discuss job ratings
- Care should be taken not to adopt too many occupational wages in an organization. It would be unwise to adopt an occupational wage for each total of point values.

27.5 JOB EVALUATION CRITERIA

A total of eight factors go into the evaluation of system of job. A position is analyzed by these factors on the basis of the skills and performance required to perform it competently, the efforts demanded by a job and the overall structure and accountability involved. Value of the job is calculated on the basis of each one of the eight factors which provides a point rating. The sum total of these point ratings gives the total point value of the job.

27.5.1 Basic Evaluation Rules

Certain rules should be followed for evaluating each position. These are as follows:

- The current position is evaluated without being influenced by what the job is likely to be in the future or what it may have been in the past.
- It is the position that is evaluated and not the job holder. The assessment of each factor is based on the job being performed competently. The exercise of assessment of performance of the job holder is altogether a distinct exercise and is not involved in the scope of the job evaluating rating.

27.5.2 Job Evaluation Factors

Following factors are considered by the job evaluation system. In certain cases, the factors and their levels are defined with minor changes in the wordings. This is done to ensure a suitable understanding between the adopted methodology and the client's environment and culture. The minor changes are done ensuring that the inter-organization consistency is not organized. The primary factor in determining compensation is an evaluation of work performed. The different factors that are utilized for establishing the internal worth of a job are: Know-How, Problem Solving, Accountability, Education, Experience, Complexity involved in the job, Scope of job, Supervision received and, Authority Exercised.

- **Know-How:** The knowledge, skill and experience is required for standard acceptable performance. This factor considers the technical and professional skills required, the required experience and the planning and organizing demanded. It also considers the requirement to work with others or through others. Figure 27.2 depicts the three dimensions of Know-How.

Technical know-how	Measures levels ranging from learning basic work to specialized techniques and knowledge to professional mastery of scientific theory.
Managerial know-how	Measures the job's requirements to integrate diversified types of supervisory or managerial activities.
Human relation know-how	Measures the degree to which the job requires practical person-to-person skills in persuasion, motivation, and selection of people.

Fig. 27.2: Three dimensions of know-how.

- **Problem solving:** The factor of problem solving considers the amount of thinking required for analyzing, creating, evaluating, and reasoning for arriving at conclusions. Further, the extent to which this thinking is circumscribed by standards is also considered by this factor. Figure 27.3 shows the two dimensions of problem solving.

Thinking environment	The degree of structure provided by the job in solving problems.
Thinking challenge	It is the complexity of the problems in the job assignment and the amount of thinking required to solve job-related problems.

Fig. 27.3: Two dimensions to problem solving.

- **Accountability:** The extent to which an employee is held accountable for the action taken and its consequences is considered by accountability. It is the measured effect of the job on end results. The factor of accountability also considers the freedom of action by taking into account the different constraints by managers and the different committees. Figure 27.4 delineates the three dimensions of accountability.

Freedom to act	Measures the relative degree to which decisions can be made, the level of authority which is needed, or the precedents, policies and procedures which must be considered before an employee can take action.
Magnitude	It is the degree of influence a position has on the organizational operations.
Impact	It is the degree to which the job affects the organizational operations. Some jobs are directly responsible for actions while others provide counsel and advice, which is used by others to take action.

Fig. 27.4: Three dimensions of accountability.

- **Education:** A level of formal education is demanded by the performance of different functions of a position. The level of education expected of a new recruit is often advisable to be considered since there is often an overlap between education and experience.
- **Experience:** This factor considers the years of practical experience required. Further, the nature of technical and managerial familiarity required in addition to formal education is also taken into account by the factor of experience.
- **Complexity:** Measured in terms of:
  - The time taken to learn and adjust to specific job requirements.
  - The level to which the job functions are defined and follow established and predictable patterns.
  - The thinking challenge required to adapt to rapidly changing circumstances and innovative or conceptual thinking needed to initiate new corporate direction.
- **Scope of job:** The complexity and scope of work factors tend to be related to the education and experience level required of a position. The calculation of points for

each of these factors is based on the application of a percentage rating of the sum of the points derived in the evaluation of education and experience.

- **Supervision received:** The extent of supervision, direction or guidance imposed on the job holder and the freedom with which the executive has to take action.
- **Authority exercised:** Authority level expressed in terms of routine expenditure, capital expenditure and investments, granting of loans, hiring and firing staff, etc.

27.6 JOB EVALUATION PROCESS

Job evaluation is a technique to rank jobs in an organization on the basis of the duties and responsibilities assigned to the job. The job evaluation process results in a job being assigned to a pay grade. The pay grade is associated with a pay range that is defined by a minimum and a maximum pay rate. A model of job evaluation process with the following steps is presented below in Fig. 27.5.

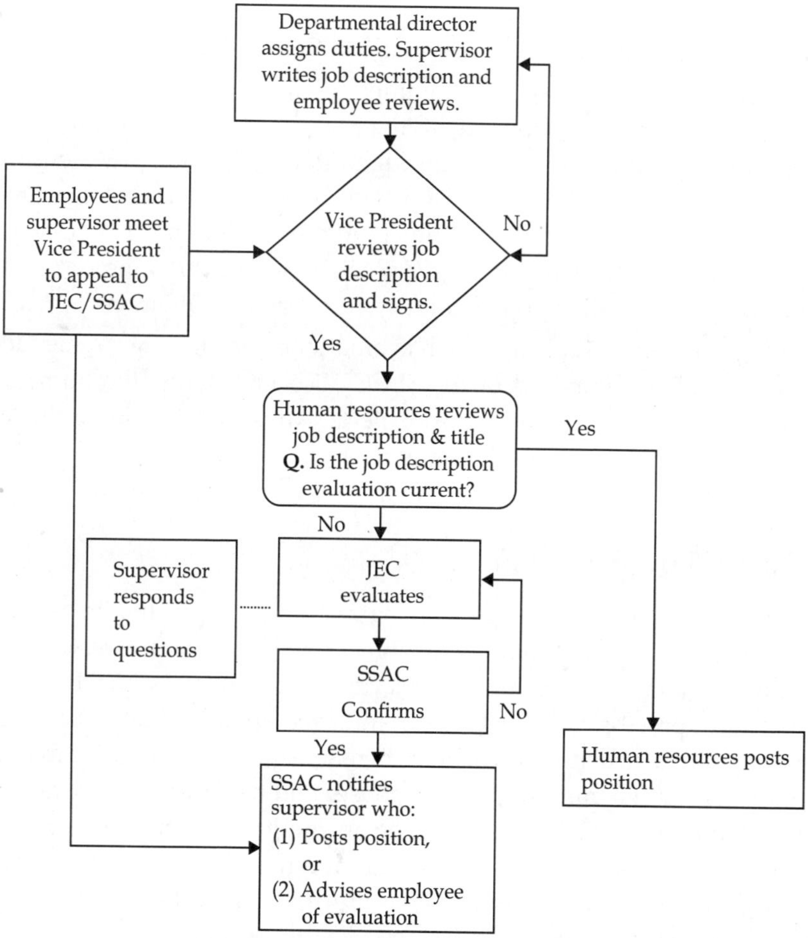

Fig. 27.5: Model of job evaluation process.

- **Job description:** The supervisor assigns duties and *writes* the job description. If there is an incumbent employee, s/he reviews it, and they both sign it. Instructions and additional assistance are available from Human Resources, if needed. The job description is a snapshot of the job as it presently exists, reflecting the current duties and responsibilities of the job and/or the incumbent.
- **Approval:** The vice president reviews job descriptions and, if s/he concurs, approves the responsibilities, requirements, and departmental organization contained within a job description presented for new evaluation, and signs it. If the vice president does not concur with the contents of the description, it is returned to the supervisor for changes.
- **Review:** Human Resources reviews the job description as submitted with the supervisor prior to evaluation by the Job Evaluation Committee. Human Resources help ensure that there is consistency and equity in the job descriptions and titles by editing them for clarity and format. If the Human Resources Office makes changes, the job description is returned to the supervisor and vice president for signature prior to being presented to the Job Evaluation Committee.
- **Evaluation:** The Job Evaluation Committee (JEC) is a multimember committee, the members of which are appointed by the Staff Salary Administration Committee (SSAC), representing employees throughout organization. JEC ensures equity among jobs through the use of established, consistent criteria for evaluation and prevents escalation of the job evaluation grades by validating changes in job content presented for review. Members of JEC receive in-depth training on job evaluation and utilize a consistently applied point system for the evaluations.
- **Confirmation:** SSAC confirms all job evaluations and titles recommended by JEC. This committee is composed of the SLCC Vice Presidents, the human resources director, and other relevant co-opted experts. After confirmation of the evaluation job description, SSAC advises the supervisor of the results of the evaluation and the title. The supervisor then advises the employee of the results of the job evaluation.

27.7 COMPUTERIZED JOB EVALUATION

Much of the time-consuming effort spent on maintaining a job evaluation program can be reduced by combining personal computers with job evaluation software. Computer-aided system simplifies the administration of job evaluation programs and provides a more expedient means of processing job evaluation information. Job data can be collected from supervisors by using a structured, machine-scoreable questionnaire. Computer software can be used to analyze the questionnaire responses and perform the job evaluation. With the advent of skill-based pay, which focuses on an employee's education, experience, and skills developed in programs, a computer program can update employee knowledge and skills as they are acquired. Pay adjustments are then made to reflect the employee's increased knowledge and skills.

28
Job Evaluation Method

28.1 INTRODUCTION

Job evaluation was defined as a process aimed at determining the relative worth or merit of a job. Job evaluation is a systematic process of establishing a basis to define the comparison between worth of different jobs. This eventually results in a wage structure that ensures equitable rates of pay to the different employees of the worker. The jobs are also compared on the basis of their content, the skills required and the responsibility involved. A job evaluation committee is involved in looking after the entire systematic process of job evaluation.

An array of methods for the systematic and planned job evaluation has been developed since 1920. However, many of these methods are not in use. The different job evaluation methods have a prime objective of establishing a ranking of different jobs on the basis of their relative worth so that an equitable pay rate can be ensured for the different jobs in the organization. The different ranking establishing methods can be broadly categorized into quantitative and non-quantitative methods.

The distinction for the two categories lies in the basis on which the jobs are ranked. In the case of non-quantitative methods, the jobs are compared as a whole with the other jobs while on the other hand in case of quantitative methods, the jobs are compared on the basis of certain selected key factors. Ranking and job classification or grading method are the most common non-quantitative methods whereas the most commonly used methods for quantitative category are the factor comparison and the point rating methods.

28.2 RANKING METHOD OF JOB EVALUATION

One of the simplest of all the non-quantitative methods is the ranking method. Some overall factor such as "job difficulty" is chosen as a basis to establish the ranking of each job relative to all the other jobs. The process initiates by comparing each job as a whole with the other and the process is continued till the evaluation and ranking of all the jobs is accomplished. The ranking is established in the order of their importance from simplest to hardest and from highest to lowest. The responsibilities, duties and demands on the job holder dictate to establish the importance of order of different jobs in an organization. The procedural steps taken to establish the order of importance are mentioned below:

- **Obtain job information:** Analysis of the job is the first step. The rankings are made on the basis of job descriptions prepared for each job.
- **Select raters and jobs to be rated:** The ranking procedure usually involves ranking of different jobs by department or in the form of clusters like that of clerical workers, factory workers, etc. This eliminates the cumbersome task to ranking all the jobs, at a time and hence the need to compare the jobs directly.
- **Select compensable factors:** The ranking for different jobs in this method can be established on the basis of just a single factor. However the ranking is done for the whole job. Also it is advisable to provide the definition of the factor(s) to the evaluators regardless of the number of factors considered. This ensures a consistent evaluation of all the jobs.
- **Rank jobs:** The ranking of jobs is the next step. Each rater is given a set of index cards. The description of each job is carried by the index cards. The ranking is done for the cards from lowest to highest.
- **Combine rating:** It is a usual practice to have ranking for different jobs from different raters individually. On the basis of similarity of duties, responsibilities, skills and the required knowledge, the division of all the ranked jobs is done into appropriate groups. The jobs receiving the same wage are the ones that fall within a particular group or classification. The rating committee then performs the task to average the ranking.

Merits: The advantages that the ranking method carries in terms of procedure, involvement of resources and operational mechanisms are listed below:

- The ranking method is one of the simplest methods.
- To put the method in effect is quite economical.
- The time involved and the paper work is less.

Demerits: Considering the validity and reliability, the following demerits of the ranking method have been established:

- There are no standards for the judgment.
- There is no process to differentiate between different jobs.
- The method suffers from sheer unmanageability with the increase in number of jobs to be evaluated.

28.3 JOB CLASSIFICATION OR GRADING METHOD

The job classification or the grading method is another simple and widely used method. There were no yardstick values in case of the ranking method, however in case of the job classification or grading method there is one such yardstick constituting of job grades. In this method too, the jobs are measured as whole jobs. The job grades or classes are established are established by an authorized committee or body. A collection of jobs that are similar in difficulty level, requiring similar skills constitutes a job grade. The information derived from job analysis forms the basis of determination of job grades. Depending on the type of jobs offered by the organization, job grades may include skilled, unskilled, laboratory assistant, office superintendent, account clerk and so on.

Jobs can be categorized in different ways. One such way to categorize the job is "class description". In this classification scheme, the jobs are categorized on the basis of their description to these correspondences. Another way is to develop certain rules for a class and then on the basis of these specific rules different jobs can be categorized into different classes. The usual way adopts to consider certain compensable factors and then according to the amount or level of compensable factors in jobs, the classes or grades description are established. Some of the compensable factors are:

- The variety and the associated difficulty level with work
- The amount of supervision received and exercised
- Judgment exercised
- The purpose and nature of interpersonal work relationships
- Responsibility
- Experience
- The amount of knowledge required.

The different steps that are generally adopted in the process of job classification are:

- To obtain information regarding the job, job description is prepared for each job.
- To identify the different levels of job, job grading description is established. The preparation of the grading description should be done in a manner to ensure that each grade level established is distinct from the grade level adjacent to it. Then on the basis of complexity of duties, responsibilities both supervisory and non-supervisory, each job is assigned to the grade classes established.
- Around 10 to 20 jobs spanning over major departments and functions, and all the grades are classified for the different grades selected.
- The key jobs are then graded. Appropriate grade levels are chosen to categorize the different key jobs. Further, their relationship to each other is also studied.
- The classification of different jobs is accomplished on the basis of grade definitions. All the jobs that fall into a particular grade are entitled to same wages. For instance, clerks can be classified into one class, junior officers in another class and top executives in the top class.

Figure 28.1 below gives an example of job description.

Grades	Job classification
Head clerk	Those handling or capable of taking a major decision on the work they do; complicated work requiring much independent thinking; able to consider details outside the control.
Senior clerk	Technically varied work, occasionally independent thinking and action due to difficult work which requires exceptional clerical ability and extensive knowledge of principles and fundamentals of the business of its department.
Clerical grade III	Pure routine concentration, speed and accuracy, works under supervision; may be held responsible for supervision.
Clerical grade II	No supervision by others, especially skilled for the job by having an exhaustive knowledge of the details.
Clerical grade I	Must have the characteristic of a second class clerk and assume more responsibilities.

Fig. 28.1: Description of job classification.

Merits: There are number of merits of the job classification method. These merits are discussed below:

- The method is relatively simpler to operate and easy to understand.
- The method is suitable for small organizations as it is economical.
- The problem of pay determination is made easier to administer.
- The job classification method is mainly useful for Government jobs.

Demerits: The method also associates with itself a number of demerits. Some of these are listed below:

- The personal bias of the committee members is one of the main hurdles to the method.
- The method is not suitable for jobs of complex nature.
- The employment of the method in different industries is rare.
- It is difficult to know how much of a job's rank is influenced by the man on the job.

28.4 POINT RATING METHOD

Evaluation of the compensable factors for each job is made by the point rating method. The point rating method involves a more detailed analytical and quantitative approach to measurement of job work. Different identifiable factors such as effort, knowledge, skills, responsibilities, hazards and so on, are used as a basis for breaking down the jobs into components. Each factor is assigned points. Depending on the importance that each factor associates with the performance of a job, weights are assigned to each of the factors. The addition of the points allocated to different factors of a job is performed. The jobs that have similar total points are placed in similar pay grades. The total sum obtained for a job forms a basis to compare different jobs in an organization.

The point rating system consists of six steps. The method is usually implemented by a job evaluation committee or by an individual analyst. The different steps are discussed below:

- **Determine critical factors:** For allocation of points, the main factors that are considered by the point rating method are:
  - Safety of other
  - Equipment or materials
  - Assisting trainees
  - Production or service quality
- **Determine the levels of factors:** Several levels are associated with each factor considered for providing the basis for ranking. This is because of the reason that the factors may vary from job to job. The analyst is then provided with an option to reward different degrees of skills, responsibility and other important factors.
- **Allocate points to sub-factors:** A point method matrix results from the factors listed down side and the levels placed across the top. Maximum possible points are awarded to each sub-factor by the job evaluation committee starting with highest level. The precise assignment of weights to each element or component of a job is ensured by the committee.
- **Allocate points to levels:** The points are allocated across each level signifying the importance of different levels. The task of allocation is done after the points have been allocated at the highest level.
- **Develop a points manual:** A point manual is prepared by the analysts. A written explanation for each job element is carried by the point manual. It outlines the expectations for the various levels of each sub-factor. This information is needed to assign jobs to their appropriate levels.
- **Apply the point system:** The relative value of each job is determined through the prepared point matrix. The process is subjective in nature. The job descriptions are compared by the specialists using the prepared point manual. The level and points for each sub-factor of every job is revealed through the comparison made between the job description and the point manual statement.

Merits: The method of point rating has certain advantages associated with it.

- The point rating method is one of the most accurate and comprehensive method of job evaluation.
- The method is subjective and as such human judgment is minimized.
- Many organizations favour this method because of it being a systematic method.
- The scales developed in this method can be used for a long time.
- The classification of jobs into different categories is easy.

Demerits: The method has some disadvantages as listed below:

- The method is time consuming.
- The point rating method is expensive too.
- It is complex and is therefore difficult for an average worker to understand.
- The amount of clerical work involved is high.
- The point rating method is not suitable for managerial jobs wherein the work content is not measurable in quantitative terms.

Figure 28.2 shows the points rating method matrix.

Compensible or critical factors	Levels			
	Minimum 1	Low II	Moderate III	High IV
1. Responsibility				
(a) Safety of other	25	50	75	100
(b) Equipment and materials	20	40	60	80
(c) Assisting trainees	5	20	35	50
(d) Product/service quality	20	40	60	80
2. Skills				
(a) Experience	45	90	135	180
(b) Education/training	25	50	75	100
3. Efforts				
(a) Physical	25	50	75	100
(b) Mental	35	70	105	150
4. Working conditions				
(a) Unpleasant	20	40	60	80
(b) Hazardous	20	40	60	80
Total points				1000

Fig. 28.2: Points rating method matrix.

28.5 FACTORS COMPARISON METHOD

The factor comparison method is a combination of both the point rating and rating methods. The jobs are ranked by comparing them with one another. The analysis is made by breaking jobs into compensable factors. The positions that can be evaluated through this system are white collar, managerial and professional positions. The following steps are taken into account for carrying out job evaluation under this method:

- **Determine the compensable factors:** The factors that are common and important in a broad range are decided first by the analysts. Some of the factors critical to evaluation of the jobs are responsibility, mental efforts, skills, physical efforts and so on. Different factors are used by different organizations for different positions.
- **Determine key jobs:** There are certain jobs that are common in an organization and also critical to the employer's market. Therefore, these jobs known as key jobs, should be selected properly. Some jobs known as common jobs are reselected since the evaluation of market rates is easier for such kind of jobs. Typically, 10-25 key jobs are selected by the committee.

- **Allocation of present wages for key jobs:** The job evaluation committee then allocates a part of each key job's current wage rate to each critical factor. The proportion wage assigned to each of the different compensable factors depends on the importance of the factor.
- The base rate is agreed upon by the company.
- **Place key jobs on a factor comparison chart:** Once the wage rates are assigned to the compensable factors of each key job, this information is transferred to a factor comparison chart. Key job titles are placed in the factor columns according to the rate of wages assigned to the job for each critical factor.
- **Evaluate other jobs:** The titles of key jobs in each column of the factor comparison chart serve as benchmarks; other non-key jobs are then evaluated by fitting them in the rate scale under each factor column.

Merits: The factors comparison method has several advantages.

- It is a more objective method of job evaluation.
- The method is flexible as there is no upper limit on the rating.
- It is fairly an easy method to explain to employees.
- The use of limited number of factors (usually five) ensures less chances of overlapping and over-weighting of factors.
- It facilitates determining the relative worth of different jobs.

Demerits: The factors comparison method also has some disadvantages.

- It is expensive and time-consuming method.
- Using the same five factors for evaluating jobs may not always be appropriate because jobs differ across and within organizations.
- It is difficult to understand and operate.

28.6 ADVANTAGES OF JOB EVALUATION

According to the International Labour Organization, job evaluation offers the following advantages:

- Job evaluation being a logical process and objective technique helps in developing equitable and consistent wage and salary structure based on the relative worth of jobs in an organization.
- By eliminating wage differentials within the organization, job evaluation helps to minimize conflict between labour unions and management and, in turn, helps to promote harmonious relations between them.
- Job evaluation simplifies wage administration by establishing uniformity in wage rates.
- It provides a logical basis for wage negotiations and collective bargaining.
- In the case of new jobs, job evaluation facilitates spotting them into the existing wage and salary structure.

- In the modern times of mechanization, performance depends much on the machines than on the worker himself/herself. In such cases, job evaluation provides the realistic basis for determination of wages.
- The information generated by job evaluation may also be used for improvement of selection, transfer and promotion procedures on the basis of comparative job requirements.
- Job evaluation rates the job, not the workers. Organizations have large number of jobs with specializations. It is job evaluation here again which helps in rating all these jobs and determining the wages and salary and also removing ambiguity in them

28.7 LIMITATIONS/DRAWBACKS OF JOB EVALUATION

In spite of many advantages, job evaluation suffers from the following drawbacks/ limitations:

- Job evaluation is susceptible because of human error and subjective judgment. While there is no standard list of factors to be considered for job evaluation, there are some factors that cannot be measured accurately.
- There is a variation between wages fixated through job evaluation and market forces. The jobs which tend to rate high as compared with the market are those of junior nurse and typist, while craft rates are relatively low (Kerr & Fisher). Weaker groups are better served by an evaluation plan than by the market, the former places the emphasis not on force but on equity.
- When job evaluation is applied for the first time in an organization, it creates doubts in the minds of workers whose jobs are evaluated and trade unions that it may do away with collective bargaining for fixing wage rates.
- Job evaluation methods lacking in scientific basis are often looked upon as suspicious about the efficacy of methods of job evaluation.
- Job evaluation is a time consuming process requiring specialized technical personnel to undertake it and, thus, is likely to be costly also.
- Job evaluation is not found suitable for establishing the relative worth of the managerial jobs which are skill-oriented. But, these skills cannot be measured in quantitative terms.
- Given the changes in job contents and work conditions, frequent evaluation of jobs is essential. This is not always so easy and simple.
- Job evaluation leads to frequent and substantial changes in wage and salary structures. This, in turn, creates financial burden on organizations.

29
Wages

29.1 THEORIES OF WAGES

According to Henry George, profit is earned by the employer and as far as the payment of wages to the labourer is concerned, it can be described as a return to a labourer of the portion the employer has received from the labourer. As far as the employer is concerned, the wages received by him is the portion of the capital produced by the labourer. Wages are a direct result of the labour itself. Thus, the return that is received by the employee in exchange of labour is known as wages received. The payment of wages may be in terms of goods and services, but is generally in terms of money.

The term wages in a broad sense implies to anything received in lieu of labour. There is a minute distinction between salary and wages. The wages are paid to the employee in proportion to the hours of labour that is put into a work; permanent form of income in the sense that it is made monthly rather than by hour.

There is a wide array of definitions for the term wages and different terminologies used according to different theories of wages. For instance, wages are referred to as nominal wages and are well distinguished from the real wages in economic theory about wages. Different theories of wages are discussed in the proceeding sections.

- **Subsistence theory of wages - iron law of wages:** There have been a number of theories on wages. The subsistence theory of wages was amongst the first of all the theories to explain and define the nature of wages. The theory is also known as the iron law of wages. David Ricardo was one of the main exponents of the theory. According to the theory, it is the subsistence levels of the workers around which the wages cluster. There will be increase in the number of workers if the wage rate is much above the subsistence level. The increase in number of workers will lead to competition which, in turn, leads to reduction of wage rates towards the cost of subsistence. However, if the wages are much below the subsistence level then there will be decrease in the size of the working population and in this case, the competition will raise the wages until it reaches the subsistence level again.
- **Surplus value theory:** The surplus value theory was propounded by Karl Marx. According to this theory, anything that is produced by the worker in excess of what

is paid in wages is known as surplus value. The capitalist's profit is constituted by this surplus value extracted from a worker. The wages according to the wage-fund theory are extracted from the fixed fund capital. There would be decrease in the amount available for payment to workers if there is a withdrawal of excess fund owing to the union pressure or through legislation. The increase in wages to workers has to be made from the profits and therefore the decline in wages to workers truly signifies the decline in savings, the savings from which the wage fund is derived.

- **Marginal Productivity Theory:** According to the marginal productivity theory, the wage payment to the workers will be equivalent to the amount of extra value added to the whole product by the workers. The bargaining theory on the other hand also considers other factors such as laws and political changes affecting the basic wages and therefore modifies the marginal productivity theory. It also acknowledges the basic assumptions of equal bargaining power of employee and employer, mobility of labour, etc., characterizing the marginal productivity theory.
- **Orthodox Labour Wage Theory:** According to the classical labour theory, the equilibrium in labour market is self-adjusting and minimal. Alan Stuart considers this simple assumption and presents a review of the orthodox labour wage theory. Stuart also considers some other alternatives.

  A simple model constituting rational individual firms and the operators or workers within the organization is reflective of the labour market equilibrium in economic analysis. In such an equilibrium environment, the workers being recognized as economic agents try to maximize their utility and try to come to terms with the market clearing wage and employment level.

  On the other hand, the wage rates are adjusted in the case where there is shock to labour supply or demand. The adjustment is done in a manner that the wage rate reaches the competitive Walrasian equilibrium.

  The consideration of labour as a tradable economic commodity is ignored by the simple model of marginal productive theory. Recently, the attention has been shifted to other sub-optimal methods and the assumptions underlying the orthodox wage theory has been relaxed.
- **Cobweb Theory:** Cobweb theory is one of the more advanced methods that have been adapted by the labour economists for assessing the labour supply adjustment. According to cobweb theory, any aberration to the labour demand curve leads to fluctuation of prices in a "cobweb" pattern. The fluctuation exists until the long-run equilibrium is achieved. There will be in effect a vertical short-run labour supply when there is a shortage of labour owing to the demand. The increased wage rate will lead to an increase in the number of workers who are willing to work. This will eventually fill the market. There is rightward shift in the vertical run supply as a result of the supply response. However, with the increasing supply and given that the quantity of workers required is fixed; there will be a surplus of workers. The

surplus is eliminated from the market by dropping the wages. There will be once again labour shortage at some point of time leading to wage cycle until long-run equilibrium is reached again.

The labour adjustment as defined by this model utilizes adaptive expectations while disregarding the rational expectations. The model is well applicable to the markets requiring heavy investments in training time and human capital. However, besides these industries, the model has lost its applicability in the other efficient labour markets.

- **Efficiency Wage Theories:** The source of imperfections in the market and the involuntary unemployment in the internal labour and dual labour market theory lies in the costs involved in human capital and the affected wage levels because of the influence from the employees within the organization. The source of profitability in case of the efficiency wage models is the asymmetric information between firms and its employees. The efficiency wage model analyzes how to pay wage above the market rate in order to optimize the marginal revenue product of labour which will be in firms' best interest.

  The phenomenon has been explained by a number of different microeconomic underpinnings. The organization or the firm may be prompted to pay an additional wage to counter the threat of shrinkage on the job. The increased wage rate will aid in eliminating any moral hazard of the employee in the form of dishonesty. This will also lead to the improvement in the general morale of workers in the firm. The Stoft's cheat-threat theory is the corollary of this argument. According to the cheat-threat theory, the thoughts of dishonest behaviour in the situations of economy nearing full employment will be less serious in case the employees are paid extra.

  A more sophisticated argument is that of the adverse selection. The firms pay an efficiency wage to attract more workers. The firms in doing so assume that workers' abilities and dependability are correlated positively to their reservation wages. The employees stand a chance of being regarded as 'lemons' by firms if the workers underbid the notion of efficiency wages. This will render the workers to become involuntarily unemployed. A sociological model was suggested by Akerlof to counter the lack of willingness by some of the American firms to fire the unproductive workers. The model is based upon raising the standards of group work norms by above equilibrium wages that defies neo-classical wage theory.

  Another explanation as described by Leibenstein says that the workers in particular of less developed nations and especially of the agrarian sector labour should be paid above the marginal product to be well-fed and clothed. These beings zero in many of the other sectors.

  All the different wage models even in the absence of institutionalism structures, account for the Pareto sub-optimal equilibrium.

29.2 THE WAGE STRUCTURE

The determination of the wage rates for the different jobs in the organization is done through the wage structure. It combines the external marketplace considered in the pay level decision with the relative value that different jobs have to the organization. The job evaluation decides on the value of the job which, in turn, relies on the job analysis to provide the information for making the appropriate analysis. The wage structure integrates the market value and the organizational value of the job. The different grades or job levels are defined by the wage structure in place and the jobs are then assigned wage rates to those grades by reference to market rates.

Wage Structure Concepts

The wage and salary rates in most of the organizations are still assigned to jobs. The organizations make pay level decisions, i.e., how much is to be paid and the pay structure decisions. Both the decisions are made simultaneously. However, the processes that are required in reaching these decisions require separate treatment. Wage relationships of all types are represented by wage structures. The issues of wage structures are dealt through the analysis of wage differentials of any kind (geographic, industry, community, or occupation). However, the primary concern within an organization is that of pay decisions and therefore the concern is with the pay difference between the jobs.

The decision makers are truly in control of the decisions regarding the wage relationships among jobs within an organization. The external forces usually influence the wage level decisions more than the decisions regarding the wage structure.

There are certain organizations where payment to the employee depends on the skillset possessed by the employee rather than on the jobs being held by the employees. However, continual skill shortages are experienced by the organization and therefore it is the job held by the employees that dictates the skill sets for measuring the contributions. The rationale is usually serious and continual skill shortages experienced by the organization.

One of the interesting features of the compensation decisions of an organization is the ability to retain the employees through the elimination of element of dissatisfaction and providing for the encouragement of the employee through the different pay level decisions. The wage structure decisions are thus aimed at encouraging employees to make a career with the organization.

Determinants of the Wage Structure

- **Economic determinants:** The occupational wage differentials according to Adam Smith, could be explained in the terms of the following components:
  - The amount of difficulty involved in a job
  - The difficulty involved in learning the job

- ○ The degree of stability of employment
- ○ The responsibility involved in a job
- ○ The chances of failure or success in the work.

This is a theory of wage structure. The complexity involved in the wage structure decisions could easily be explained through Adam's standards of worth. The price that an item brings in a market in a situation where the demand and supply are equal is known as the market value of an item. The value that the buyer or seller anticipates by analyzing the functions of an item is the use value of the item. The use value of an item will vary amongst individuals and also with the time.

- **Job worth:** The important differences amongst the employers in the decisions to wage structure could be well established through the concept of worth and the concept of internal labour markets. The organizations making use of the market value are the ones that fill their jobs from outside. In other words, one can say that such organizations have relatively open internal labour markets. The wage and salary surveys are utilized by such organizations in making the wage structure decisions. On the other hand, the concept of use value is emphasized by the organizations filling their jobs from inside, i.e., organizations with relatively closed internal labour markets.
- **Training:** The primary factor in the human capital analysis and therefore the job worth is the requirements demanded by training in terms of difficulty, length and also on the source of training, i.e., employers, society or the individuals. Different job values are yielded through the interaction between the ability and training requirements. This depends on the required scarcity of the ability and the number of people who try to make it in the occupation and fail.
- **Employee tastes:** Another important economic factor is the taste and preference of an employee. There is a difference in opinion of the people liking and disliking their occupation. There are numerous disadvantages as well as non-monetary advantages associated with a job. The occupational choice is strongly influenced by the expectation of the workers towards future earnings. In the same manner, the labour supplies are influenced too. Unfortunately, the information pertaining to the labour market is far from perfect. Further, the response is more prompt to labour market shortages than that to the oversupplies.
- **Unions:** The wage structures are also affected by the type of union, i.e., craft union or industrial union as reflected by the economic analysis. The favour is towards absolute increase of wages by the industrial unions which consists of heavy proportions of semiskilled members. However, an industrial union may consist of a highly differentiated wage structure. This is true for the organizations where the employees are representatives of the industrial unions. Further, such industrial unions pay less attention to percentage differentials in comparison to the craft unions.

- **Social determinants:** The pre-established status distribution in the society plays the major role in setting of wages according to the just-price theory. A systematic regulation of the wages was required to keep each class in its customary place in the society. The just-price theory laid emphasis on the equity, tying of wages to the status and the preservation of the customary relationships. The marketing forces generally operate to low differentials owing to the fact that the social forces play a crucial role in deciding what is customary and accepted. The slow response of supply to price is one of the main reasons of the predomination of the social forces. The effect of raising pay by the supply shortages is more effective in comparison to the supply surpluses lowering the pay.
- **Organizational determinants:** The jobs developed by the organization are with the sole purpose of getting their work done. A special economic meaning could be attached to labour services only in relation to the particular jobs in which they are performed. The organization in our economic system plays a vital role in designing a job and then selecting the employees to fill these created jobs. Thus one of the major sources of contribution of an employee is towards the jobs created by the organization which is also their primary determinant for their rewards.

  The different organizations are structuring the labour market with the help of the jobs created and the pay decisions about them. Different organizations differing in technology, competitive economics, management competence and objective bargaining are involved in designing and thus creating jobs. Therefore, it is quite obvious that there will be difference in the job created by one organization and the other. The decisions going into the creation of jobs are subject to revisions with the changing market conditions and technology.

29.3 WAGE FIXATION

The wage fixing process over the last decade has absorbed the notion that the increase in the pay is directly linked to the productivity. Thus the pay fixing system is based on the underlying principle that the pay in the wages cannot be contemplated without offsetting the productivity. An increased pay is suggestive of the increased productivity. Therefore, increased productivity provides a sufficient justification for the increased pay. The enterprise agreement encapsulates the link between productivity and pay which suggests that the increased pay is a result of specific changes in the work practices. The productivity models are put in place in different cases that provide an automatic link between the pay and the increased productivity. The changes in work practices lead to increased productivity. However, it is disadvantageous as well since it would be considered only a factor and sufficient one for increases in the pay.

The three categories in which the wage fixing can be categorized are:

- The basic 'minimum wage' provides for bare subsistence and is at the level of poverty line.

- The second falls in the category of the 'fair wage' which is little above the 'minimum wage'.
- The last category is that of the 'living wage' which provides for the basic level.

However, clear demarcation of the above levels of the wage structure is not possible.

The first basic principle regarding the wage structure decisions is that a minimum wage is mandatory to be paid by the organization irrespective of the extent of the profits, the availability of workers at lower wage rates and the financial condition of the organization or the firm. The minimum wage thus applies to all the industries, both big and small. Thus, a lowest limit is set that ensures that the wages cannot sink below the specified limit whatever may be the circumstances.

The fairness of the wages is the second principle. Thus, the wages must be sufficiently high to provide the family with shelter, food, medical care, and clothing and ensure education to the children. However, the wage provided should not exceed the wage earning capacity in the class of establishment to which a worker belongs.

The earning capacity and the workload are the two main factors relating to the fair wages. However, a fair wage must not be confused with the living wage. The living wage not only ensures the fairness in the wage and provides for the essentials mentioned for the fair wage but is wage that would provide for the frugal comfort with an ability to provide for old age and evil days.

29.4 WAGE PAYMENT

There are four statutes that regulate the payment of wages in India.

- The Payment of Wages Act, 1936
- The Minimum Wages Act, 1948
- The Equal Remuneration Act, 1976
- The Inter-State Migrant Workmen (Regulation of Employment and Conditions of Service) Act, 1979

The Payment of Wages Act, 1936

The Government of India wrote to the local governments in 1926, to clearly understand the position with regard to the delay of payment in wages to a person employed in an organization. The information collected was placed before the Royal Commission on Labour appointed in 1929. The Payment of Wages Bill, 1933 was introduced as a result of the report of the Commission, Government of India. This was re-circulated in the legislative assembly to elicit opinions. The bill lapsed after a motion was tabled in favour of the bill to a select committee and the motion couldn't be passed. On 15th February, 1935 the Payment of Wages Bill was introduced after a thorough revision of the earlier bill. The Bill was based on the principles on which the earlier bill was based. The select committee presented its report and incorporated the recommendations and again introduced the Bill in 1935 in the legislative assembly which was passed.

The Minimum Wages Act, 1948

The lower level of wages, substantially low for certain labour in certain organizations in comparison to the wages paid in the industries for similar nature and amount of labour gave rise to the concept of minimum wages.

A draft convention on the minimum wages was adopted by the International Labour Conference of the International Labour Organization in 1928 at Geneva. The Convention asked the member nations to put in place a mechanism that would ensure minimum wage rates for the workers employed in different industries. This was to be especially adopted for workers employed in industries where wages were exceptionally low and industries lacked an efficient mechanism for regulating the wages. Assurance of every effort to ensure the payment of standard wages was made at the Preparatory Asian Regional Labour Conference of International Labour Organization held at New Delhi in 1947 and then at the 3rd session of the Asian Regional Labour Conference.

Thus, the need of it was thus during the World War II that the fixation of minimum wages in India received impetus. This was undertaken to ensure the protection of the interests of the immobilized personnel in hunt of employment in industries. A Bill to provide for machinery for fixing and revision of minimum wages was prepared and discussed at the 7th session of the Indian Labour Conference in November, 1945. It was introduced in the Central Legislative Assembly on 11th April, 1946.

The Equal Remuneration Act, 1976

The Constitution of India - Part IV relating to the Directive Principles of State Policy - Article 39 envisages that the State shall direct its policy, among other things, towards securing that there is equal pay for equal work for both men and women. In order to give effect to this provision, in the year which was being celebrated as the International Women's Year, President of India promulgated the Equal Remuneration Ordinance, 1975.

On 26th September, 1975 to provide for the payment of equal remuneration to men and women workers and for the prevention of discrimination, on the grounds of sex, against women in the matter of employment. To replace the said Ordinance of 1975, the Equal Remuneration Bill was introduced in the parliament.

29.5 SALARY ADMINISTRATION

Determining appropriate compensation for an incumbent in an administrative and professional (A&P) position is left largely to the discretion of the administrative superior of that position. Salary administration for A&P positions is not subject to the same constraints as those for classified positions. Appropriate compensation levels and ranges are determined by the administrative superior of these positions based on his or her subjective assessment of the position, the variety of activities required to successfully fill the position, the relevant marketplace for incumbents of such positions, and a variety of other subjective variables.

Procedure

- **Initial appointment:** The total compensation to be offered to an individual assuming an A&P position will be specified in his or her appointment letter upon initial appointment. Many academic A&P positions may encompass duties other than administrative duties (e.g., teaching, research, clinical service). In negotiating terms of employment with the academic A&P employee, the administrative superior will discuss and document the relative proportions of duties and will note the amount of compensation that is associated with the administrative aspects of the position. The amount of compensation that is associated with the administrative aspects of the position will be in addition to the negotiated rate of compensation associated with the teaching, research, or clinical service aspects of the position. This additional compensation will be stated in both the institutional operating budget and his or her annual appointment letter.

  Retaining the administrative portion of total compensation will depend on continued incumbency in the specific A&P position and may be proportionally reduced upon a change in present time appointment or administrative duties, or discontinued should the incumbent change jobs within the institution. In those situations in which the duties for the A&P employee are proportioned among administrative duties and teaching, research, or clinical service activities, salary increases will be awarded proportionally as long as the conditions of the original appointment are in effect.

- **Salary increases:** Requests for salary increases for A&P employees are normally submitted as part of departmental and/or operating unit budget requests and may be approved as such to take effect at the beginning of each fiscal year. Requests for salary increases outside this process are made to the chief through the head of the affected organizational unit and are subject to budgetary constraints as well as approval by the administration.

  Promotions or reclassification from one A&P position to another may also be requested and accomplished through the operational budget process. Requests for such actions outside this process should be made to the chief through the head of the affected operating unit. They are subject to salary constraints as well as approval by UT System administration when necessary.

- **Merit awards:** Merit awards are provided to recognize truly extraordinary job performance and productivity that are well above and beyond that normally expected. The actual salary percentage associated with a merit award will be determined by the management each time such awards become available; however, merit awards should not exceed ten per cent of base salary. Requests for exceptions should be directed to the Manager, Human Resources.

  A lump sum merit is a one-time award, not added to base pay that can be awarded to an employee for meritorious job performance. Meritorious job performance is defined as either consistently high level of job performance over a sustained period of time; or successful completion of an assigned project that had a significant positive impact on the department. Documentation must be provided and a copy maintained in the employee's personnel file within the department concerning the specific nature of this activity and its impact.

The criteria that follow, apply to either type of merit award; all criteria must be met in order for such actions to be processed:

- The amount of either type of merit award can be in any amount up to 10 per cent of the employee's current base salary.
- An employee may receive only one of each type of merit award per fiscal year. The total amount for merit awards of either type cannot exceed 10 per cent in a fiscal year.
- An employee cannot be guaranteed in advance a payment of a lump sum merit for achieving performance targets.
- An A&P employee must have completed six months of continuous service with the management prior to any merit award increase.
- At least six months must have elapsed since the employee's last salary change or transfer from another department before a lump sum merit can be awarded.
- A current written performance appraisal conducted within the last twelve months must be on file.
- Lump sum merits can be awarded anytime during the fiscal year and must be in accordance with payroll guidelines.
- Lump sum merits are subject to availability of funds.
- A lump sum merit may be paid from any fund source. Payment from a grant fund will be up to each individual granting agency.

- **Administrative supplement:** A temporary administrative pay supplement may be given to an A&P employee under certain circumstances. An administrative pay supplement is defined as a temporary pay supplement paid at the discretion of the designated budgetary official for specific situations when an employee assumes substantial, additional responsibilities on an interim basis for an extended period of time, generally not to exceed one year. The temporary pay supplement is discontinued when the employee is no longer responsible for the additional responsibilities.
- **Salary adjustment:** As a guideline, salary adjustments should not be greater than 10 per cent of the A&P employee's current salary. Should it be found that a salary adjustment greater than 10 per cent be required, HR Compensation should be consulted.

SECTION X
INDUSTRIAL LEGISLATION

30
Industrial Legislation

30.1 NEED FOR INDUSTRIAL LEGISLATION

Labour legislation that is adapted to the economic and social challenges plays three crucial roles:

- It establishes a legal system that facilitates productive individual and collective employment relationships, and therefore a productive economy.
- By providing a framework within which employers, workers and their representatives can interact with regard to work-related issues. It serves as an important vehicle for achieving harmonious industrial relations based on workplace democracy.
- It provides a clear and constant reminder and guarantee of fundamental principles and rights at work which have received broad social acceptance and establishes the processes through which these principles and rights can be implemented and enforced.

But experience shows that labour legislation can only fulfill these functions effectively if it is responsive to the conditions of the labour market and the needs of the parties involved. The most efficient way of ensuring that these conditions and needs are taken fully into account is if those concerned are closely involved in the formulation of the legislation through processes of social dialogue. The involvement of stakeholders in this way is of great importance in developing a broad basis of support for labour legislation and in facilitating its application within and beyond the formal structured sectors of the economy.

30.2 THE FACTORIES ACT, 1948

Objectives of the Act

- To ensure adequate safety measures and to promote the health and welfare of the workers employed in factories.
- To prevent haphazard growth of factories through the provisions related to the approval of plans before the setting up of a factory.

Applicability of the Act

- Applicable to the whole of India including Jammu & Kashmir.
- Covers all manufacturing processes and establishments falling within the definition of 'factory'.
- Applicable to all factories using power and employing 10 or more workers, and if not using power, employing 20 or more workers on any day of the preceding 12 months.

Scheme of the Act

The Act consists of 120 Sections and 3 Schedules.

- Schedule 1 contains list of industries involving hazardous processes.
- Schedule 2 is about the permissible level of certain chemical substances in work environment.
- Schedule 3 consists of list of modifiable diseases.

Important Provisions of the Act

Facilities and Conveniences

- The factory should be kept clean.
- There should be arrangement to dispose of wastes and effluents. Ventilation should be adequate.
- Reasonable temperature for comfort of employees should be maintained.
- Dust and fumes should be controlled below the permissible limits.
- Artificial humidification should be at prescribed standard level.
- Overcrowding should be avoided.
- Adequate lighting, drinking water, latrines, urinals and spittoons should be provided.

Welfare

- Adequate facilities for washing, sitting, storing clothes when not worn during working hours.
- If a worker has to work in standing position, sitting arrangement to take short rests should be provided.
- Adequate first-aid boxes should be provided and maintained.

Facilities in case of large factories: Following facilities are required to be provided by large factories:

- Ambulance room if 500 or more workers are employed.
- Canteen if 250 or more workers are employed. It should be sufficiently lighted and ventilated and suitably located.
- Rest rooms/shelters with drinking water when 150 or more workmen are employed.

- Crèches if 30 or more women workers are employed.
- Full-time welfare officer if factory employs 500 or more workers.
- Safety officer if 1000 or more workmen are employed.

Safety

- All machinery should be properly fenced to protect workers when machinery is in motion.
- Hoists and lifts should be in good condition and tested periodically.
- Pressure plants should be checked as per rules.
- Floor, stairs and means of access should be of sound construction and free from obstructions.
- Safety appliances for the eyes, dangerous dusts, gas, and fumes should be provided.
- Worker is also under obligation to use the safety appliances. He should not misuse any appliance, convenience or other things provided.
- In case of hazardous substances, additional safety measures have been prescribed.
- Adequate firefighting equipment should be available.
- Safety officer should be appointed if the number of workers in the factory is 1000 or more.

Working Hours

- A worker cannot be employed for more than 48 hours in a week.
- Weekly holiday is compulsory. If he is asked to work on weekly holiday, he should have full holiday on one of three days immediately or after the normal day of holiday.
- He cannot be employed for more than 9 hours in a day.
- At least half an hour rest should be provided after 5 hours.
- Total period of work inclusive of rest interval cannot be more than 10.5 hours.
- A worker should be given a weekly holiday. Overlapping of shifts is not permitted.
- Notice of period of work should be displayed.

Overtime Wages

- If a worker works beyond 9 hours a day or 48 hours a week, overtime wages are double the rate of wages payable.
- A workman cannot work in two factories.
- There is restriction on double employment.
- However, overtime wages are not payable when the worker is on tour.
- Total working hours including overtime should not exceed 60 hours in a week and total overtime hours in a quarter should not exceed 50 hours.

Employment of Women

- A woman worker cannot be employed beyond 7.00 pm. State Government can grant exemption to any factory or group or class of factories. Shift change can be only after weekly or other holiday and not in between.

Leave

- A worker is entitled in every calendar year annual leave with wages at the rate of one day for every 20 days of work performed in the previous calendar year, provided that he had worked for 240 days or more in the previous calendar year. Child worker is entitled to one day every 15 days. While calculating 240 days, earned leave, maternity leave up to 12 weeks and layoff days will be considered, but leave shall not be earned on those days.
- Leave can be accumulated up to 30 days in case of adult and 40 days in case of child. Leave admissible is exclusive of holidays occurring during or at either end of the leave period. Wage for period must be paid before leave begins, if leave is for 4 or more days.
- Leave cannot be taken for more than three times in a year. Application for leave should not normally be refused.

Wages for overtime and leave salary: Wages for leave encashment and overtime will include dearness allowance and cash equivalent of any benefit. However, it will not include bonus or overtime.

Child Employment

- Child below the age of 14 should not be employed.
- Child above 14 but below 15 years of age can be employed only for 4.5 hours per day or during the night.
- He should be certified fit by a certifying surgeon.
- He cannot be employed during night between 10 pm to 6 am.
- A person over 15 but below 18 years of age is called an 'adolescent'. He can be employed as an adult if he has a certificate of fitness for a full day's work from a certifying surgeon. An adolescent is not permitted to work between 7 pm and 6 am.
- There are more restrictions on employment of female adolescents. Register of child workers should be maintained.

Display on notice board: A notice containing abstract of the Factories Act and the rules made thereunder, in English and local language should be displayed. Name and address of Factories Inspector and the certifying surgeon should also be displayed on notice board.

Obligation regarding hazardous processes/substances: Information about hazardous substances/processes should be given. Workers and general public in the vicinity should be informed about dangers and health hazards. Safety measures and emergency plan should be ready. Safety Committee should be appointed.

30.3 INDUSTRIAL DISPUTES ACT, 1947

Prior to the year 1947, industrial disputes were settled under the provisions of the Trade Disputes Act, 1929. Experience of the working of the 1929 Act revealed various defects, which needed to be overcome by a fresh legislation. Accordingly the Industrial Disputes Bill was introduced in the Legislature. The Bill was referred to the select committee. On the recommendations of the select committee, amendments were made in the original Bill.

The Industrial Disputes Act, 1947 came into existence in April 1947. It was enacted to make provisions for investigation and settlement of industrial disputes and for providing certain safeguards to the workers.

Definition of Industrial Disputes

An industrial dispute may be defined as a conflict or difference of opinion between the management and workers on the terms of employment. It is a disagreement between an employer and employees' representative; usually a trade union, regarding wages, etc., and other working conditions can result in industrial actions. When an industrial dispute occurs, both the parties, that is, the management and the workmen, try to pressurize each other. The management may resort to lockouts while the workers may resort to strikes, picketing or gheraos.

As per Section 2(k) of Industrial Disputes Act, 1947 an industrial dispute is defined as any dispute or difference between employees and employers, or between employers and workmen, or between workmen and which is connected with the employment or non-employment or the terms of employment or with the conditions of labour, of any person.

Objectives of the Act

The objective of the Industrial Disputes Act is to secure industrial peace and harmony by providing machinery and procedure for the investigation and settlement of industrial disputes by negotiations. The Act also lays down:

- The provision for payment of compensation to the workman on account of closure or layoff or retrenchment.
- The procedure for prior permission of appropriate government for layingoff or retrenching the workers or closing down industrial establishments.
- Unfair labour practices on the part of an employer or a trade union or workers.

Applicability

The Industrial Disputes Act extends to whole of India and applies to every industrial establishment carrying on any business, trade, manufacture or distribution of goods and services irrespective of the number of workmen employed therein. Every person employed in an establishment for hire or reward including contract labour, apprentices and part time employees to do any manual, clerical, skilled, unskilled, technical, operational or supervisory work, is covered by the Act.

This Act though does not apply to persons mainly in managerial or administrative capacity, persons engaged in a supervisory capacity and drawing > 1600 p.m. or executing managerial functions and persons subject to Army Act, Air Force and Navy Act or those in police service or officer or employee of a prison.

Important Provisions of the Act

- Defines industry, industrial dispute, layoff, lockout, retrenchment, trade union, strike, wages, workman, etc.
- Provides machinery for investigating and settling disputes through work committees, conciliation officers, boards of conciliation, courts of enquiry, labour courts, tribunals and voluntary arbitration.
- Reference of dispute for adjudication.
- Awards of labour courts and tribunals.
- Payment of wages to workers who have pending proceedings in High Courts.
- Rights of appeal.
- Settlements in outside conciliation.
- Notice of change in employment conditions.
- Protection of workmen during pendency of proceedings.
- Strike and lockout procedures.
- Layoff compensation.
- Retrenchment compensation.
- Proceedings for retrenchment.
- Compensation to workmen in case of transfer of undertakings.
- Closure procedures.
- Reopening of closed undertakings.
- Unfair labour practices.
- Recovery of money due from employer.
- Penalties.
- Obligations and rights of employees.

30.4 THE TRADE UNIONS ACT, 1926

The Trade Unions Act, 1926 provides for registration of trade unions with a view to render lawful organization of labour to enable collective bargaining. It also confers on a registered trade union certain protection and privileges.

The Act extends to the whole of India and applies to all kinds of unions of workers and associations of employers, which aim at regularizing labour management relations. A trade union is a combination whether temporary or permanent, formed for regulating the relations not only between workmen and employers but also between workmen and workmen or between employers and employees.

Registration

Registration of a trade union is not compulsory but is desirable since a registered trade union enjoys certain rights and privileges under the Act. Minimum seven workers of an establishment (or seven employers) can form a trade union and apply to the Registrar for its registration. The application for registration should be in the prescribed form and accompanied by the prescribed fee, a copy of the rules of the union signed by at least 7 members, and a statement containing the names, addresses and occupations of the members making the application.

- The name of the trade union and the addresses of its head office.
- The titles, names, ages, addresses and occupations of its office bearers.
- If the union has been in existence for more than a year, then a statement of its assets and liabilities in the prescribed form should be submitted along with the application.
- The registrar may call for further information for satisfying himself that the application is complete and is in accordance with the provisions, and that the proposed name does not resemble.
- On being satisfied with all the requirements, the registrar shall register the trade union and issue a certificate of registration, which shall be conclusive evidence of its registration.

30.5 INDUSTRIAL EMPLOYMENT ACT, 1946

The Industrial Employment (Standing Orders) Act (herein after being referred as "the Act" or said Act) was enacted in 1946 and the scope of extent includes whole of India. The said Act is applicable to all the industrial establishments which employ or had employed hundred or more workmen during a year. However, the appropriate government after issuing notification in its Official Gazette extends the provisions of this Act to any industrial employment employing less than hundred workers or the number specified in the notice during a year.

The main object of the Act is to bring about uniform terms and conditions of service in various industrial establishments. Such uniform terms of employment ensure to the employer that once such terms are implemented, the employed workmen cannot change them to their detriment or prejudice of their rights and interests. Such standing orders or terms of services act as expressed or written conditions or statutory guidelines for the aspiring workmen to accept the same before joining the industrial establishment. The standing orders also function as a bulwark to maintain peace and stability in the industrial establishment and promotes efficiency and productivity.

Standing orders are thus, a set of rules pertaining to the subjects mentioned in the schedule to the Act. The standing orders are to be certified by a certifying officer. A certifying officer is either a Labour Commissioner or a Regional Labour Commissioner and also includes any other officer appointed by the appropriate government through notification in the Official Gazette.

As soon as the said Act becomes applicable to the industrial establishment, the employer of that establishment is required to submit to the certifying officer five draft copies of the standing orders which he intends to adopt for his establishment. Such draft standing orders sent by the employer for approval must adhere to the model standing orders and must contain all the aspects mentioned in the schedule which are applicable to his industrial establishment. The draft must be attached with the details of the number of workmen employed in the industrial establishment along with the names of the trade union, if any.

The draft standing orders shall stand certified if they are in compliance with the relevant provisions stated in the schedule to this Act or they must adhere to the other provisions of this Act. The onus lies upon the certifying officer to check the reasonableness and justifiability of the draft standing orders before approving. The standing orders must comply with the provisions of this Act and if any such specification is found unreasonable by the certifying officer, he must deny certifying the same.

The certifying officer, after receiving the draft standing orders from the employer, shall forward a copy of the same to the trade union (if any) or to the workmen in the prescribed manner along with a notice to raise objections, if any. Such objections are to be brought forward within 15 days from the date of receipt of the notice. Further, the certifying officer shall consider the objections raised and provide an opportunity of being heard to the workmen and employer and then shall proceed to carry out necessary amendments, after which he shall certify the standing orders. The copies of the certified standing orders must be sent to both the employer and employees within seven days of such certification. The certifying officer is empowered to maintain a register under Section 8 of this Act, wherein he can maintain a record of all the certified standing orders certified by him and he is also entitled to furnish a copy of the same to any person upon payment of prescribed fees.

The Act authorizes the employer or trade union or workmen to oppose to the certified standing orders and make an appeal before the appellate authority within 30 days from the date on which the copies are forwarded to the employer and workmen. The decisions made by the appellate authority shall be final. The appellate authority may either confirm the standing orders certified by the certifying officer or amend the same and send the copies of it within seven days from the date of its order to the employer or the workmen representative. However, it is pertinent to note that the appellate authority is not empowered to set aside the order of the certifying officer, it can give assent or modify the standing orders.

The standing orders shall come into force or be in operation on the expiry of 30 days from the date of sending of authenticated copies to the employer or the workmen. In case of any appeal to the appellate authority, then upon the expiry of seven days from the date on which the copies were sent to the appellate authority.

30.6 PAYMENT OF WAGES ACT, 1936

Application of the Act

The Act will apply to persons employed in any factory or employed (otherwise then in a factory) upon any railway by a railway administration or, either directly or through a sub-contractor, by a person fulfilling a contract with a railway administration, and to persons employed in an industrial or other establishment.

Here "factory" means a factory as defined in Section 2(m) of the Factories Act, 1948 (63 of 1948) and includes any place to which the provisions of that Act have been applied under section 85(1) thereof.

"Industrial or other establishment" means any:

- Tramway service, or motor transport service engaged in carrying passengers or goods or both by road for hire or reward
- Air transport service other than such service belonging to, or exclusively employed in the military, naval or air forces of the Union or the Civil Aviation Department of the Government of India
- Dock, Wharf or Jetty
- Inland vessel, mechanically propelled
- Mine, Quarry or Oil-field
- Plantation
- Workshop or other establishment in which articles are produced, adapted or manufactured, with a view to their use, transport or sale
- Establishment in which any work relating to the construction, development or maintenance of buildings, roads, bridges or canals, or relating to operations connected with navigation, irrigation, or to the supply of water or relating to the generation, transmission and distribution of electricity or any other form of power is being carried on.

30.7 WORKMEN'S COMPENSATION ACT, 1923

The Workmen's Compensation Act, 1923 provides for payment of compensation to workmen and their dependants in case of injury or accident (including certain occupational diseases) arising out of and in the course of employment and resulting in disablement or death. The Act applies to railway servants and persons employed in any such capacity as is specified in Schedule II of the Act. The Schedule II includes persons employed in factories, mines, plantations, mechanically propelled vehicles, construction works and certain other hazardous occupations.

The amount of compensation to be paid depends on the nature of the injury and the average monthly wages and age of workmen. The minimum and maximum rates of compensation payable for death (in such cases, it is paid to the dependents of workmen) and for disability have been fixed and is subject to revision from time to time.

A Social Security Division has been set up under the Ministry of Labour and Employment, which deals with framing of social security policy for the workers and implementation of the various social security schemes. It is also responsible for enforcing this Act. The Act is administered by the State Governments through Commissioners for Workmen's Compensation.

The main provisions of the Act are:

- An employer is liable to pay compensation:
  - If personal injury is caused to a workman by accident arising out of and in the course of his employment;
  - If a workman employed in any employment contracts any disease, specified in the Act as an occupational disease peculiar to that employment.
- However, the employer is not liable to pay compensation in the following cases:
  - If the injury does not result in the total or partial disablement of the workman for a period exceeding three days.
  - If the injury, not resulting in death or permanent total disablement, is caused by an accident which is directly attributable to:
    - » The workman having been at the time of the accident under the influence of drink or drugs; or
    - » The willful disobedience of the workman to an order expressly given, or to a rule expressly framed, for the purpose of securing the safety of workmen; or
    - » The willful removal or disregard by the workman of any safety guard or other device which has been provided for the purpose of securing safety of workmen.
- The State Government may, by notification in the Official Gazette, appoint any person to be a Commissioner for Workmen's Compensation for such area as may be specified in the notification. Any commissioner may, for the purpose of deciding any matter referred to him for decision under this Act, choose one or more persons possessing special knowledge of any matter relevant to the matter under inquiry to assist him in holding the inquiry.
- Compensation shall be paid as soon as it falls due. In cases where the employer does not accept the liability for compensation to the extent claimed, he shall be bound to make provisional payment based on the extent of liability which he accepts, and, such payment shall be deposited with the Commissioner or made to the workman, as the case may be.
- If any question arises in any proceedings under this Act as to the liability of any person to pay compensation (including any question as to whether a person injured is or is not a workman) or as to the amount or duration of compensation (including any question as to the nature or extent of disablement), the question shall, in default of agreement, be settled by a commissioner. No civil court shall have jurisdiction to settle, decide or deal with any question which is by or under this Act required to be settled, decided or dealt with by a commissioner or to enforce any liability incurred under this Act.

- The state government may, by notification in the Official Gazette, direct that every person employing workmen, or that any specified class of such persons, shall send at such time and in such form and to such authority, as may be specified in the notification, a correct return specifying the number of injuries in respect of which compensation has been paid by the employer during the previous year and the amount of such compensation together with such other particulars as to the compensation as the state government may direct.

Whoever fails to maintain a notice-book which he is required to maintain; or fails to send to the Commissioner a statement which he is required to send; or fails to send a report which he is required to send; or fails to make a return which he is required to make, shall be punishable with fine.

30.8 PAYMENT OF BONUS ACT, 1965

The Payment of Bonus Act provides for payment of bonus to persons employed in certain establishments on the basis of profits or on the basis of production or productivity and for matters connected therewith.

It extends to the whole of India and is applicable to every factory and to every other establishment where 20 or more workmen are employed on any day during an accounting year.

Eligibility for Bonus

Every employee receiving salary or wages upto Rs. 3500 p.m. and engaged in any kind of work whether skilled, unskilled, managerial, supervisory, etc., is entitled to bonus for every accounting year if he has worked for at least 30 working days in that year.

However, employees of LIC, universities and educational institutions, hospitals, Chamber of Commerce, RBI, IFCI, UTI and social welfare institutions are not entitled to bonus under this Act.

Disqualification for Bonus

Notwithstanding anything contained in the Act, an employee shall be disqualified from receiving bonus, if he is dismissed from service for fraud or riotous or violent behaviour while in the premises of the establishment or theft, misappropriation or sabotage of any property of the establishment.

Minimum/Maximum Bonus Payable

Minimum Bonus

- The minimum bonus which an employer is required to pay even if he suffers losses during the accounting year or there is no allocable surplus. It is 8.33% of the salary or wages during the accounting year, or

- Rs. 100 in case of employees above 15 years and Rs. 60 in case of employees below 15 years, at the beginning of the accounting year, whichever is higher.

Maximum Bonus

If in an accounting year, the allocable surplus, calculated after taking into account the amount 'set on' or the amount 'set of' exceeds the minimum bonus, the employer should pay bonus in proportion to the salary or wages earned by the employee in that accounting year subject to a maximum of 20% of such salary or wages.

Time Limit for Payment

The bonus should be paid in cash within 8 months from the close of the accounting year or within one month from the date of enforcement of the award or coming into operation of a settlement following an industrial dispute regarding payment of bonus. However, if there is sufficient cause, extension may be applied for.

Duties of Employer

- To calculate and pay the annual bonus as required under the Act.
- To submit an annual return of bonus paid to employees during the year, in Form D, to the inspector, within 30 days of the expiry of the time limit specified for payment of bonus.
- To co-operate with the inspector, produce before him the registers/records maintained, and such other information as may be required by them.
- To get his account audited as per the directions of a labour court/tribunal or of any such other authority.

Rights of Employer

An employer has the following rights:

- Right to forfeit bonus of an employee, who has been dismissed from service for fraud, riotous or violent behaviour, or theft, misappropriation or sabotage of any property of the establishment.
- Right to make permissible deductions from the bonus payable to an employee, such as, festival/interim bonus paid and financial loss caused by misconduct of the employee.
- Right to refer any disputes relating to application or interpretation of any provision of the Act, to the Labour Court or Labour Tribunal.

Rights of Employees

- Right to claim bonus payable under the Act and to make an application to the government, for the recovery of bonus due and unpaid, within one year of its becoming due.

- Right to refer any dispute to the Labour Court/Tribunal Employees, to whom the Payment of Bonus Act does not apply, cannot raise a dispute regarding bonus under the Industrial Disputes Act.
- Right to seek clarification and obtain information, on any item in the accounts of the establishment.

Recovery of Bonus Due

- Where any bonus is due to an employee by way of bonus, employee or any other person authorized by him can make an application to the appropriate government for recovery of the money due.
- If the government is satisfied that money is due to an employee by way of bonus, it shall issue a certificate for that amount to the collector who then recovers the money.
- Such application shall be made within one year from the date on which the money became due to the employee.
- However, the application may be entertained after a year if the applicant shows that there was sufficient cause for not making the application within time.

Offences and Penalties

For contravention of the provisions of the Act or rules the penalty is imprisonment up to 6 months, or fine up to Rs. 1000, or both.

For failure to comply with the directions or requisitions made the penalty is imprisonment up to 6 months, or fine up to Rs. 1000, or both.

In case of offences by companies, firms, body corporate or association of individuals, its director, partner or a principal officer responsible for the conduct of its business, as the case may be, shall be deemed to be guilty of that offence and punished accordingly, unless the person concerned proves that the offence was committed without his knowledge or that he exercised all due diligence.

30.9 EMPLOYEES PROVIDENT FUND SCHEME, 1952

The Constitution of India under "Directive Principles of State Policy" provides that the State shall within the limits of its economic capacity make effective provision for securing the right to work, to education and to public assistance in cases of unemployment, old-age, sickness & disablement and undeserved wants.

The Employees' Provident Fund Organization (EPFO) is a statutory body of the Government of India under the Ministry of Labour and Employment. It administers a compulsory contributory Provident Fund Scheme, Pension Scheme and an Insurance Scheme. It is one of the largest provident fund institutions in the world in terms of members and volume of financial transactions that it has been carrying on.

Applicability of the Employees' Provident Fund Scheme, 1952

The Employees' Provident Fund and Miscellaneous Provisions Act, 1952 applies to the whole of India.

Employees' Provident Fund and Miscellaneous Provisions Act, 1952 is applicable to:

- Every establishment which is engaged in any one or more of the industries specified in Schedule I of the Act or any activity notified by Central Government in the Official Gazette. (**List of Industries/Establishments**)
- Employing 20 or more persons.
- Cinema theatres employing 5 or more persons.

The Act does not apply to:

- The co-operative societies employing less than 50 persons and working without the aid of power. [16(1)(a)]
- The establishment to which this Act applies shall continue to be governed by this Act, even if the number of employees falls below 20 at a later date. [1(5)]
- Establishments under the control of state/central govt. & employees who are getting benefits in the nature of 16(1)(b) contributory P.F. or old age pension as per rules framed by the Government [16(1)(b)]
- Establishment set up under any central, provincial or state Act and the employees who are getting benefits in the nature of contributory P.F. or old age pension as per rules. [16(1)(c)]

SECTION XI
VALUE ANALYSIS

31
Value Analysis

31.1 INTRODUCTION

Value analysis is an organized process that leads to improvement in the cost of the product for its intended function. The process may utilize different techniques and tools in order to achieve the desired set of objectives. The process of value analysis is universal and is used by different manufacturing units and the organizations to analyze their products or services offered by them. In case of new products, the organized process of value analysis and its principles is applied during the development and design phase of the product.

The main concern of the value analysis is to identify and therefore eliminate the features of the products that add no extra value to the functionality of the product. However, these features lead to the increment in the cost of the product and services as a whole. Therefore, the main objective of value analysis lies in providing a better performing product at an optimal cost. It's a much better option against substituting an already existing product with an inferior solution. The principles in the value analysis process guide all the actions required for any ideas of improvements in the existing product and therefore translation of these ideas to fetch commercial gains for the company and therefore its customers. The process of value analysis thus aims to achieve Total Quality Management (TQM) to satisfy the different clients and customers. The world leading companies such as Sony, Panasonic, Hewitt Packard, Nissan, etc., have made use of the value analysis process to fetch major business returns. Certain requirements need to be fulfilled for performing an efficient value analysis. These include an in-depth knowledge of the different manufacturing processes, the knowledge associated with the product, costs due to poor design of the product leading to product failure. All the mentioned inputs are vital to take appropriate decisions regarding the design of both the process and the product in order to obtain lower cost of the product and hence enhanced customer value.

It was after the second world war, the concept of value analysis technique evolved at the General Electric during the late 1940s. Since the inception, many new techniques have been developed and supplemented with the basic concept of value analysis. These new techniques became integral with the basic value analysis process. The growing competition amongst the different companies to analyze their products and services and improve them to meet the ever growing demands of customized products of the customers, the popularity of the value analysis process has grown exponentially.

31.2 DEFINITION OF VALUE ANALYSIS

The process of value analysis is a systematic process that is aimed at the existing product design to improve the functions of the product after comparing the existing product function with the requirements of the customer and clients. The aim is to provide an improved product at lowest cost which is consistent with the specified performance and the needed reliability.

The definition of value analysis can be reduced to the definitions to certain key points and elements:

- Value analysis is a formal, organized and systematic process of evaluation and analysis. The process requires managerial input for its proper control, planning and co-ordination.
- The function of the product is at the centre of the concept. The process considers the functional requirements of the customer. A review process to understand the functionality of the product must be included.
- A level of satisfaction between the product and the derived value by the customer can be established through adequate understanding of the use of the product and thus the required specifications can be established.
- The formal and systematic process must meet the different functional specifications and the performance criteria in order to provide value to the customers.
- A systematic process to improve the design of the product must be established. The design improvements should take place to yield benefits to the company through lower cost of production while maintaining the value of the product.

31.3 DEFINING COST AND VALUE

Two elements need to be considered while attempting to improve the value of a product. The first one is known as the "use value" of the product which is concerned with the use of the product. "Esteem value" is the second element which comes from the ownership. The difference between the two can be clearly depicted in a luxury car and the basic small car. From the point of view of the "use value" both the cars offer same function, i.e., safe economic travel. However, the luxury car has a higher "esteem value". A gold-plated ballpen and a disposable pen is another example to mark the difference between the two.

Understanding the nature of different types of costs associated with a product is essential for any given product. The education process is important even though there is no direct relationship between the associated cost for the factory and the value, both use and esteem, to the customer. Around 80% of the cost incurred in manufacturing could be established once the design drawing has been released. The manufacturing cost is thus a fixed component at this juncture. The costs that are included are the materials cost, the cost for the technology employed and the likes. The design process therefore, fixes a major portion of the total cost of the product. Hence, a periodic review is necessary to recover any avoidable cost that can be removed throughout the life of the product. This may be done by establishing new techniques, tools, materials, etc. This should be accompanied by the reduction in cost while maintaining the use value to the customer.

There are three important costs that are associated with a product:

- Cost of the parts purchased: The cost related to the supply of materials and parts involved in the manufacturing of the product.
- Cost of direct labour used to convert the raw materials into useful products.
- Cost of factory overheads that recover the expenses of production.

Although the above costs are important, yet the organizations have focused mainly on the different labour costs. The different activities such as time study, work study, motion study, automation, etc., have compressed the labour costs and as a result there is very little to be gained for the companies if they further attempt to reduce this. Greater gains are associated with redesigning and analysis of the products to remove extra materials and the overhead costs. A much broader look towards the way in which the total cost in the factory accumulates can be had by adopting the above way of the total costs. One can easily establish the relation between costs and the generated value. Following are the new sources of the costs and therefore the evaluations made will include these new sources too.

- Cost of manufacture
- Cost of assembly
- Cost of poor quality
- Cost of warranty

The key to adequately exploit the process of value analysis lies in understanding how the different costs are accumulated rapidly in a factory to the understanding of design to dispatch of the end product. All the activities and the principles of the value analysis are aimed at reduction and removal of the unavoidable cost while maintaining the value of the product. The objective of value analysis also identifies the largest source of cost reduction and is thus a systematic and formal process.

31.4 FOCUS OF VALUE ANALYSIS

The main objective of the value analysis process thus lies in managing the functionality of the product while meeting the requirements of the customer value. Let's consider the example of an electric kettle. The manufacturing units came up with varieties of kettles with a variety of different types of metal-based boiling device. The heating of water is the value attached to the electric kettle. Therefore, through its attached value one can predict its functionality which includes safety, reliability, capacity, etc. A designer would explore the possibility of plastic kettle with the same functionality of heating water. The plastic in comparison to metal will also have the same function to contain and boil the water. However, the action of using plastic will not only save weight but also the cost. Thus it would be disadvantageous for a company to not review the design process considering plastic as the material of the electric kettle. The example of electric kettle thus clearly explains that the concept of value analysis is important to consider for a company to compete against its rivals in the market.

It becomes critical of a company to identify the elements of costs that are unnecessary and provide no functional value to the product. The reduction of such cost elements then becomes the primary concern of an organization. Once the cost elements are identified, the main objective of the value analysis process will then lie in removing the identified cost elements. The removal of cost elements should not adversely affect the quality, machinability, reliability, function required by the customer. Thus, the target of all the value analysis activities is to highlight such cost elements as opposed to simple redesigning of the product with no real purpose attached to the re-engineering exercise.

Rules that govern the application of the value analysis process are as under:

- The costs compromising the reliability and quality of a product should not be removed: This is because the yield will be lower customer value which will attract complaints and ultimately will lead to product withdrawal.
- There should be no compromise on the sales of the product: The aspect of sales of a product makes the product attractive to the market and therefore gives it an appeal value.
- The cost to ownership of a product for a customer will increase with the reduction in the maintainability of the product.

The process of value analysis is shown in Fig. 31.3. It depicts the detailing of the costs being gradually decomposed to a high level of detail. The figure shows the development of knowledge about the costs of a product. The assessment of the recoverable costs associated with the current design becomes easier at this juncture of the development phase of the product. These then can be targeted for reduction to yield which will ultimately result in reduced cost with the same functionality and hence the same customer value.

31.5 WHY USE VALUE ANALYSIS?

A number of reasons exist to necessitate the process of value analysis as a means to logical cost reduction. The different reasons can be broadly categorized into two main categories of sources: the ones lying within the business and secondly those that are a result of stimulation from the market. Within the business design related issues, the design process itself is one of the main reasons behind exercising the process of value analysis. The lack of control mechanism for the review and feedback of the product on entering the production stage is another reason behind the systematic value analysis process. The problems associated with the design process are listed below:

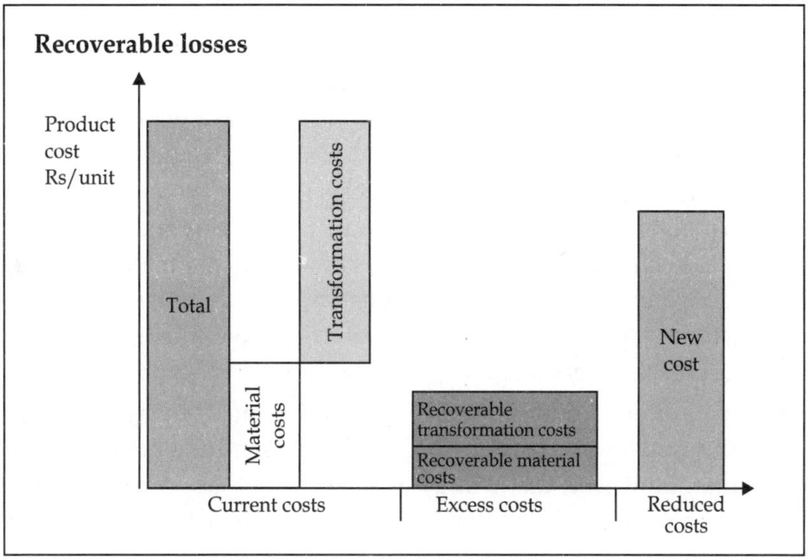

Fig. 31.1: Decomposition of the cost elements.

- The best practices required to produce an optimal design may not be known to the designer. Further, a poor understanding on the technologies and the new materials for making a new product may often lead to cost implications of one design over another. The review process therefore aims to provide the basis for incorporating the new materials and technologies in order to achieve the major aim of cost reduction. The process also offers vital feedback to the designer regarding the performance of the design in production.
- The drawing from the designer may incorporate the new technology that has been replaced by the manufacturing unit. The value analysis intends to consider the replaced technology to process the products smoothly through the production stage.
- The traditional and proven solution may often lead a designer to believe that the particular solution as suggested is the best and will therefore lead to an optimal solution. However, the traditional practices may not incorporate the requirements of the modern customer and therefore may produce a product that may not at all provide the value as demanded by the customer. The value analysis process thus makes the designer evaluate the level of fit between the requirements of the customer and the solution provided by the customer.
- The time pressure owing to the customer requirements and market competition may force a designer to produce an inefficient design. Value analysis therefore makes adequate planning for the different characteristics of the product and therefore decides the relative costs of different design stages. The designer may be forced to compromise the quality of design in order to meet the pressure to launch the product in the market.

The above-mentioned problems, obviously lead to frustration amongst the designers and also discontentment for the other employees in the business. The poor quality of design owing to the commercial pressure may impact the workers in the factory to produce the product which is not the optimal one. The production operators face problems to account for quality standards and therefore need to slow down the rate of manufacturing the product and hence the output. Thus, extra costs will be generated in a factory for any deviation caused in the optimal design of the product. The value analysis process thus aids in reduction of these extra cost elements. The systematic and formal process also yields to learn from the past experience and therefore constantly enhance the ability to create better designs which will involve less time of production. This will further lead to competitive edge in the market for the organization.

The product will offer to provide the consumer the most sought optimal value with enhanced reliability and lowest cost if the product is designed and manufactured optimally in the first instance. However, this will go against the law of probability. Therefore, the main objective of value analysis is to maintain the value aspect of a product to meet the customer needs through a periodic review. The periodic review will continuously improve the status of the product in the competitive market. For any organization, the key to succeed is to constantly improvise and differentiate its product and services from the others in the market. Value analysis thus leads a manufacturing unit to eradicate the different design weaknesses before the product enters the production phase. It also aids in eliminating the costs that would be passed on to the customer. In essence, value analysis is used to maintain a fit between the product, low costs, and high perceived customer value.

The different internal reasons for conducting the value analysis exercise include the following:

- There are certain products with known problems that are produced continuously from the pilot production stage and require remedial and corrective actions.
- Different companies have introduced the standard components, rationalization programmes in order to avoid the explosion of demand of the unique product which emanates from the market pressure from suppliers to produce products with different ranges and to supply the same to meet the market demand. The reduction of cost is of prime importance especially for those in mature markets to help them compete against the cheaper imports.
- The products are required to comply with the different safety requirements in the market and therefore incorporate the different safety legislations in the product. The value analysis activities must be used to review such information related to the safety legislations and to ensure that the product manufactured complies with the same.
- Value analysis is often used to combat the perpetual and expected price reductions between a supplier and a customer. Therefore as a protective measure, many businesses employ value analysis to reduce costs and to protect their own profit margins.

- Corrective Action: To redress the known problems with the existing product designs or to reduce the costs associated with failure (including warranty, complaints and poor quality within the factory and with the customer).

In conditions where the market determines the price, any attempt to reduce costs or recover losses through redesign and improvement activities will provide a major return to the business throughout the life of the product. This total lifecycle saving can amount to a large financial saving.

Market Induced Reasons

There are many modern competitive trends and pressures that make the value analysis approach a valuable activity within any business. These pressures include:

- **Pricing practice:** The traditional approach to setting the price of a product has been to determine the costs of the product and then to add a 'margin' to provide the profit (known as 'cost plus' pricing). However, in the modern competitive environment, the market tends to determine the acceptable price that can be commanded for a product. As such, companies with high costs and a relatively fixed market price will command less profit if costs are not managed properly and reduced continuously. The value analysis process accommodates this need to manage and continuously seek ways of reducing product costs.
- **The advent of E-commerce:** The new information technology available to customers means that product purchasing is now a global exercise. Therefore, in order to maintain a relationship with an existing customer and to protect this relationship, enhancing the value and lowering the costs of the existing products is vital to competitiveness.
- **Reducing complexity:** The general trend in European industry is to rationalize the number of suppliers to a business and to reduce the vast number of parts that were traditionally bought and stocked. Therefore, the ability to redesign products to incorporate common parts will lead to financial savings in space and the costs of inventory.
- **Compliance with quality regulations:** Most of the quality management systems, such as ISO9000 series, require companies to operate a formal design review process to ensure that the quality of the product can be assured. This is an element of the quality accreditation system that is monitored and audited by external agencies. As such, companies that fail to comply with these procedures will fail to qualify for the quality award and can lose business as a result.
- **New technology and materials:** The discovery and invention of new processes and materials means that this form of innovation can be incorporated within the existing product designs such that the reliability and quality of the product can be improved whilst simultaneously reducing costs. This market intelligence and the ability to take advantage of innovation for product designs are vital to improving the performance of the product and the factory.

- **Environmentalism:** The growing awareness of environmental issues is reshaping the buying behaviour of customers and consumers. It is effectively redefining the esteem value of a product and can, through legislation, affect what materials can be used in the production of products and therefore environmental pressures serve to redefine the 'use' value through changes in product specifications (for example, CFC gases in refrigerators and aerosols). In addition many companies, notably vehicle producers, have begun to direct attention towards reducing the weight (and material content) of purchased parts to meet environmental and efficiency targets for themselves.

31.6 TYPES OF VALUE ANALYSIS EXERCISES

Value Analysis for Existing Products

One of the best approaches to value analysis is simply to select an existing product that is sold in relatively large volumes. This product, or product family, will tend to have a great deal of the basic information, and documented history, which can be used quickly as opposed to a newly introduced product where such a history is not available. An existing product unites all the different managers in a business, each with an opinion and list of complaints concerning the ability to convert the design into a 'saleable' product. Therefore, any team that is created for the purpose of value analysis will understand their own problems but not necessarily the cause of these problems across the entire business. These opinions regarding poor performance (and documented evidence of failures) are vital to the discussions and understanding of how the product attracts costs as it is converted from a drawing to a finished product. These discussions therefore allow learning to take place and allow all managers to understand the limitations to the scope of product redesign and re-engineering activities. These issues include:

- The inability to change the existing product designs due to the need to redesign tooling and the expense of such an initiative.
- The project team may have a finite duration before the project is concluded and therefore time will dictate what can be achieved.
- The high levels of purchased costs may imply a need to engage with suppliers in the value analysis process. This initiative will be constrained by a number of issues such as the timing of the project, the availability of resources from the supplier, the location of the suppliers, and other constraints.

Value analysis for New Products – Value Engineering

For new products, the team will need to modify the value analysis approach and will operate in an environment that is less certain and has poor levels of available information upon which to make decisions. In this case, the analysis and systematic process of review for new products is known as Value Engineering (VE). The VE approach is similar to that of value analysis but requires a much greater level of investment by the organization in terms of the skilled, experienced and proficient human resources seconded to the group.

Value Analysis for Product Families: Horizontal Deployment

The final form of value analysis results when there is scope for the 'horizontal deployment' of the results of a value analysis exercise with a single product or family of products. Under conditions where the value analysis project team finds commonalties with many products manufactured by the company, then it is possible to extend the benefits to all these other products concurrently. In this manner, all affected products can be changed quickly to bring major commercial benefits and to introduce the improvement on a 'factory-wide basis'. This is particularly the case when supplying companies offer improvements that affect all the products to which their materials or parts are used. The horizontal deployment activity has many advantages both in terms of financial savings and also the relatively short amount of time required to introduce the required changes to the product design.

Competitive Value Analysis

Value analysis techniques are not simply the prerogative of the business that designed the product. Instead value analysis is often used as a competitive weapon and applied to the analysis of competitor products in order to calculate the costs of other company's products. This is often termed 'strip down' but is effectively the reverse of value analysis. Here the value analysis team understands the design and conversion costs of a competitor product. The results of the analysis is to understand how competitor products are made, what weaknesses exist, and at what costs of production together with an understanding of what innovations have been incorporated by the competitor company.

It is recommended that the best initial approach, for companies with no real experience of value analysis, is to select a single product that is currently in production and has a long life ahead. This approach offers the ability to gain experience, to learn as a team, and to test the tools and techniques with a product that has known characteristics and failings. In the short term it is most important to develop the skills of value analysis, including understanding the right questions to ask, and finally to develop a skeleton but formal process for all value analysis groups to follow and refine.

32
Use of Value Analysis

32.1 KEYS TO SUCCESS

There are certain key points for the success of the value analysis programme. Once the value analysis programme is started, it becomes difficult to correct any errors in the project plan. Further, these key points will be useful to avoid any kind of frustration. Development of team that consists of appropriate individuals is one of the main steps to conduct the value analysis programme smoothly. The individuals should be drawn from different backgrounds of managerial skills that can handle the costs associated with the design, supply and other related activities; manufacturing, etc. The team must focus on a particular product or family of similar products to conduct the value analysis programme. There are other key factors for the success of the programme which are discussed below:

- **Gain approval of the senior management:** Approval for conducting the value analysis programme should be taken from the senior management. A mandate and endorsement from the senior management provides for legitimacy and importance to the project in an organization. The hurdles to the progress of the exercise made by the created formal team are also eliminated.
- **Enlist a senior manager as a champion:** A senior management individual should be chosen as a leader of the value analysis programme. The selected individual should serve to report the progress of the project directly to the board of directors. The chosen leader is expected to remain associated with the entire team for the entire span of the project.
- **Establish the reporting procedure:** A reporting procedure must be established for the team. A plan developed must be formal and should be able to serve as a means of controlling and evaluating the achievements of the exercise against time.
- **Present the value analysis concept and objectives of the team to all the middle and senior managers:** The related aspects and concepts of the value analysis programme should be communicated widely to the other employees of the organization that will include the different middle and senior managers of the organization. This is

necessary to gain support and confidence. Particularly managers from all levels of the organization should be communicated about the exercise that will be able to support the project either by directly assigning the staff or indirectly through the provision of data.

A list of certain business functions intended to receive **regular communication of the progress** should be prepared. The list may consist of certain functions that may even be not involved directly with the project. The process will help the employees within the organization to be well informed about the findings of the team involved and hence the progress made. Through such a process, a momentum is maintained as widely as possible in the team.

- **Select the product:** A suitable product or family of products may be selected for the first study.

  The **objectives of the project** should be mentioned and written down clearly. The key points to be considered for regular review should also be noted down. The targets to be achieved by the project should be estimated. The writing exercise provides a framework and reference point for the exercise. A focus and attention on the outputs of the project can be established which will lead to smoother functioning of the value analysis programme.
- **Train the team:** The selected team should be trained adequately both for the basic process of value analysis and the basic team building activities. The understanding of the concept and the nature of project is essential to the success of the value analysis programme.

32.2 STAGE 1: ORIENTATION PHASE

The orientation phase of the value analysis programme is concerned mainly with the selection and development of the value analysis team and also on the selection of the appropriate product for making the study. The overview of the implementation phase is depicted in Fig. 32.1 ahead.

Forming the Value Analysis Team

A proper and efficient control mechanism in the form of value analysis should be put in place after ensuring that there is no fault of any individual if the cost accumulates. For real financial and efficiency savings, it is critical to adopt a 'company-wide' perspective for the different value analysis activities. The value analysis programme will address the losses in the factory which may include slow processing times, excess material loss during conversion to final product, etc. Further, the tangible costs lying outside the manufacturing unit such as the warranty returns and complaints from the customer are also taken care by the efficient value analysis programme. A team of individuals needs to be created to respond properly to this cumulative approach. The individuals should be selected from the areas and departments from which these costs arise. In order to gain an understanding of the cause and effect relationship between sub-optimal designs, product margin and value generation, development of the cross-functional team is also vital.

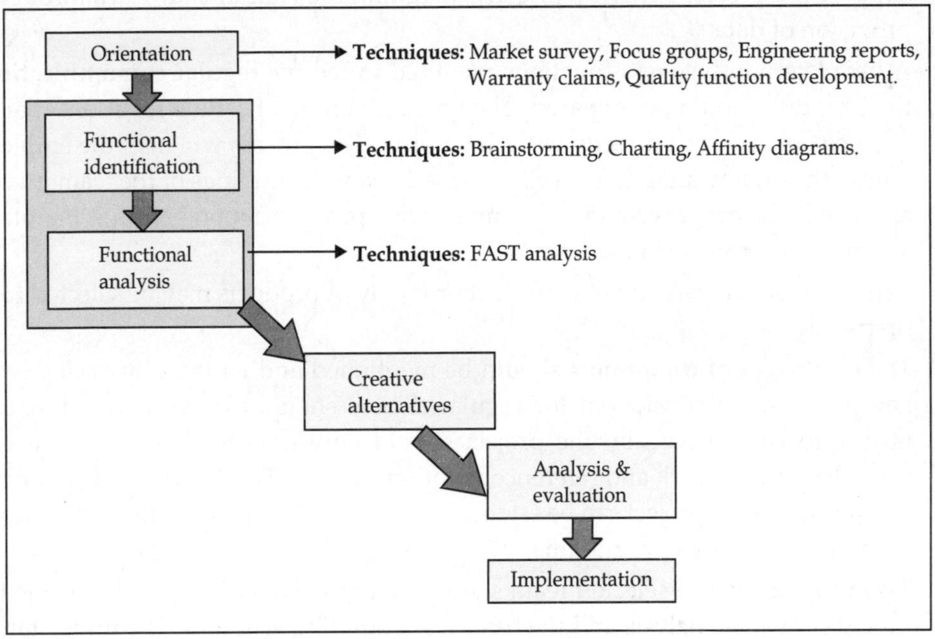

Fig. 32.1: Different stages in value analysis.

Many individuals are involved in a formal and systematic value analysis approach that helps achieve the objective of lowering the cost while maintaining the value of the product. The resources available with the company and the objective of the programme will decide the exact make-up of the entire value analysis team. The value analysis team should consist of the stakeholders in the product design and the manufacturing process who should form within the company and as well as external, i.e., customers or suppliers.

Thus a team should comprise the individuals that have an impact on the costs of the product. The individuals will be drawn from the technical as well as the managerial backgrounds. The individuals in the team from different backgrounds will have an understanding of the product and the associated failure. The individuals will always have a solution to the difficulties and will therefore be able to overcome them.

In order to have a right mix of the different individuals, a generalized skillset is preferred over the specialist skillset. The addition of individuals with generalized skillset is a powerful addition to the value analysis team. The quality of results obtained for the value analysis programme depends upon the combination of the generalized and specialist skillset and hence on the collective ability of the team involved in the programme. It is, therefore essential to carefully plan the implementation stage so that the appropriate and suitable personnel in the business organization could be directed to the value analysis project. A value analysis programme may be seen as an investment made by a business organization in order to reap the benefits of minimized costs. It offers the best skillset to accomplish the objective of lower cost. Therefore, the possession of right skillset by the different individuals of the team is important. Further, they should be capable enough to work as a team throughout the lifespan of the programme. The different representatives of the team conducting the value analysis programme should include the following:

- **Designers:** The knowledge of related design activities is an essential to the early stages of the development of the product. The designers provide the expertise to select optimal material, the product specifications, etc.
- **Manufacturing engineers and production engineers:** The individuals from these disciplines have a direct impact on the cost associated with the product and have the ability to make an efficient product with much reduced cost. Industrial engineers, production managers are other related personnel who have a direct link to manage the different processes and hence obtain the product with the overall reduced cost.
- **Purchasing specialists:** The knowledge of purchasing requirements is another skill-set that is required in a team involved for conducting the value analysis programme. These employees have a detailed knowledge of the purchasing requirements. The requirements emanate from the product design which is then converted into material specifications.
- **Operational staff:** The individuals who are directly responsible for the manufacturing of products and services are the important group of individuals in the value analysis programme team. They are the vital source of information for the difficulties concerning and associated with the manufacturing and assembly of the product.

The creation of the value analysis programme team should be done as quickly as possible. The team should then be trained on the general skills to assist in the development of the cross-functional groups. To understand the different activities and processes right from the initiation of the product design till the dispatch of the product is one of the foremost activities that are conducted by the value analysis programme team to mark the initiation of the value analysis process. Each member of the team understands as to what happens in the process of product conversion. They meet the different individuals involved in the production process and look after the difficulties and problems faced by them. There is a possibility that certain members of the value analysis programme team may be new enough to have carried out such activities. It becomes the sole responsibility for a team member concerned with certain specific area of the product conversion to provide an overview of the related activities in the area. Any operational concerns should be addressed accordingly for the employees involved in the particular area of working.

Selecting the Product

The next stage after the formation of the value analysis programme team is the selection of the product or the family of products to be undertaken for the study. There are certain commercial attributes that will make the value analysis process more commercially important. Further, these attributes will also add to profitability characteristic to the business. The criteria and attributes that can be applied in the product selection stage include products with:

- **Large generated customer complaints, costly warranty returns and those with known problems.** The level of frustration of the customer about the product was so high that the product attracted complaints and criticism. The complaints and criticism received must be corrected as quickly as possible to maintain the value of the product to the customer. Further, there are products that have known problems within the manufacturing unit and are equally important. Therefore, such products must be dealt with to rectify the internal errors before being dispatched to the customer. The products with known problems are of major importance to many of the business organizations. This is because they attract huge costs and return no true value from the consumer or business perspective. It is common to find large investments made by the different organizations on the rework and final inspection of the product to ensure a very high level of quality to the consumer. It is therefore these products that offer a higher degree of potential savings that can be achieved by the value analysis team.
- **Forecast sales volumes that are due to rise, grow or maintain a high level of sales.** Such products are key products to the business and are therefore important to the value analysis activities. These products are often known as runners, because of their weekly appearance in the production programmes. Conversely, there are certain products that are referred to as strangers which undergo manufacturing cycle infrequently with the low annual sales. The cost savings associated with strangers are very low because of the lack of sales volumes and economies of such volumes. While on the other hand, the prospect of cost saving from the runners is very high due to the high volume of sales.
- **Below average margins.** The products with below average margins, i.e., the products with negative or poor margin of profit; will attract attention of the value analysis team since the contribution of such items to the long-term survival of the business is low. Although, the selection of the product for the study depends upon the criteria that is specific to the business, it is always a general practice to start with a product with high volumes of sales and entailing high profit rather than with the product that requires certain rectifications and therefore doesn't yield profit to the business organization. Further, a better skillset is required at the disposal of the value analysis project team for the latter product type in comparison to the product of the first type. Thus, it is always advisable to leave the loss-making products until there is improvement of the skill set in the organization.

Preparation

After making the suitable selection of the product for study, a proper understanding is required to be built by the team members regarding the different components of the product under study. To ensure this, the team must understand the functions of the product which could be done by experiencing the product. Getting acquainted with the product is the first stage in the functional analysis which provides an overview of the product under study. The proper understanding of the different stages of the product development till its dispatch to the customer will lead to the development of the base upon which the latter analysis will be based. This will help in refinement of the functionality and costs. The stage is referred to as the gathering stage where the team is expected to collect basic information about the product under study. The team of individuals engaged in conducting the value analysis programme is expected on their part to collect information for the different items such as: a fully assembled product, product parts mounted on a board, product sub-assemblies and competitor products.

32.3 STAGE 2: FUNCTIONAL ANALYSIS

The next stage in the value analysis programme is the initiation of the product analysis through the proper identification of the functions of a product or service. This stage is known as the functional analysis stage. The use demanded of a product by the consumer of the product and the esteem value provided by the product together define the term 'Function'. The effective working of the product is solely dependent on the functions of the product, which in turn, contribute to the salability of the product. The several stages in the functional analysis stage are discussed hereunder.

Describe the Functions

The analysis of the different functions that a product undertakes is the first step in the functional analysis stage of the value analysis programme. A brainstorming session is conducted to list the basic functions of the product and services under study.

The two main types of functions that a customer requires are the work and sell functions. For example, in case of a postage stamp, the authorized carriage and the evidence of payment are the work functions whereas attracting for identification and allowing for collection opportunity are the sell functions desired by the consumer. The entire brainstorming session must be recorded and the results obtained from the session must be noted on a standard form for this activity.

The process of identification of the different functions of a product or service is one of the most important stages of the value analysis programme. Therefore, this stage takes longer duration to exercise itself. A different solution may be produced if the functions are chosen inappropriately. A tree diagram approach is adopted to record the different functions discovered by the team. This approach is often referred to as the FAST (Function Analysis System Technique) method in value analysis programme.

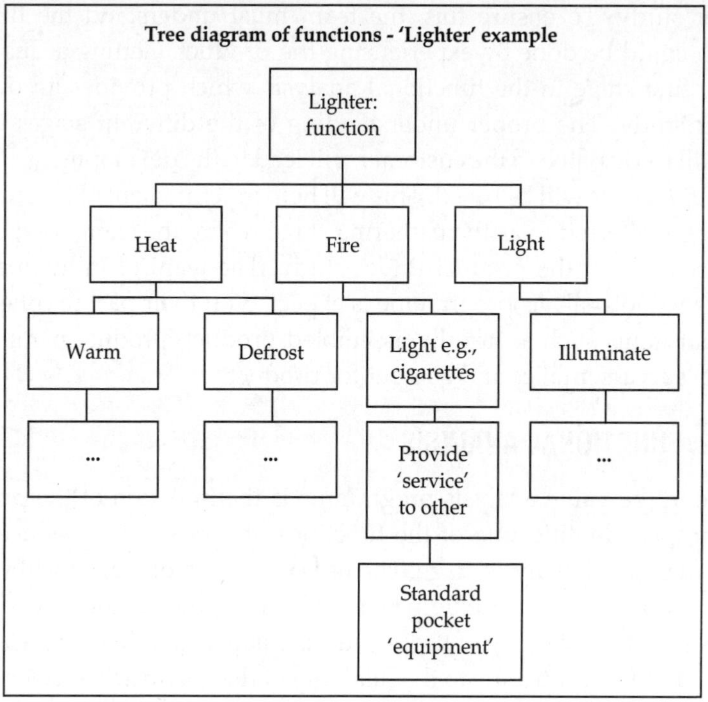

Fig. 32.2: Tree diagram.

Rank the Functions by Pair-wise Comparison

The next step uses pair-wise comparison to rank the functions. This is often done as a group activity, reaching a consensus about each pair. It works like this: each function is compared for importance with each other function, using, e.g., a table (Fig. 32.3). The most important of the two functions is identified and written on the table. Always decide which function is more important, do not allow the 'cop out' of saying that both are equally important.

Then the group decides if the difference in importance is minor (1 point), medium (2 points), or major (3 points). The group discussion on importance usually makes this easy, and points made are written on the table. After all the pairs have been compared, the scores for each function are added up - the higher the score, the more important the function. Experiences here show that in most studies one or two functions emerge as being by far the most important ones. These functions are those to concentrate subsequent efforts on. This stage of identifying the most important or 'basic' functions is very important from the point of view of gaining group consensus.

Pairwise comparison: Example - 'Lighter'

Functions:	**A:** Lights cigarettes and candles **B:** Provides light **C:** Provides heat, e.g., defrost

A vs B	**A: 1**	**Score:** A: 4 points B: 2 points C: 0 points
B vs C	**B: 2**	
A vs C	**A: 3**	

Key to points: 1. Little more important/better
2. Significantly more important/better
3. A lot more important

Fig. 32.3: Pairwise comparison.

32.4 STAGE 3: CREATIVE BRAINSTORMING

This step requires a certain amount of creative thinking by the team. A technique that is useful for this type of analysis is brainstorming which allows all the members of the team to participate and for some strange yet ultimately commercial ideas to be promoted amongst the team. This stage is concerned with developing alternative, more cost-effective ways of achieving the basic function. All rules of brainstorming are allowed, and criticism needs to be avoided as it could cease the flow of ideas. Simply, list down all ideas, not regarding whether they sound apparently ridiculous. Various 'tricks' can be used, such as:

- **Deliberate short periods of silence:** These deliberate periods of reflection allow the team members to refocus their thoughts and to avoid the trap of following one line of thought too far.
- **Writing ideas on cards anonymously:** This approach is particularly good for team members who are shy or feel inferior to the specialists in the group. Using this approach, each team member is issued a number of paper cards to write their ideas. At a point in time, all the cards are collected, discussed and grouped. This is a good way of gaining high levels of participation from the entire team.
- **Sequencing suggestions in a 'round-robin' fashion:** This process involves the team situated at a table. Each person nominates an idea for the team and then the responsibility passes to the person on his or her right. As the process unfolds, several cycles of the entire table will produce a large number of ideas which will eventually become exhausted. Therefore, the team will amass a great quantity of ideas for discussion in a relatively short time period.

- **Making sketches:** Many of the specialists in the group will be more comfortable drawing their ideas rather than verbalizing them. This is true of engineers who find verbalizing complex solutions difficult but drawing them somewhat easier. In this process, the teams are allowed to draw potential improvement ideas for discussion.
- **Explaining the product to an 'extra-terrestrial' customer:** This process is interesting and somewhat challenging, as the team must describe the functionality to a person that has no concept of the product or its application. This process sounds easy but in reality is quite difficult as the team will constantly review their efforts to describe the product and therefore add greater levels of detail that often go unexpressed.

This process usually involves a high degree of humour and is a fun activity that ensures everyone in the team understands the functionality of the product. In effect, this process creates a common understanding and a baseline that can be shared with all team members regardless of their level of specialist knowledge.

These techniques have been proven to generate high levels of enthusiasm, high levels of participation and also a high quantity and quality of innovation. The real key is to make the process fun and allow individuals to 'spark' ideas from their other team members. It is also a good way of 'becoming the customer' and undertaking a critical review of value by looking at the product in a neutral manner. It should be noted that many people have unrealistic expectations of this process and expect radical innovations in product design and often this is not the case. Breakthrough innovations are possible but it is more important to improve in the right direction and allow the team to 'up-skill'. As such, any improvement in cost effectiveness is a worthy result and one that benefits the company - a major radical breakthrough is either the result of new innovations that are available since the design of the product or other factors. In addition, a radical innovation implies that the initial design of the product must have been particularly poor and this is seldom the case. Designs tend to be more or less right and are always capable of improvement towards the optimal cost stage.

32.5 STAGE 4: ANALYSIS AND EVALUATION

The third stage is to evaluate the 'cost' and 'worth' of each function. This is not an exact process but allows the existing cost of the product to be apportioned between the functions based on the assumptions that have been made by the team. The worth is determined by estimating the lowest cost of producing each basic function if cut down to its minimum. The **value potential** is therefore the difference between the cost and the worth figures. In some cases it is necessary for the team to take a break while specialist team members, or seconded resources, evaluate the costs and feasibility of some of their suggestions that have been generated.

At this stage, the options available to the team are therefore to modify the design of the product to:

- **completely eliminate the part** from the design as it serves no useful purpose and has no customer value but only a cost; and
- **replace, substitute or modify the part** and therefore lower the cost of the product by making an improvement to it.

The results of these team deliberations and evaluations of the different alternatives and potential changes can be recorded using a cost-benefit chart. This chart displays the costs of the improvement on one axis, and the associated benefits along the other. At this point, the team has developed and justified improvements to the product and this stage usually concludes with a project report with recommendations. In addition, the team will develop a brief presentation to senior management as a summary of their findings and recommendations. The presentation and report will usually contain the following sections:

- The subject, product and value analysis project team brief, mandated by senior management.
- The business conditions and justification to improve the cost performance or value enhancement of the product.
- The current costs of the product and the failures in the conversion process that represent the hidden costs of poor design.
- An analysis of the product and its functionality for customers.
- The proposed changes and the commercial reasons for it.
- The comparison of actual costs now and post-implementation costs.
- The savings year on year based on future expected volumes.
- The expenditure items required.
- The process of implementing the change and the proposal (including timing of the different phases).
- A list of issues that could not be resolved by the team but are worthy of future analysis.
- A complete list of appendices containing all the materials collected, used and recorded during the life cycle of the team.

The next stage is to gain a formal agreement by the senior management team to proceed and schedule the implementation of the recommended changes.

32.6 STAGE 5: IMPLEMENTATION

The final stage of the value analysis team is to report the findings to the senior management team and to gain permission to implement the findings of the report. This is the most rewarding stage as the many hours of brainstorming; classification and calculation begin to become 'the new product' and 'the new way of manufacturing'. At this point, each product or service that is conducted is done so with the knowledge that it generates profit for the business and generates value for the customer in the most effective and efficient way. It should be noted that changes need to be scheduled in order to prevent 'change overload' within the factory whereby many elements of a product are replaced or modified and also to allow specialist departments such as the purchasing department to make the necessary changes to material and part specifications. These activities need to be phased to avoid the chaos of multiple changes happening at once and to allow the anticipated cost savings to be tracked and monitored.

Indeed, it is necessary to track the improvement in the quality performance of the product (in the factory) over many months before the improvements can be proven to work. This is especially true where the company has to run down the existing stocks of the problem part before introducing the modified part.

SECTION XII
LEADERSHIP

33
Leadership

33.1 INTRODUCTION

Leadership is a process by which an executive can direct, guide and influence the behaviour and work of others towards accomplishment of specific goals in a given situation. Leadership is the ability of a manager to induce the subordinates to work with confidence and zeal.

Leadership is the potential to influence behaviour of others. It is also defined as the capacity to influence a group towards the realization of a goal. Leaders are required to develop future visions, and to motivate the organizational members to achieve the visions.

According to Keith Davis, "Leadership is the ability to persuade others to seek defined objectives enthusiastically. It is the human factor which binds a group together and motivates it towards goals."

Leadership is an important function of the management which helps to maximize efficiency and to achieve organizational goals. The following points justify the importance of leadership in a concern.

- **Initiates action:** Leader is a person who starts the work by communicating the policies and plans to the subordinates from where the work actually starts.
- **Motivation:** A leader proves to be playing an incentive role in the concern's working. He motivates the employees with economic and non-economic rewards and thereby gets the work from the subordinates.
- **Providing guidance:** A leader has to not only supervise but also play a guiding role for the subordinates. Guidance here means instructing the subordinates the way they have to perform their work effectively and efficiently.
- **Creating confidence:** Confidence is an important factor which can be achieved through expressing the work efforts to the subordinates, explaining them clearly their role and giving them guidelines to achieve the goals effectively. It is also important to hear the employees with regards to their complaints and problems.

- **Building morale:** Morale denotes willing co-operation of the employees towards their work and getting them into confidence and winning their trust. A leader can be a morale booster by achieving full co-operation so that they perform with best of their abilities as they work to achieve goals.
- **Builds work environment:** The management gets things done from the people. An efficient work environment helps in sound and stable growth. Therefore, human relations should be kept into mind by a leader. He should have personal contacts with employees and should listen to their problems and solve them. He should treat employees on humanitarian terms.
- **Co-ordination:** Co-ordination can be achieved through reconciling personal interests with organizational goals. This synchronization can be achieved through proper and effective co-ordination which should be primary motive of a leader.

33.2 LEADER VS MANAGER

Leadership and managership are two synonymous terms. Leadership doesn't require any managerial position to act as a leader. On the other hand, a manager can be a true manager only if he has got the traits of a leader in him. By virtue of his position, a manager has to provide leadership to his group. A manager has to perform all five functions to achieve goals, i.e., planning, organizing, staffing, directing, and controlling. Leadership is a part of these functions. Leadership as a general term is not related to managership. A person can be a leader by virtue of qualities in him. For example: leader of a club, class, welfare association, social organization, etc. Therefore, it is true to say that, "All managers are leaders, but all leaders are not managers."

A leader is one who influences the behaviour and work of others in group efforts towards achievement of specified goals in a given situation. On the other hand, a manager can be a true manager only if he has got traits of leader in him. Managers at all levels are expected to be the leaders of work groups so that subordinates willingly carry instructions and accept their guidance. A person can be a leader by virtue of all qualities in him.

Leaders and Managers can be compared on the following basis:

Basis	Manager	Leader
Origin	A person becomes a manager by virtue of his position.	A person becomes a leader on basis of his personal qualities.
Formal rights	Manager has got formal rights in an organization because of his status.	Rights are not available to a leader.
Followers	The subordinates are the followers of managers.	The group of employees whom the leaders lead are their followers.
Functions	A manager performs all five functions of management.	Leader influences people to work willingly for group objectives.
Necessity	A manager is essential to a concern.	A leader is required to create cordial relation between a person working in and for organization.

Stability	It is more stable.	Leadership is temporary.
Mutual relationship	All managers are leaders.	All leaders are not managers.
Accountability	Manager is accountable for self and subordinates' behaviour and performance.	Leaders have no well-defined accountability.
Concern	A manager's concern is organizational goals.	A leader's concern is group goals and member's satisfaction.
Followers	People follow a manager by virtue of his job description.	People follow them on voluntary basis.
Role continuation	A manager can continue in office till he performs his duties satisfactorily in congruence with organizational goals.	A leader can maintain his position only through day-to-day wishes of followers.
Sanctions	A manager has command over allocation and distribution of sanctions.	A leader has command over different sanctions and related task records. These sanctions are essentially of informal nature.

33.3 LEADERSHIP THEORIES

Great Man Theory (1840s)

The Great Man theory evolved around the mid 19th century. Even though no one was able to identify with any scientific certainty, which human characteristic or combination of, were responsible for identifying great leaders. Everyone recognized that just as the name suggests; only a man could have the characteristic(s) of a great leader.

The Great Man theory assumes that the traits of leadership are intrinsic. That simply means that great leaders are born; they are not made. This theory sees great leaders as those who are destined by birth to become a leader. Furthermore, the belief was that great leaders will rise when confronted with the appropriate situation. The theory was popularized by Thomas Carlyle. Just like him, the Great Man theory was inspired by the study of influential heroes. In his book "On Heroes, Hero-Worship, and the Heroic in History", he compared a wide array of heroes.

In 1860, Herbert Spencer, an English philosopher disputed the Great Man theory by affirming that these heroes are simply the product of their times and their actions the results of social conditions.

Trait Leadership Theory (1930s–1940s)

The trait leadership theory believes that people are either born or are made with certain qualities that will make them excel in leadership roles. That is, certain qualities such as intelligence, sense of responsibility, creativity and other values puts anyone in the shoes of a good leader. In fact, Gordon Allport, an American psychologist, "...identified almost 18,000 English personality-relevant terms".

The trait theory of leadership focused on analyzing mental, physical and social characteristics in order to gain more understanding of what is the characteristic or the combination of characteristics that are common among leaders.

There were many shortfalls in the trait leadership theory. However, from a psychology of personalities approach, Gordon Allport's studies are among the first ones and have brought, for the study of leadership, the behavioural approach.

- In the 1930s, the field of psychometrics was in its early years.
- Personality traits measurement weren't reliable across studies.
- Study samples were of low level managers.
- Explanations weren't offered as to the relation between each characteristic and its impact on leadership.
- The context of the leader wasn't considered.

Many studies have analyzed the traits among the existing leaders in the hope of uncovering those responsible for one's leadership abilities! In vain, the only characteristics that were identified among these individuals were those that were slightly taller and slightly more intelligent!

Behavioural Theories (1940s–1950s)

In reaction to the trait leadership theory, the behavioural theories offer a new perspective, one that focuses on the behaviours of the leaders as opposed to their mental, physical or social characteristics. Thus, with the evolutions in psychometrics, notably the factor analysis, researchers were able to measure the cause and effect relationship of specific human behaviours from leaders. From this point forward anyone with the right conditioning could have access to the once before elite club of naturally gifted leaders. In other words, leaders are made not born.

The behavioural theories first divided leaders in two categories. Those that were concerned with the tasks and those concerned with the people. Throughout the literature these are referred to as different names, but the essence is identical.

Contingency Leadership Theories (1960s)

The contingency leadership theory argues that there is no single way of leading and that every leadership style should be based on certain situations, which signifies that there are certain people who perform at the maximum level in certain places; but at minimal performance when taken out of their element.

To a certain extent contingency leadership theories are extensions of the trait theory, in the sense that human traits are related to the situation in which the leaders exercise their leadership. It is generally accepted within the contingency theories that leaders are more likely to express their leadership when they feel that their followers will be responsive.

Transactional Leadership Theories (1970s)

Transactional leadership theories, also known as exchange theories of leadership, are characterized by a transaction made between the leader and the followers. In fact, the theory values a positive and mutually beneficial relationship.

For the transactional theories to be effective and as a result have motivational value, the leader must find a means to align to adequately reward (or punish) his follower, for performing leader-assigned task. In other words, transactional leaders are most efficient when they develop a mutual reinforcing environment, for which the individual and the organizational goals are in sync.

The transactional theorists state that humans, in general, seek to maximize pleasurable experiences and to diminish unpleasurable ones. Thus, we are more likely to associate ourselves with individuals that add to our strengths.

Transformational Leadership Theories (1970s)

The transformational leadership theory states that this process is by which a person interacts with others and is able to create a solid relationship that results in a high percentage of trust, that will later result in an increase of motivation, both intrinsic and extrinsic, in both leaders and followers.

The essence of transformational theories is that leaders transform their followers through their inspirational nature and charismatic personalities. Rules and regulations are flexible, guided by group norms. These attributes provide a sense of belonging for the followers as they can easily identify with the leader and its purpose.

33.4 CONVENTIONAL TRAITS

A leader has multidimensional traits in him which makes him appealing and effective in behaviour. The following are the requisites to be present in a good leader:

- **Physical appearance:** A leader must have a pleasing appearance. Physique and health are very important for a good leader.
- **Vision and foresight:** A leader cannot maintain influence unless he exhibits that he is forward looking. He has to visualize situations and thereby has to frame logical programmes.
- **Intelligence:** A leader should be intelligent enough to examine problems and difficult situations. He should be analytical who weighs pros and cons and then summarizes the situation. Therefore, a positive bent of mind and mature outlook is very important.
- **Communicative skills:** A leader must be able to communicate the policies and procedures clearly, precisely and effectively. This is helpful in persuasion and stimulation.
- **Objective:** A leader has to have a fair outlook which is free from bias and which does not reflect his willingness towards a particular individual. He should develop his own opinions and should base his judgment on facts and logic.

- **Knowledge of work:** A leader should precisely know the nature of work of his subordinates because it is then he can win their trust and confidence.
- **Sense of responsibility:** Responsibility and accountability towards an individual's work is very important to bring a sense of influence. A leader must have a sense of responsibility towards organizational goals because only then he can get maximum of his capabilities exploited in a real sense. For this, he has to motivate himself and arouse and urge to give best of his abilities. Only then he can motivate the subordinates to the best.
- **Self-confidence and willpower:** Confidence in himself is important to earn the confidence of the subordinates. He should be trustworthy and should handle the situations with his willpower.
- **Humanist:** This trait to be present in a leader is essential because he deals with human beings and is in personal contact with them. He has to handle the personal problems of his subordinates with great care and attention. Therefore, treating the human beings on humanitarian grounds is essential for building a congenial environment.
- **Empathy:** It is an old adage "stepping into the shoes of others". This is very important because fair judgment and objectivity comes only then. A leader should understand the problems and complaints of employees and should also have a complete view of the needs and aspirations of the employees. This helps in improving human relations and personal contacts with the employees.

From the above qualities present in a leader, one can understand the scope of leadership and its importance for scope of business. A leader cannot have all traits at one time. But a few of them help in achieving effective results.

33.5 DOMAINS IN LEADERSHIP

The Four Domains

To better understand and explain the four domains of strength, here is a brief rundown. While you could argue some themes should be moved around, this is a helpful way to better understand how each strength – at a general level – helps individuals and teams see a bigger picture in accomplish their goals.

- **Executing themes:** These nine themes are the most hard working of the bunch. They tend to get things done, with speed, precision, and accuracy. They put in the hard work now, so that when it's time to move, they are ready. Putting ideas into action is the the strengths of this domain.
  - Achiever
  - Arranger
  - Belief
  - Consistency
  - Deliberative
  - Discipline

- Focus
- Restorative
- Responsibility

- RestorativeI**Influencing themes:** These eight themes enable individuals or groups to sell the big ideas. They are able to take charge, speak up and be heard. They are extremely helpful when you need to reach a broader audience, or meet a bigger goal. This can happen both internally with the team, or to external constituents. They tend to influence forward.
    - Activator
    - Maximizer
    - Command
    - Self-Assurance
    - Communication
    - Significance
    - Competition
- **Relationship building themes:** While certainly not the only themes that deal with people (because they're all about people), these nine themes have an innate ability to take the human component into the equation. They look at how individuals fit into the bigger pictures, and can create pathways for them to thrive. They make strong relational connections that bind a group together around a cause, idea or each other.
    - Adaptability
    - Includer
    - Developer
    - Individualization
    - Connectedness
    - Positivity
    - Empathy
    - Relator
    - Harmony
- **Strategic thinking themes:** When a plan needs to be made, or a new idea created for solving a problem, these eight themes can help accomplish that. Whether it's thinking into a current problem, or dreaming about how to overcome tomorrow, the strategic thinking themes can take a thought or idea and look for the best way to move forward on it.
    - Analytical
    - Input
    - Context
    - Intellection
    - Futuristic
    - Learner
    - Ideation
    - Strategic

SECTION XIII
OPERATIONS RESEARCH

34
Linear Programming

34.1 INTRODUCTION

The linear programming (LP) uses the following generalized format:

Maximize $Z = C_1X_1 + C_2X_2 + ... + C_nX_n$

Subject to

$$a_{11}X_1 + a_{12}X_2 + ... + a_{1n}X_n \leq b_1$$
$$a_{21}X_1 + a_{22}X_2 + ... + a_{2n}X_{2n} \leq b_2$$
$$\vdots \quad \vdots \qquad\qquad \vdots \quad \vdots$$
$$a_{m1}X_1 + a_{m2}X_2 + ... + a_{nm}X_n \leq b_n$$

where, $X_1, X_2, X_3, ..., X_n \geq 0$.

The graphical method can be used if the number of variables is two for a problem under consideration. However, Simplex method can be used for problems involving more than two variables.

34.2 DEVELOPMENT OF LINEAR PROGRAMMING MODELS

The development of LP models is illustrated through the examples discussed in this section:

Example 1: A manufacturing unit manufactures two types of products *A* and *B*. Each product makes use of lathe and shaper machine. It takes four hours to machine product *A* on lathe while five hours on shaper machine. For product *B*, it takes six hours to machine it on lathe and ten hours on shaper machine. The total number of hours for lathe and shaper are 40 hours and 60 hours respectively. Product *A* sells for a profit of Rs. 8.00 and product *B* sells at profit of Rs. 6.00. Determine the number of units of products *A* and *B* to be produced to maximize the profit.

Solution: The data for the problem under consideration is summarized in the Table below.

Machine	Product		Limit on Machine (hours)
	A	B	
Lathe	4	6	40
Shaper	5	10	60
Profit/Unit	8	6	

Let the number of units for product *A* be X_1 and that for product *B* be X_2

The linear programming model for the problem under consideration will be as follows:

Maximize $Z = 8X_1 + 6X_2$

Subject to: $4X_1 + 6X_2 \leq 40$

$5X_1 + 10\,X_2 \leq 60$

$X_1, X_2 \geq 0$

Example 2: Doctor proposes a nutrition scheme for babies. The babies can opt for either Type I or Type II food. These are available in standard packets of 50 grams. The cost for Type I and Type II foods are Rs. 3 and Rs. 2 respectively. Table below summarizes the vitamin available in each type of food and also the minimum vitamin requirement. Determine the optimal combination of the two food types in such a way that the minimum vitamin requirement is fulfilled at minimum cost.

Vitamin	Vitamin availability per packet		Limit on machine (hours)
	Food Type I	Food Type II	
1	1	1	8
2	5	7	6
Cost/packet	3	2	

Solution: Let the number of packets for food type I be X_1 and X_2 be the number of packets for food Type II. The linear programming model for the problem under consideration is as below:

Maximize $Z = 3X_1 + 2X_2$

Subject to: $X_1 + X_2 \geq 8$

$5X_1 + 7X_2 \geq 6$

$X_1, X_2 \geq 0$

34.3 GRAPHICAL METHOD

The graphical method is preferred when the number of variables in the linear programming model is two. The method is demonstrated using two different examples:

Example 3: Use the graphical method to solve the following linear programming model:

Maximize $Z = 6X_1 + 8X_2$

Subject to: $5X_1 + 10X_2 \leq 60$

$$4X_1 + 4X_2 \leq 40$$
$$X_1, X_2 \geq 0$$

Solution: Plot the above constraints on XY plane, i.e., plot the following equations:

$$5X_1 + 10X_2 = 60$$
$$4X_1 + 4X_2 = 40$$

The graph will look as shown in Fig. 34.1. The feasible region is the shaded region A-B-C-D as shown.

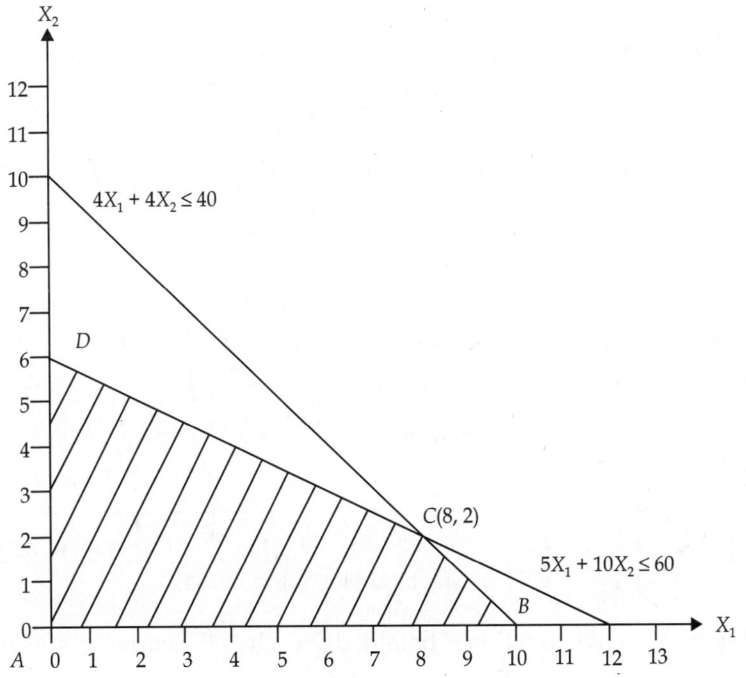

Fig. 34.1: Graphical plot of Example 3.

The value of the objective function is calculated at each of the corner points of the polygon.

i.e., $Z(A) = 6 \times 0 + 8 \times 0 = 0$

$Z(B) = 6 \times 10 + 8 \times 0 = 60$

$Z(C) = 6 \times 8 + 8 \times 2 = 64$

$Z(D) = 6 \times 0 + 8 \times 6 = 48$

Since the objective is to maximize the value of Z, hence the values corresponding to maximum of Z should be selected. Therefore, $X_1 = 8$ and $X_2 = 2$.

Example 4: Use the graphical method to solve the below linear programming model:

Minimize $Y: 2X_1 + 3X_2$

Subject to: $X_1 + X_2 \geq 6$

$7X_1 + X_2 \geq 14$

$X_1, X_2 \geq 0$

Solution: The plot for two constraint equations is shown in Fig. 34.2. The feasible region is indicated by the shaded region.

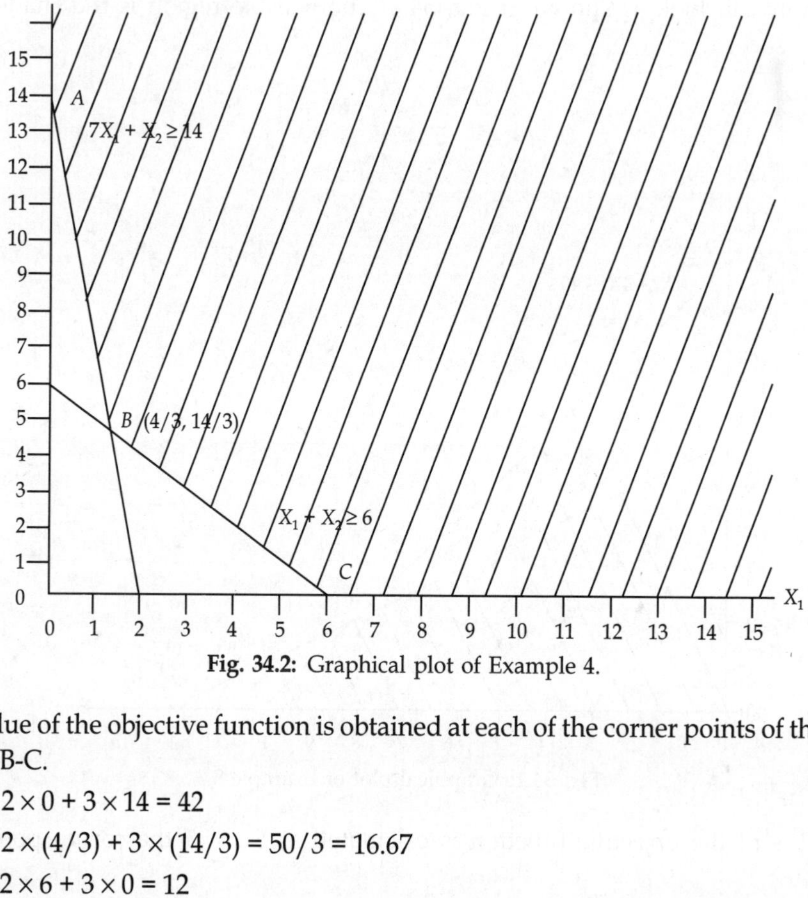

Fig. 34.2: Graphical plot of Example 4.

The value of the objective function is obtained at each of the corner points of the feasible region A-B-C.

$Y(A) = 2 \times 0 + 3 \times 14 = 42$

$Y(A) = 2 \times (4/3) + 3 \times (14/3) = 50/3 = 16.67$

$Y(C) = 2 \times 6 + 3 \times 0 = 12$

Since the objective is to minimize the objective function, therefore the values corresponding to minimum values should be selected to give the optimal solution. Therefore $X_1 = 6$ and $X_2 = 0$.

34.4 SIMPLEX METHOD

Following numerical explains the Simplex method.

Example 5: Solve the following linear programming model using Simplex method:

Maximize $Y = 5X_1 + 10X_2$

Subject to: $5X_1 + 10X_2 \leq 60$

$4X_1 + 4X_2 \leq 40$

$X_1, X_2 \geq 0$

Solution: The above model is first reduced to canonical form as follows:

Maximize $Y = 5X_1 + 10X_2 + 0S_1 + 0S_2$

Subject to: $5X_1 + 10X_2 + S_1 = 60$

$4X_1 + 4X_2 + S_2 = 40$

$X_1, X_2 S_1, S_2 \geq 0$

The initial simplex table will appear as shown in Fig. 34.3.

CB_i	C_j	6	8	0	0		
	Basic variable	X_1	X_2	S_1	S_2	Solution	Ratio
0	S_1	5	10	1	0	60	60/10 = 6**
0	S_2	4	4	0	1	40	40/4 = 10
	Z_j	0	0	0	0	0	
	$C_j - Z_j$	6	8*	0	0		

*Key column, **Key row

Fig. 34.3: Initial simplex table.

Key element is obtained at the intersection of key row and key column.

$C_j - Z_j$ is the relative contribution. Here, C_j is the objective coefficient for the *j*th variable. The objective function value of the problem at this iteration is zero, i.e., the value of Z_j against the solution column is the value of the objective function.

Optimality Condition

For maximization problem, if all $C_j - Z_j = 0$, then optimality is reached. Otherwise, select the entering variable with the maximum $C_j - Z_j$ value.

[For minimization problem, if all $C_j - Z_j$ are greater than or equal to zero, the optimality is reached; otherwise, select the entering variable with the most negative value.]

In Fig. 34.3, all the values for $C_j - Z_j$ are not less than or equal to zero. Hence, the solution can be improved further. $C_j - Z_j$ is maximum for the variable X_2. Therefore, X_2 enters the basis. This is known as the *entering variable*, and the corresponding column is called the *key column*.

Feasibility Condition

To maintain the feasibility of the solution in each iteration, do the following:

- Find the ratio between the solution value and the respective value in the key column value in each row.

- Then, select the variable from the present set of basic variables w.r.t. the minimum ratio (break tie randomly). This is the leaving variable and the corresponding row is called the *key row*. The value at the intersection of the key row and key column is called key element or pivot element.

In Fig. 34.3, the leaving variable is S_1 and row 1 is the key row. The key element is 10.

The next iteration is shown in Fig. 34.4. In this figure, the basic variable S_1 of Fig. 34.3 is replaced by X_2

$$\text{New value} = \text{Old value} - \frac{\text{Key column value} \times \text{Key row value}}{\text{Key value}}$$

Using the above equation, the new values calculated are shown in Fig. 34.4.

	C_j	6	8	0	0		
CB_i	Basic variable	X_1	X_2	S_1	S_2	Solution	Ratio
8	X_2	1/2	1	1/10	0	6	6/(1.2)= 12
0	S_2	2	0	-2/5	1	15	16/2 = 8**
	Z_j	4	8	4/5	0	48	
	$C_j - Z_j$	2*	0	-4/5	0		

*Key column, **Key row

Fig. 34.4: Iteration 1.

The solution in Fig. 34.4 is not optimal. Hence, the variable X_1 is selected as the entering variable and after computing the ratios, S_2 is selected as the leaving variable. The next iteration is shown in Fig. 34.5.

	C_j	6	8	0	0	
CB_i	Basic variable	X_1	X_2	S_1	S_2	Solution
8	X_2	0	1	1/5	-1/4	2
6	X_1	1	0	-1/5	1/2	8
	Z_j	6	8	2/5	1	64
	$C_j - Z_j$	0	0	-2/5	-1	

Fig. 34.5: Iteration 2.

In the above shown iteration, all the $C_j - Z_j$ are negative and hence the optimal solution is reached. Therefore, the corresponding optimal solution is $X_1 = 8$ units and $X_2 = 6$ units.

35
Project Management

35.1 INTRODUCTION

The interrelated sequences of activities that are required to be implemented before the completion of task constitute a project. The precedence relationship leads to the connection of different activities in a logical sequence. An activity cannot be started until and unless its immediate preceding activities are completed. Some typical examples of a project are the following:

- House construction
- Factory commissioning
- Ship construction
- Steam boiler fabrication
- Bridge construction
- Dam construction
- Power plant commissioning
- Equipment and machinery undergoing shutdown maintenance
- Launching of new product
- New weapon system launch
- National elections conductance
- New technology development
- Railway coaches construction

Generally, for the construction of public utilities, organizing mega events and for large industrial projects, project management finds applications. Since many of the industrial activities are mainly the project management problems, hence the role of project management is considered to be vital. The examples of industrial activities where project management finds applications are that of fabrication of boilers, satellite launching, launching of new product, organization of R&D projects, etc.

The same project can be repeated either by the same organization or by different organizations. Although the same project carried out repeatedly by different organizations, is unique in itself by nature. There will some key selected cities where the product will be launched in case of the launching of new project. Other cities will be selected for the new product launch depending upon the priorities fixed by the marketing department of the organization. Since the estimates of time will be different for different activities of a project, there will be different project schedules for different cities. This may be due to varying environmental conditions for different cities. In certain cases, there may be addition or deletion of certain activities. A detailed planning effort will be required for planning project schedules for a different place and at different times. So, if a project is repeated at a different place/different time, then a detailed planning effort is required.

To obtain solutions for scheduling and controlling of different activities, an analytical treatment is carried out. This is done by representing a project in the form of network of activities. A network consists of a set of nodes that are connected through a set of arcs. A network provides for the precedence relations amongst the different activities. Therefore, one can define a project network as collection of different precedence relations amongst different activities.

A project can be represented on a network in two ways:

- Activities on Arrows Diagram (AOA Diagram)
- Activities on Nodes Diagram (AON Diagram)

For project management, the AOA diagram is commonly used. Two examples below illustrate the concepts clearly.

Example 1: For the construction of community hall, the required activities are listed below. The table also summarizes the predecessor(s).

Activity	Description	Immediate predecessor(s)
A	Approval of plan	
B	Preparation of site	
C	Making arrangement of materials	A
D	Excavation for foundation	B
E	Carpentry work for window and door supporting frame	A
F	Laying of foundation	C,D
G	Raising wall from foundation to window base	F
H	Raising wall from window base to lintel level	E,G
I	Roofing	H
J	Electrical fitting and firing	I
K	Plastering	J,L
L	Making windows and doors and fitting them	A
M	White washing	K
N	Clearing the site	M

Construct a project network for the above set of activities.

Solution: The above set of activities can be represented through a network as shown in Fig. 35.1.

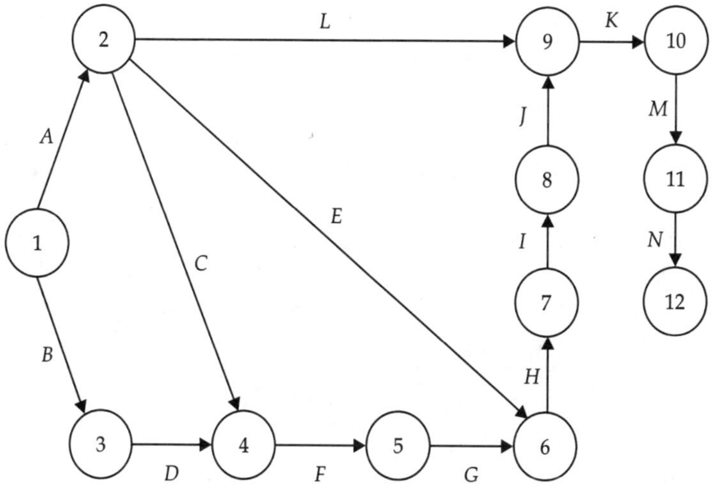

Fig. 35.1

From the above network one can see that the concurrent activities are activity *A* and activity *B*. The activities *C*, *L* and *E* can only be started after the completion of activity *A*. Similarly, activity *F* can be started only after the completion of activities *B* and *F*. Likewise, explanation for other activities can be held.

Example 2: Group discussion, written test and interviews are held in different professional institutes for making selection of students. There are many activities that are required to be conducted before the written test, say for instance deciding the date for conductance of all the related events. The precedence relation could be used to obtain the coordination amongst different activities to accomplish the whole task of selecting and admitting students to any professional course. An ineffective operation of the entire system for a delay at any stage will be the result. The precedence relation for the different activities involved is depicted in Fig. 35.2. The corresponding network for the entire project is shown in Fig. 35.3.

Activity	Description	Immediate predecessors
A	Decide the date, time of the entrance test, group discussion and interview	
B	Decide the examination venue(s)	*A*
C	Call for application through advertisement	*A*
D	Print application form	*A*
E	Despatch applications	*D*, *C*
F	Receive and process applications and send hall tickets	*E*, *B*
G	Set question paper	*A*
H	Arrange invigilators, and examiners	*B*
I	Make seating arrangements	*F*
J	Conduct examination	*G*, *H*, *I*
K	Valuation and announcement of entrance test result	*J*
L	Conduct group discussion and interview	*K*
M	Publish admission result	*L*

Fig. 35.2: Precedence relationships for professional course admission process.

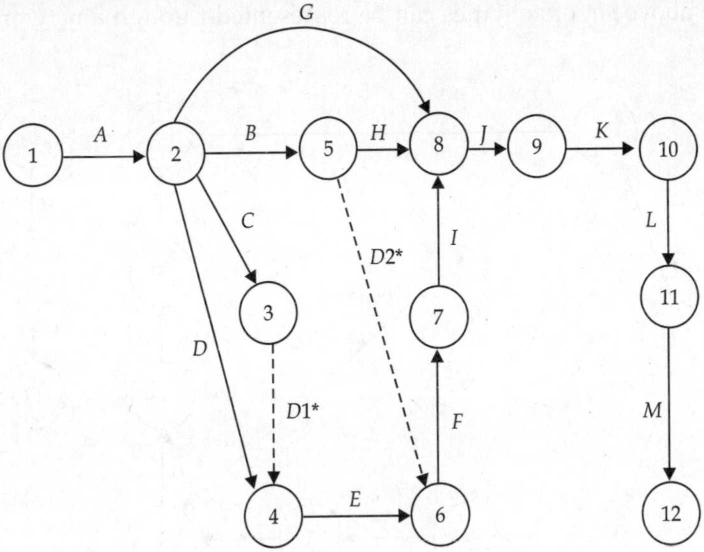

*D1 and D2 are dummy activities

Fig. 35.3: Network for professional course admission process.

The two main basic techniques in project management are:

- Critical Path Method (CPM),
- Project Evaluation and Review Technique (PERT).

The timings for different activities in CPM are deterministic in nature whereas in PERT three main time estimates used for an activity are: optimistic time, pessimistic time and most likely time.

35.2 PHASES OF PROJECT MANAGEMENT

There are three phases for project management: planning, scheduling and controlling. Following steps are involved in the planning phase:

- The project is divided into distinct activities.
- For each activity, the estimated time required is calculated.
- The precedence relations between different activities are established.
- The network diagram is finally constructed.

The start and end times for each activity is determined by the scheduling phase. The time chart or the Gantt chart may be used to summarize the start and end times for each and every activity. The amount of slack time if present for an activity must also be summarized on the same chart. It should be noted that there is always a slack for the non-critical activities.

Continuous monitoring is done in the control phase that uses the arrow diagram and time chart. Progress reporting is also done in the control phase. If any variation is found in the proposed schedule, the same may be updated in the control phase.

35.3 GUIDELINES FOR NETWORK CONSTRUCTION

The different terminologies that are used in the construction of a network are discussed below:

- **Node:** The start and end of an activity is represented using a node.
- **Branch/Arc:** The actual activity consuming certain amount of resources is represented using the Branch/Arc.
- **Precedence relations of activities:** Following information is provided through the precedence relations for any activity:
  - The preceding activities.
  - The following activities.
  - The concurrent activities.

Following is required for network construction:

- List of different individual activities of a project,
- The activity duration estimates
- Precedence relations amongst the different activities of a project.

Rules for Network Construction

For the construction of AOA diagram, the following primary rules are used:

- The tail of an activity is the starting event and the ending event of an activity is known as the head event.
- There should be unique starting node.
- The completion of the network should be represented by a unique node.
- Not more than one arc should be used to represent an activity.
- The two different activities are not needed to have the same starting and ending nodes.
- A dummy activity may be used for indicating the precedence relationship. It's an imaginary activity and the duration is zero for such an activity.

35.4 CRITICAL PATH METHOD (CPM)

The concept of CPM is demonstrated in this section through an example.

Example 3: Figure 35.4 shows the summary of the activities involved in a project. The project is divided into 16 activities.

Activity	Immediate predecessor	Duration (months)
A		1
B		4
C		2
D	*B*	2
E	*B*	3
F	*A, D*	3
G	*A, D*	2
H	*B*	1
I	*C, E*	3
J	*C, E*	2
K	*F*	3
L	*G, H, I*	6
M	*G, H, I*	5
N	*J*	2
P	*K, L*	4
Q	*M, N*	7

Fig. 35.4: Project details.

The following questions need to be answered:

- Construction of CPM
- Determination of critical path
- Computation of free and total floats for non-critical activities

Solution:

- **CPM** is shown in Fig. 35.5.

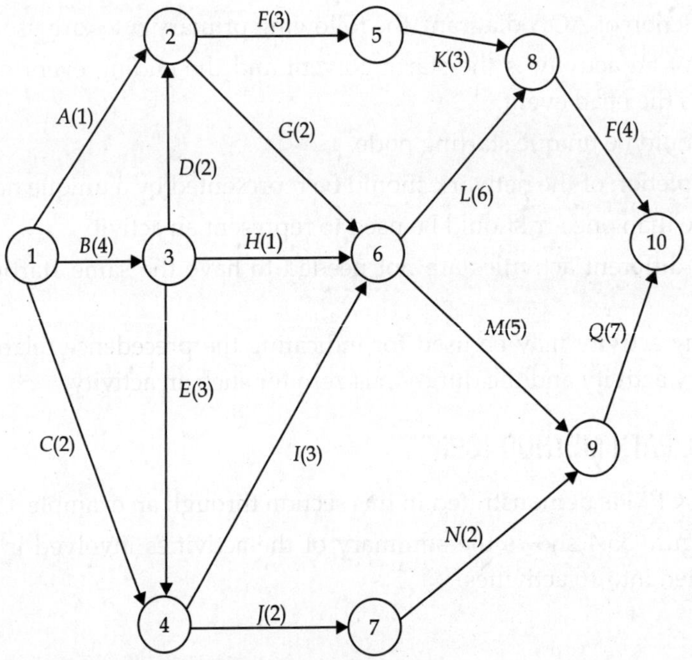

Fig. 35.5: CPM network.

- **Determination of critical path:** The longest path in a network is known as the critical path of a project network. The critical path in a project may be identified by firstly listing all the possible paths between the start node and the end node of a project. The path with the maximum sum of activity times on that path is selected as the critical path.

  However, the above method becomes inefficient for a large network and the details like total and free floats will not be established.

  A different approach to identify the critical path consists of the following two phases:
  - The determination of earliest start time (ES) for all the nodes is done in Phase 1. Phase 1 is also known as the forward pass.
  - The latest completion time (LS) is determined in Phase 2. This phase is also known as the backward pass.

  Let d_{ij} = duration of activity (I, j)

  ES_j = earliest start time of the activities emanating from node j

  LC_j = latest completion time of all the activities terminating at node j

Then, earliest start time and latest completion time can be calculated using the equations 1 and 2:

$$ES_j = \max_i \lfloor ES_i - D_{ij} \rfloor \quad (1)$$

$$LC_i = \min_j \lfloor LC_j - D_{ij} \rfloor \quad (2)$$

The calculation for earliest start time has been shown for node 3:

$$ES_3 = \max_{i=1} \lfloor ES_1 - D_{1,3} \rfloor = 0 + 4 = 4$$

The calculation for the latest completion time is shown for node 9:

$$LC_9 = \max_{j=10} \lfloor LC_{10} - D_{9,10} \rfloor = 22\text{-}7 = 15$$

The calculations for other nodes are shown in Fig. 35.6.

The following conditions should be satisfied for an activity (i, j) to be qualified for being critical:

- $ES_i = LC_i$
- $ES_j = LC_j$
- $ES_j - ES_i = LC_j - LC_i = D_{ij}$

The critical activities as identified after implementing the above conditions are shown with cross lines in Fig. 36.6. The corresponding critical path is 1–3–4–6–9–10 (*B–E–I–M–Q*).

- **Determination of total floats and free floats:** The total float may be defined as the amount of time through which an activity may be delayed without impacting the total project completion time. This can be calculated using equation 3:

$$TF_{ij} = LC_j - ES_j - D_{ij} \quad (3)$$

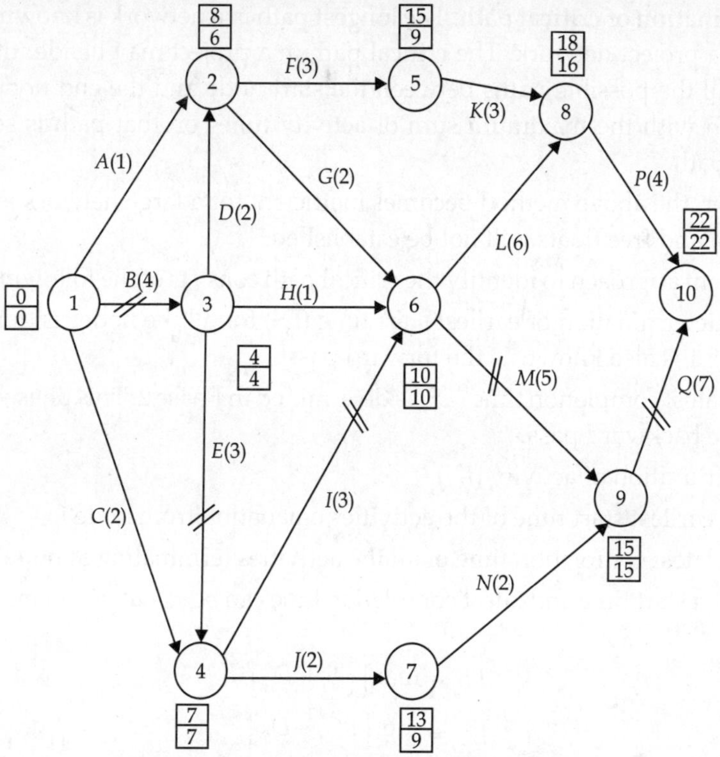

Fig. 35.6: Network with critical path calculations.

The free float on the other hand may be defined as the amount of time the activity can be delayed without impacting the earliest start time of the immediate successor activity. This is calculated using equation 4 below:

$$FF_{ij} = ES_j - ES_i - D_{ij} \tag{4}$$

The summary of the calculations of total and free float is shown in Fig. 35.7.

Activity (i, j)	Duration (D_{ij})	Total float (TF_{ij})	Free float (FF_{ij})
1–2	1	7	5
1–3	4	0	0
1–4	2	5	5
2–5	3	6	0
2–6	2	2	2
3–2	2	2	0
3–4	3	0	0
3–6	1	5	5
4–6	3	0	0
4–7	2	4	0
5–8	3	6	4
6–8	6	2	0
6–9	5	0	0
7–9	2	4	4
8–10	4	2	2
9–10	7	0	0

Fig. 35.7: Total floats and free floats.

It should be noted that any critical activity will have zero total and free float. Using this concept too, one can determine the critical path.

35.5 GANTT CHART/TIME CHART

The preparation of the Gantt chart is the next step followed after the network calculations. The start and completion time of each and every activity is represented on this chart. The calendar schedule for the whole project could be clearly delineated through this chart.

The levelling of resources could also be done using the Gantt chart. The schedule of the non-critical activities could be adjusted whenever there are limitations on the available resource(s) (manpower, equipment, money, etc.). This helps to level the resource requirements smoothly throughout the project execution. Even if there is no restriction on any resource, it is the usual practice to smooth out the resource requirements by resource levelling technique.

The Gantt chart for the example under consideration is shown in Fig. 35.8.

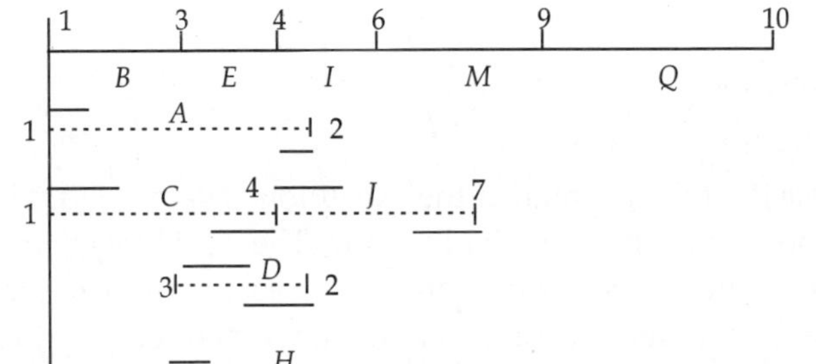

Fig. 35.8: Time chart/Gantt chart.

In Fig. 35.8, the thick line represents the schedule for various critical activities [(1,3), (3,4), (4,6), (6,9) and (9,10)]. The horizontal dashed lines represent the total time span over which a non-critical activity can be performed.

As stated earlier, a non-critical activity will have float in excess of its time duration. So, it is possible to adjust the start and completion time of any non-critical activity over its entire range shown by the dashed lines without delaying the project's completion time. Infinite number of schedules is possible for the non-critical activities. But to give a finite number of schedules, we consider only two types of schedules:

- Earliest start schedule
- Latest start schedule

These are shown by continuous horizontal lines over and below the dashed line showing the time range for execution of a given non-critical activity, respectively.

35.6 PERT (PROJECT EVALUATION AND REVIEW TECHNIQUE)

The activity durations in reality may be probabilistic in nature. Therefore, the probabilistic considerations should be incorporated in obtaining the time durations of the activities in a project.

Following three estimates are used:

- a = optimistic time
- b = pessimistic time
- m = most likely time

The *optimistic time* is a time estimate if the execution is very good. The *pessimistic time* is a time estimate if the execution is very badly done. The *most likely time* is a time estimate if execution is normal. The probabilistic data for project activities generally follow beta distribution. The formula for mean (μ) and variance (σ^2) of the beta distribution are as follows:

$$\mu = (a + 4m + b)/6 \qquad (1)$$

The range for the time estimates is from a to b. The most likely time will be anywhere in between the range from a to b.

The expected project completion time = $\sum \mu_i$, where μ_i is the expected duration of the ith critical activity.

The variance of the project completion time = $\sum_i \sigma_i^2$, where σ_i^2 is the variance of the ith critical activity in the critical path.

As a part of statistical analysis, we may be interested in knowing the probability of completing the project on or before a given due date (C), or we may be interested in knowing the expected project completion time if the probability of completing the project is given.

For the purpose of this analysis, the Beta distribution is approximated to standard normal distribution whose statistic is given by:

$z = (x - \mu)/\sigma$, where x is the actual project completion time; μ = expected project completion time (sum of the expected durations of the critical activities); σ = standard deviation of the expected project completion time (square root of the sum of the variances of all the critical activities).

Therefore, $P(x \le C)$ represents the probability that the project will be completed on or before the C time units. This can be converted into the standard normal statistic z as follows:

$$P[(x - \mu)/\sigma] \le (C - \mu)/\sigma = P[z \le (C - \mu)/\sigma]$$

SECTION XIV
INDUSTRIAL SAFETY

36
Safety Engineering

36.1 EVOLUTION OF SAFETY

The big level expansion started taking form with the beginning of nineteenth century but safety could not become the concern of industries. With expansion of industrial behaviours, the sizes of industries multiplied and so did the number of workers in individual industries. The productivity of workers increased at tremendous rate and also the product excellence was visibly controlled and improved. Though, all these growths did not produce any concern to human values, safety, and common well-being of factory workers.

Through the beginning of twentieth century, lack of safety concern and consciousness began to speak upon the health of the industry. Adverse health effects began to run rampant in job spaces. The number of serious industrial accidents began to rise. It was then that a few enlightened and progressive factory managers started feeling the necessity of abating the causes of rising number of accidents, serious injuries to workers and poor health circumstances in job spaces.

The early thrust started with taking care of cuts and bruises and broken bones of factory workers. The responsibility was mainly entrusted upon personnel managers, maintenance foremen, or plant engineers. Such persons tried to evolve methods of safe working through providing guards on machines, shields on implements or through creation workers to use gloves and wear glasses throughout some specific action. Soon these persons were replaced through safety engineers or supervisors and safety managers. Such requirement was felt greatly through two industry giants, viz., steel industry and rail road establishment. Yet the personnel made responsible to prevent accidents were not specifically trained for the job but were chosen from accessible force based upon their wide experience in a scrupulous industry.

The situation sustained until 1912 when in USA *Cooperative Safety Congress* was organized. The electrical engineers from steel industry took lead in organizing this congress. It resulted in the establishment of *National Safety Council* (NSC) in USA. This body was given charter to take responsibility after prevention of accidents and development of safety programmes. In post-1920 era, many safety codes were formulated through American Standards Association.

The onset of Second World War caused a setback to safety movement both in Europe and America. This era was marked through workers' demand for higher wages, their insistence on unionizing any union rights. There was a perceptible transformation in government attitude towards sacrificing safety thoughts in favour of desire to win war. The management also urbanized false notion that safety was a non-productive action. This setback was short existed and soon the attitudes of governments and management started paying more attention to safety characteristics of industrial workers.

The industries started including newer characteristics in safety concerns. The noise, dust, fumes, heat, mists, and radiation, etc., got incorporated in the rising lists of hazards in industry. This became necessary because the industrial behaviours widened extremely and scopes of industrial behaviours expanded. This renewal of interest was followed through governments paying more attention to safety programmes and big industries began to organize special training to their engineers. These steps helped augment the number of suitably trained personnel in the region of industrial safety. New disciplines were added to safety practice in industry. These were: industrial hygiene, health physics, ergonomics, design engineering, illumination engineering, audiology, and workers' compensation claim management. Each of these meadows had twin targets of safeguarding workers' health and life and improving productivity. Tremendous amount of research job and enunciation of safety theories propelled safety practices into academic body of knowledge and information. It has now become possible for engineers and managers to specialize in safety engineering and safety management through education. It has now become imperative that a chief executive of an industry is equally conscious of safety and excellence. Safety, health, and environmental controls have become essential staff functions. In mainly industries today safety is one of the significant industrial behaviours beside manufacturing, research, design and development, purchase, sales, service and profits.

36.2 IMPROVEMENTS REQUIRED

The outlining of connection of safety engineering, with excellence, productivity, profit, etc., has also tended to make impediments in successful implementation of safety programmes. The safety professionals tend to become overzealous and often are inclined to neglect cost-benefit ratio and payback of their practices. It has also been observed that several workers illustrate resistance to adopt new safety events when confronted first time. A successful safety drive often comes after a number of false starts.

Successful safety programmes are management initiated but workers dependent. It is always significant to take cognizance of workers' comprehension of safety and any specific safety programme. In a survey, a big cross-part of workers was consulted and it was established that employees of big organizations are more safety conscious than those of little organizations. The common feeling in the middle of workers was that safety was the responsibility of the management. They also thought government should create rules for safety and intervene more regularly in this regard. They thought sound safety programmes, training and drills were necessary for safety of workers. A little proportion of workers only thought that they were adequately trained and showed dependence on coworkers for safety thinking that they knew better. It was noted in the survey that the employees who did not receive safety training were liable to experience twice as several on-the-job accidents as those who had received safety training. The workers who had met accidents were not ready to accept their responsibility towards accidents while approximately 85% of them agreed that accidents could have been avoided.

The common consensus among the workers was that safety programmes and training should be organized, frequent inspection and enforcement of safety rules be followed, better and, more safety equipment be provided and their maintenance be ensured.

36.3 SAFETY ORGANIZATION

Every industry necessity has a safety organisation with well-defined objectives and well-recognized functions. It has been experienced that safety policies often fail if safety functions are distributed or made section of behaviours of many departments. Under the system of distributed responsibilities, the safety functions have often been accounted to corporate managers through personnel and human resource department, operational office or legal office. Such practices had often obliterated the successful implementation of safety programmes.

Safety functions become successful if they are controlled through a single department with safety personnel interacting with other behaviours functionally. A top stage corporate manager necessity supervises safety organisation in a big industry. Safety director or manager at industry stage may give statement to corporate manager. There may be many managers reporting to safety director who would take care of special safety functions such as fire, environment, occupational health, claim for compensation, etc. These managers will necessarily interact with all other departments wherever workers are involved.

Stage 1

This is a corporate stage and there should be a company director who will be occupied in formulating safety policies at corporate stage. These policies will be issued from time to time if changes are made. He will have to see that safety audits are made at proper times. His necessity is readily accessible for required advice and guidance to all safety personnel. The company director necessity appoints a common manager safety at company stage.

Stage 2

This is at company stage and will directly give statement to the corporate director. He has to continuously monitor safety policies of the company and bring in relation to the necessary improvement in the light of directives issued from time to time. His necessity also sees that the directives and policies are in accordance with governmental regulatory standards. He should give guidance and assistance for training of safety personnel at several stages and necessity conduct safety audits. The necessity sees that safety records are properly maintained and data and information concerning safety status of the company are accessible.

Stage 3

This stage works at plant stage and would directly give statement to common manager safety. There necessity is four plant safety managers as recognized through four plant safety functions, namely fire safety, environmental management, occupational health, and professional service. Specific circumstances and size of plant may dictate combining two or three of these functions under a single plant stage manager but in all cases the functions should remain separate and identifiable. The development of procedure of implementing safety events on job performance and analyzing safe job performance, readiness and preparedness to trade with emergency situations are the main necessities at this stage. Equally importantly it is the stage where interactions with other behaviours are mainly likely to take layoff. Therefore, a plant manager will coordinate with managers in the regions of design, manufacture, purchase, sale, R&D, etc. A plant manager will have the full responsibility to investigate the injuries to a worker occurring on job/location and create statement to the higher officials.

Stage 4

This stage comprises representatives of safety departments working at shop floor stage or with workers. The personnel will actually implement safety procedures, train workers on procedures, and guide them to adoption of procedure. They will give all support for maintenance of environment and its preservation. Extremely importantly the personnel at stage 4 will conduct safety drills.

36.4 SAFETY FUNCTIONS

In the statement in relation to the safety organization, several functions have been mentioned. Yet, a clear account is lacking. Without much elaboration, a list of safety functions is presented here. The safety functions are:

- Environmental management
- Health and safety information system
- Industrial hygiene
- Industrial safety
- Occupational health
- Property conservation
- Safety in material handling
- Workers' compensation claim management

36.5 WORKPLACE OPERATIONS REQUIRING SAFETY

The operations performed through workers in their workplace are of dissimilar nature but they involve some machine, equipment, and materials. The safety precautions are adopted for machines and operations performed on them. Several operations require hazardous material or material in hazardous state. Here some operations which are either machine/ equipment or material specific are described which would require safety practices to be involved. No effort will be made to describe the safety procedure to be adopted.

- Electrical assembly and fabrication
- Electronic assembly and cleaning
- Use of electrical apparatus
- Use of chemical mediators and chemical treatments
- Use of biological materials and treatments
- Use of acidic and alkaline materials
- Toxic vapour applications
- Use and manufacture of mists, dust
- Use of boiler and of compressed air and gas
- Use of combustible and toxic gases and liquids
- Processing of radioactive sources and treatments
- Painting and mixing of paints
- Spraying of paints and liquid metals
- Welding gas and electric, brazing and soldering
- Wood cutting and working
- Sawing metal and wood
- Sanding
- Sand blasting and shot peening
- Burning and furnace application
- Casting and foundry practice
- Digging
- Climbing
- Masonry job
- Hoisting and lifting
- Machining on lathes and mills
- Shearing
- Cutting
- Drilling
- Jointing

36.6 SAFETY BENEFITS

An industry or a company that follows safety programmes is benefited in many ways. The benefits are shared/flanked by employer and employees directly and consumers are indirectly benefited. A sound safety policy will avoid or reduce greatly the accidents whereby the employer will save cost of lost man-hours and down-machine time. The employer will also save on paying compensation and replacement or repair of equipment. The employees feeling safe in job will illustrate better productivity. Also since a sound safety policy will guarantee an adequate compensation, the employees will do a job without apprehension and psychological pressure. The latter factor often causes accidents. The increased productivity and excellence consciousness will produce goods which will be to the liking of the customer.

37
Occupational Safety

37.1 OCCUPATIONAL HEALTH PROBLEMS

Many health troubles have been established to be rooted in kind of job, equipment and job layoff. It was in the eighteenth century when definite observations were made that workers suffered from job specific diseases. The occupational diseases were established to have dealings with handling of harmful materials, with irregular or unnatural movements of the body and the environment in which the worker worked. In the nineteenth century, the Industrial Revolution brought such changes as introduction of inanimate power to replace man and animal power and also substitution of machines for people. The steam power which replaced animal power posed new threats of injuries which could at times turn fatal. Introduction of new methods for converting raw materials also opened risks of injuries and diseases. A distant reaching consequence of Industrial Revolution was organization and specialization of job resulting in division of job. The specialization unluckily resulted in boredom and inattentiveness causing augment in workplace accidents.

The pioneer efforts in the region of occupational safety were encouraged through specific health troubles. Lung troubles in coal miners were perceived as major health problem in 1800s. The problem was overcome through providing good ventilation and reducing number of working hours. Though, the problem recurred in the beginning of twentieth century both in Great Britain and USA. The resurgence of these troubles invited many governmental and legislative reforms in occupational safety. The coal mining worldwide has posed troubles of health and accidents. Roof collapse and flooding has caused several deaths. Efforts through technology, legislation, and enforcement are continuously made to create mining operation safe.

Silicosis has been recognized as yet another problem faced among miners and tunnel borers when they have to dig through silica. Intense interest for safety against silicosis was aroused in last quarter of last century when electronic industry by silicon based devices grew with highest pace. Mercury poisoning due to use and discharge of mercury nitrate and methyl mercury into water were accounted in 1940s. Again legislative actions were brought in force to fight the menace. Asbestos fibres of microscopic size released from ageing asbestos products are capable of causing lung cancer. The asbestos has been used for many structures and as insulator in power industry. While its use is now cut down to minimum, special equipment and training are mandatory for workers occupied in removal of asbestos from old structures.

Besides materials that are mixed, the rising diversity of materials like many kinds of steels, nonferrous alloys, plastics, composites by fibres and plastics bring their own hazards throughout processing, machining, and casting. There are many procedures being added to extensive conventional procedure list. Explosive forming and explosive welding, photochemical machining, laser machining and chemical machining have introduced disease and accident related risks. The automation of traditional and non-traditional machining procedures have also enlarged the active region of injuries. Many procedures of painting and plating involve continuous breathing of air laden with dangerous compounds. The other procedures of similar nature are grinding, vitreous enameling, and pottering.

Older Worker

Features of Illnesses and Injuries

Just as to the New Jersey Census of Fatal Occupational Injuries, more workers of age 55 and above (n = 234) died than younger workers in three categories: transportation incidents (42% versus 34%), falls (18% versus 14%), and fires/explosions (6% versus 3%) from 1991-2000. The majority of the 234 fatal injuries in older workers throughout this era occurred in the occupations of operators, fabricators, and labourers (34%), precision manufacture, craft, and repair (23%), and technological, sales, and administrative support (15%). Industry clusters mainly affected were construction (20%), government (15%), and transportation and public utilities (15%).

In 2001, a total of 160,231 injuries and illnesses in those of age 55 and older in private industry nationwide required recuperation or absence from job beyond the day of the incident, just as to the U.S. Department of Labour's Bureau of Labour Statistics (BLS). Whereas there were 5930 nonfatal occupational injuries and illnesses that resulted in lost work time in the middle of workers aged 55 and older in the New Jersey private sector. Mainly, of these, reports were in the occupational category of operators, fabricators, and labourers. The industry division mainly affected was services. The nature of injury/illness accounted regularly was mainly sprains and strains. The source of injury/illness was floor and ground surfaces, and falls on the similar stage was mainly the general incident accounted.

Also, in 2001, workers employed in New Jersey State and local governments, experienced a total of 2189 nonfatal occupational injuries and illnesses involving days absent from job. For these workers, mainly the reports were in service occupations and in the services industry. Like their private industry counterparts, the nature of injury/illness mainly accounted was sprains/strains. The mainly frequent source of injury/illness was floor or ground surfaces. Falls on similar stage, overexertion, and coming in touch with substance and equipment were the general incidents accounted.

Furthermore, a BLS revise on median days absent from job—the key survey measure of severity—accounted that older workers may sustain especially disabling circumstances such as broken bones and multiple injuries more regularly than younger workers; and similar injuries, such as a fracture, requires a longer recuperation time for older workers. This revise also indicated older workers became disabled through a fall more often than younger workers.

What can the Older Worker do?

Talk about medical circumstances and your skill to job with your personal physician. Underlying medical circumstances may put you at increased risk and susceptibility to injury. Early discovery and treatment of sensory impairments (hearing loss or visual impairment) can reduce your risk for injury. Wellness plays a critical section - take steps to lower your risk of disease. Augment your knowledge in relation to the chronic diseases such as heart disease, cancer, diabetes, osteoporosis, and arthritis.

Understanding the role these circumstances can play in rising occupational injury is the first step towards reducing your risk of injury. Chronic diseases are in the middle of the 'mainly general' and costly of all health troubles, but they are also in the middle of the 'mainly preventable'.

37.2 TAKING CARE OF OCCUPATIONAL SAFETY

The important development in occupational safety and health has been the introduction of legislative events adopted through many governments. Such legislations have specifically been based upon the principle of assuring safe and healthful working circumstances to every working man and woman with the objective of preserving human possessions.

The occupational health and safety Acts have purposes including the following:

- Encouraging employers and employees to reduce workplace hazards.
- Implementing new safety and health programmes.
- Improving the existing safety and health programmes.
- Encouraging research to innovate ways of dealing with workplace safety and health troubles.
- Establishing the rights of employers and employees concerning improvement of workplace safety and health.
- Monitoring the job-related injuries and illness through a system of reporting and record-keeping.
- Raising number and improving the competence of safety and health professionals through organized training.
- Generating information data on injuries, diseases, training programmes and safety personnel.

The occupational safety Acts are planned to cover all employees (even if single) and all kinds of employers from manufacturing and construction to retail and service organisation. The specific regions to be taken care of through Acts are: fire protection, electrical installations, sanitation, air excellence maintenance and repair of machines, posting of notices and warnings, reporting of accidents and illness, maintaining written compliance programmes and training employees. It is imperative that government should frame rules that are enforceable. The rules which cannot be enforced create employees and employers equally disillusioned and the safety is affected. It is further essential that the employers should know the standards applicable to their industrial practices. Provision of protection equipment and gears may be at times hard and costly but employers forced through safety rules enforcement power will have to create all arrangements in workplace. Many examples of protection events may vary from such easy items as safety hats, overalls, hand gloves, eye shields, or goggles to radioactive safety gears and radiation measuring devices. The last mentioned are not only necessary in nuclear processing plants but also establishment occupied in radiological non-destructive testing.

The Coverage

This ordinance covers approximately all workplaces. In addition to factories, construction locations and catering establishments, other spaces, such as offices, laboratories, shopping arcades, educational organizations also approach under the ambit of the law. Though, there are a few exceptions, namely:

- An aircraft or vessel in a public layoff;
- The layoff occupied through the driver of a land transport vehicle when it is in a public layoff (but other employees working in the vehicle are sheltered);
- Domestic premises at which only domestic servants are employed; and
- Spaces where only self-employed persons work.

The Roles of the Duty holders

Under this ordinance, everyone has a role to play in creating a safe and healthy workplace.

- Employers should contribute to safety and health in their workplaces through:
  - providing and maintaining plant and job systems that do not endanger safety or health;
  - arrangement for ensuring safety and health in connection with the use, handling, storage or transport of plant or substances;
  - providing all necessary information, instruction, training, and supervision;
  - providing and maintaining safe access to and egress from the workplaces; and
  - providing and maintaining a safe and healthy job environment.

- Occupiers of premises should take responsibility for ensuring that
  - the premises;
  - the means of access to and egress from the premises; and
  - any plant or substance kept at the premises

  are safe and without risks to health to any person working on the premises, even if they do not directly employ that person on the premises.
- Employees should also contribute to safety and health in the workplaces through:
  - taking care for the safety and health of persons at the workplace; and
  - by any equipment or following any system or job practices provided through their employers.

Enforcement of the Ordinance

The Commissioner for Labour is empowered to issue improvement notices and suspension notices against action of workplace which may make an imminent hazard to the employees. Failure to comply with the notices constitutes an offence punishable through a fine of HK$200,000 and HK$500,000 respectively and imprisonment of up to 12 months.

Occupational Safety and Health Regulation

The Occupational Safety and Health Regulation, made under the ordinance, sets down some vital necessities for accident prevention, fire precaution, workplace environment management, hygiene at workplaces, first aid, as well as what employers and employees are expected to do in manual handling operations. The main provisions of the Regulation are:

- To prevent accidents through:
  - Ensuring that the plant is properly intended, constructed and maintained and that all dangerous sections are effectively guarded;
  - Ensuring that all dangerous regions are securely fenced.
- To prevent fire through:
  - Providing illuminated 'EXIT' signs in excess of all exits and clear directions to them;
  - Keeping all means of escape in a safe condition and free from obstruction;
  - Making sure that all exit doors can easily be opened from inside the workplace or are unlocked;
  - Providing appropriate and adequate fire safety events.
- To give a safe and healthy job environment by:
  - Keeping the workplace clean and ensuring that it is adequately lit and ventilated;
  - Providing adequate drainage.
- To ensure hygiene by:
  - Providing adequate lavatory and washing facilities, as well as adequate supply of drinking water.

- To give first aid by:
  - Keeping adequate first aid facilities on the premises and appointing designated employees to take care of this.
- To ensure safe manual handling operations through:
  - Assessing and reviewing risks to the safety and health of employees who undertake manual handling operations;
  - Providing proper training and other necessary protective events for employees who undertake manual handling operations.

37.3 STANDARDS FOR OCCUPATIONAL SAFETY AND HEALTH

Many standards to serve the cause of occupational safety and health are formulated. The industries are required to adhere to such standards. The standards are described here in brief.

37.3.1 Confined Space Standards

Many examples of workplace exist in industrial practice where spaces are characterized through many restrictions. Such spaces are recognized as:

- Manholes,
- Exhaust ducts,
- Boilers,
- Silos,
- Vats,
- Pipelines,
- Underground vaults,
- Storage tanks, etc.

The features of such confined spaces are: limited openings for entry and exit, poor natural ventilation, no continuous human occupancy. The employer's necessity ensures safety of employees when working in such confined legroom and employee's necessity does not have any adverse health effect. Only specified permitted employee's necessity is allowed to enter such spaces. It means that the industry necessity has permit system if job is to be done in these spaces. The standards necessity is formulated to.

- identify spaces that can be entered through permit,
- restrict entry to recognized legroom only to permit holders,
- adopt such job practices which would avoid hazard, and
- monitor the circumstances in confined legroom to see any hazardous situation likely to arise and to seal the legroom occasionally to clean or remove any cause of hazard.

All industries concerned in such confined legroom necessity are made to follow these standards irrespective of number of workers.

37.3.2 Hazardous Waste and Material Standards

Besides many industries—chemical, metallurgical, textile, leather, nuclear—there are several situations where workers are subjected to hazardous materials. The other group comprises firefighters, police officers, ambulance and several hospital personnel. Standards in respect of occupational hazards are formulated to take care of the following.

- Each worker necessity has undergone training to identify, evaluate, and manage hazardous material. His necessity is able to give an emergency response to hazardous situation.
- Each hazardous location necessity be examined and evaluated for its features before workers are allowed entry. This will pre-decide anti-hazard method and procedure.
- A location management programme necessity identifies zonal plan, communication point, and station for medical assistance. Out of many inculcated job habits in hazardous environment, teamwork necessity takes precedence.
- Prior training on specific hazardous material necessity is always undertaken.
- Periodical medical examination of workers handling hazardous waste/material is required to be arranged.
- Besides engineering controls to restrict exposure risk, the workers necessity use personal protective gear and equipment.
- Air monitoring to measure hazardous material necessity be a routine practice.
- The identities including names, official location, and specialization of key personnel necessity are widely publicized among the workers dealing with such materials and situations.
- The workers leaving the hazard filled legroom necessity follow decontamination procedure.
- There necessity for contingency plans to trade with emergency situation in which coordination of all concerned department of the company and any outside agency necessity be ensured.

37.4 RECORD KEEPING

Systematic procedure for collecting information on employees' health, working circumstances and any accidents require be to recognized in a company. Many differences had flanked by employers and employees in respect of both health circumstances and safety events. The employers have complained that government sponsored documents could be interpreted in dissimilar ways whereas the employees had the grudge that organization came to know about the emerging safety regions quite belatedly. The requirement of record keeping may contain the following:

- Good excellence of records necessity is prepared in simplified method.
- Records should cover stakes of all vulnerable employees.
- Employees should have access to records.
- Guidelines for record keeping necessity are clearly outlined.

It is significant to have general average for recording and reporting occupational illness and injury in dissimilar organizations. One such average defines an occupational injury as cut, fracture, sprain, or amputation resulting from a job related accident or from exposure involving a single incident in job environment. An occupational illness is defined as any abnormal condition or disorder other than one resulting from occupational injury caused through working in the existing working environment. Chronic illnesses or diseases resulting from inhalation, absorption, ingestion, or direct get in touch with toxic substances or harmful mediator's necessity also are incorporated in lists. All occupational illnesses or injuries resulting in one or more of the following necessity are accounted.

- Death of one or more workers.
- Absence from job for one or more days.
- Restricted motion or restriction to the job an employee can do.
- Loss of consciousness of one or more workers.
- Transfer of a worker to another job.
- Treatment required through a worker which is not in the first aid list.

A sound policy of keeping information and maintaining transparency may be fulfilled through creating records of individual and a summary of all incidents. It is easily understood that record keeping in two formats will greatly help improve working circumstances of employees while facilitating employers in implementing safety and prevention of illness programme related to any job. Such record keeping may also bring out lacunae in safety policies, require for training or lack of protecting equipment. The government agencies may also stay an eye on industry in respect of occupational health and safety.

37.5 INCIDENCE RATES

From records rates of incidences such as injury, illness, death, number of hours restricted from job can be calculated as percentage of total number of hours worked. All these data are recorded in the Log given in format B. The total number of hours worked is calculated on the foundation of 40 hours per week.

If T denote total number of hours worked through all employees, then the incidence rate

$$\text{IR} = N \times \frac{\text{No. of weeks in a year} \times \text{No. of hr. in week}}{T} \times 100$$

Number of weeks in a year is usually taken as 50, with allowance two week non-working days.

Instance

Number of employees that received first aid and did not work for 3-4 hours, and the factory worked for 50 weeks throughout the year. Number of employees is 40. Calculate total number of accessible hours for job, injury incidence rate, rate of cases in which job days were lost, rate of cases in which job hours were lost.

Solution

Number of hours worked by all employees during the year

T = 40 employees × 50 weeks × 40 hours per week

= 80, 000 hours

Injury rate $(IR)_i = 5 \times ((50 \times 40)/\ 80,000) \times 100 = 12.5\ \%$

Rate of cases in which number of days were lost

$(IR)_{wd} = 2 \times ((50 \times 40)/80,000) \times 100 = 5\%$

Rate of cases in which work hours were lost

$(IR)_{wh} = 3 \times ((50 \times 40)/\ 80,000) \times 100 = 7.5\%$

Work hours lost = 2 workers absent for 2 days × working hours per day + 3 workers lost work hours of 4 each

$$= 2 \times 2 \times 8 + 3 \times 4 = 32 + 12 = 44 \text{ hours}$$

Rate of work hours lost

$= (44/80,000) \times 100 = 0.055\%$

37.6 INFORMATION DISSEMINATION

The purpose of record keeping is best served if information is timely disseminated. The employees are required to be informed on all health issues concerning them and this purpose is easily achieved through posting information and notices. The site of posting should be permanent and the one where notices are displayed routinely. Following should be displayed regularly.

- Rights and responsibilities of employees in respect of occupational health and injuries. The government agencies often print and publish posters in this context. Such posters are displayed from time to time in general spaces like clubs, lunch rooms and job lay.
- The notices and citations received from government regulating agencies are likewise displayed. A copy of notice relating to any safety violation should be displayed close to the location of violation. Such notice necessity remains displayed for three days or until violation is corrected whichever is earlier.
- The summary sheet of all incidences of illness and injury as presented in Log sheet of format B necessity is displayed in the beginning of calendar year. This Log sheet necessity remains displayed for an era of one month.

- Copies of safety rules as stipulated in industrial laws should be provided to any employee who demands it.
- The records of any steps taken through management for safety of workers in respect of hazardous materials and other risky practices should be accessible to employees on demand.

37.7 GOVERNMENT RESPONSIBILITIES

Besides passing legislations, creation rules and regulations the government has to keenly watch health and safety circumstances of the industry. Government establishes agencies to keep watch on industries and businesses. Such agencies may be accorded compliance power through inspection, surveillance, meetings, and interviews. They may also reserve the right to test samples of materials understood to be causing health troubles. The personnel from compliance power may visit a workplace or many workplaces in an establishment, any location, or facility of any organization. Such visits are made without prior intimation and providing any information prior to visit is violation of Law. Only under exceptional circumstances the employers require to be informed of inspection.

Throughout the visit the employers are required to illustrate all facilities to protect employees from illness and injuries, appraise power of their safety programmes and training, and also illustrate records of illness and injury kept in Log format. The inspectors may like to meet employers and employees in joint as well as separate meetings. The locations of potential risks and hazardous material will normally receive greater attention and questioning. The compliance officer necessity of course carries his identity and authorization and is presented on request. Such inspection visits are often preceded through opening conferences in which representatives of employers and employees are present. They are also followed through closing conference in which open discussions and remarks through both employers and employees will be encouraged.

The compliance officer necessity follows the visit through actions in the light of law applicable to scrupulous industry. The follow-up action could be an easy statement (citation) in which violations are mentioned and warnings given with time limits prescribed to remove violation. The follow-up action could also be imposition of fine within legally prescribed limits or even notice for closure of industry. The employer will, of course, have the right to appeal and challenge any action in the court of law. The citation served through compliance power will be required to mention the following:

- Other than serious violation – which is not likely to result in death or serious physical harm? There may be discretionary penalty on each violation.
- Willful violation – which the employer commits intentionally and knowingly. The employer establishes awareness of circumstances volatile of safety and health events and takes no steps to eliminate them.

- The penalty may be imposed for willful violation depending upon whether it is first time or repeated. Repeat violation may be of any order or intensity that attracts strict action from compliance power.
- Failure to correct prior violation.

In addition to serving citation on violations of rules the compliance power has to look at all the records of incidences of illness and injuries, posting of reports and citations, notifying rules and potential risks and also arrangement of training. Falsification of records of illnesses or injuries is to be taken extremely seriously through inspection authorities. All these actions are to be taken with express intent of improving working circumstances of workers and minimizing occupational ill health and injuries.

Through legal procedure and rights, the employer is permitted to appeal to power or challenge a penalty in the court of law. The employer will be required to spell out clearly the steps taken for compliance, additional time required for further compliance and reasons for delay, the steps taken to protect employees from job related risks throughout interim era. The employer will also have to assure that detailed information has been properly posted for the benefit of the employees.

SECTION XV
ENGINEERING ECONOMICS

38
Elements of Economics

This chapter discusses the elements of economics and the interaction between its various components. This is followed by an analysis of the need and scope of engineering economics. Later, elements of cost and break-even analysis are presented.

38.1 ECONOMICS

Economics is the science that deals with the production and consumption of goods and services and the distribution and rendering of these for human welfare.

The following are the economic goals.

- A high level of employment
- Price stability
- Efficiency
- An equitable distribution of income
- Growth

Some of the above goals are interdependent. The economic goals are not always complementary; in many cases they are in conflict. For example, any move to have a significant reduction in unemployment will lead to an increase in inflation.

38.1.1 Flow in an Economy

Households and businesses are the two major entities in a simple economy. Business organizations use various economic resources like land, labour and capital which are provided by households to produce consumer goods and services which will be used by them. Business organizations make payment of money to the households for receiving various resources. The households, in turn, make payment of money to business organizations for receiving consumer goods and services. This cycle shows the interdependence between the two major entities in simple economy.

38.1.2 Law of Supply and Demand

An interesting aspect of the economy is that the demand and supply of a product are interdependent and they are sensitive with respect to the price of that product. The interrelationships between them are shown in Fig. 38.1.

From Fig. 38.1 it is clear that when there is a decrease in the price of a product, the demand for the product increases and its supply decreases. At the same time, lowering of the price of the product makes the producers restrain from releasing more quantities of the product in the market. Hence, the supply of the product is decreased. The point of intersection of the supply curve and the demand curve is known as the equilibrium point. At the price corresponding to this point, the quantity of supply is equal to the quantity of demand. Hence, this point is called the equilibrium point.

Factors Influencing Demand

The shape of the demand curve is influenced by the following factors:

- Income of the people
- Prices of related goods
- Tastes of consumers

If the income level of the people increases significantly, then their purchasing power will naturally improve. This would definitely shift the demand curve to the north-east direction as shown in Fig. 38.1. A converse situation will shift the demand curve to the south-west direction.

If, for instance, the price of television sets is lowered drastically its demand would naturally go up. As a result, the demand for its associated product, namely VCDs would also increase. Hence, the prices of related goods influences the demand of a product.

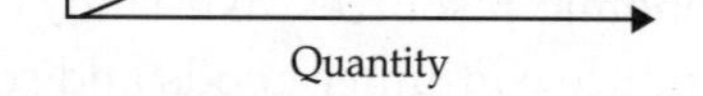

Fig. 38.1. Demand and supply curve.

Over a period of time, the preference of the people for a particular product may increase, which in turn, will affect its demand. For instance, diabetic people prefer to have sugar-free products. If the incidence of diabetes rises naturally there will be increased demand for sugar-free products.

Factors Influencing Supply

The shape of the supply curve is affected by the following factors:

- Cost of the inputs
- Technology
- Weather
- Prices of related goods

If the cost of inputs increases, then naturally, the cost of the product will go up. In such a situation, at the prevailing price of the product the profit margin per unit will be less. The producers will then reduce the production quantity, which in turn, will affect the supply of the product. For instance, if the prices of fertilizers and cost of labour are increased significantly, in agriculture, the profit margin per bag of paddy will be reduced. So, the farmers will reduce the area of cultivation, and hence the quantity of supply of paddy will be reduced at the prevailing prices of the paddy.

If there is an advancement in technology used in the manufacture of the product in the long run, there will be a reduction in the production cost per unit. This will enable the manufacturer to have a greater profit margin per unit at the prevailing price of the product. Hence, the producer will be tempted to supply more quantity to the market.

Weather also has a direct bearing on the supply of products. For example, demand for woollen products will increase during winter. This means the prices of woollen goods will be increased in winter. So, naturally, manufacturers will supply more volume of woollen goods during winter.

Again, take the case of television sets. If the price of TV sets is lowered significantly, then its demand would naturally go up. As a result, the demand for associated products like VCDs would also go up. Over a period of time, this will lead to an increase in the price of VCDs, which would result in more supply of VCDs.

38.2 CONCEPT OF ENGINEERING ECONOMICS

Science is a field of study where the basic principles of different physical systems are formulated and tested. Engineering is the application of science. It establishes varied application systems based on different scientific principles. From the discussions in the previous section, it is clear that price has a major role in deciding the demand and supply of a product. Hence, from the organization's point of view, efficient and effective functioning of the organization would certainly help it to provide goods/services at a lower cost which in turn will enable it to fix a lower price for its goods or services.

The following section discusses the different types of efficiency and their impact on the operation of businesses and the definition and scope of engineering economics.

38.2.1 Types of Efficiency

Efficiency of a system is generally defined as the ratio of its output to input. The efficiency can be classified into technical efficiency and economic efficiency.

Technical Efficiency

It is the ratio of the output to input of a physical system. The physical system may be a diesel engine, a machine working in a shop floor, a furnace, etc.

Technical efficiency (%) = (Output/Input) * 100

The technical efficiency of a diesel engine is as follows:

Technical efficiency (%) = (Heat equivalent of mechanical energy produced/Heat equivalent of fuel used) × 100

In practice, technical efficiency can never be more than 100%. This is mainly due to frictional loss and incomplete combustion of fuel, which are considered to be unavoidable phenomena in the working of a diesel engine.

Economic Efficiency

Economic efficiency is the ratio of output to input of a business system.

Economic efficiency (%) = (Output/Input) * 100 = (Worth/Cost) * 100

'Worth' is the annual revenue generated by way of operating the business and 'cost' is the total annual expenses incurred in carrying out the business. For the survival and growth of any business, the economic efficiency should be more than 100%.

Economic efficiency is also called 'productivity'. There are several ways of improving productivity.

- Increased output for the same input
- Decreased input for the same output
- By a proportionate increase in the output which is more than the proportionate increase in the input
- By a proportionate decrease in the input which is more than the proportionate decrease in the output
- Through simultaneous increase in the output with decrease in the input.

Increased output for the same input: In this strategy, the output is increased while keeping the input constant. Let us assume that in a steel plant, the layout of the existing facilities is not proper. By slightly altering the location of the billet-making section, and bringing it closer to the furnace which produces hot metal, the scale formation at the top of ladles will be considerably reduced. The molten metal is usually carried in ladles to the billet-making section. In the long run, this would give more yield in terms of tonnes of billet produced. In this exercise, there is no extra cost involved. The only task is the relocation of the billet-making facility which involves an insignificant cost.

Decreased input for the same output: In this strategy, the input is decreased to produce the same output. Let us assume that there exists a substitute raw material to manufacture a product and it is available at a lower price. If we can identify such a material and use it for manufacturing the product, then certainly it will reduce the input. In this exercise, the job of the purchase department is to identify an alternate substitute material. The process of identification does not involve any extra cost. So, the productivity ratio will increase because of the decreased input by way of using cheaper raw materials to produce the same output.

Less proportionate increase in output is more than that of the input: Consider the example of introducing a new product into the existing product mix of an organization. Let us assume that the existing facilities are not fully utilized and the R&D wing of the company has identified a new product which has a very good market and which can be manufactured with the surplus facilities of the organization. If the new product is taken up for production, it will lead to:

- An increase in the revenue of the organization by way of selling the new product in addition to the existing product mix.
- An increase in the material cost and operation and maintenance cost of machineries because of producing the new product.

If we examine these two increases closely, the proportionate increase in the revenue will be more than the proportionate increase in the input cost. Hence, there will be a net increase in the productivity ratio.

When proportionate decrease in input is more than that of the output: Let us consider the converse of the previous example, i.e., dropping an uneconomical product from the existing product mix. This will result in the following:

- A decrease in the revenue of the organization.
- A decrease in the material cost, and operation and maintenance cost of machinery.

If we closely examine these two decreases, we will see that the proportionate decrease in the input cost will be more than the proportionate decrease in the revenue. Hence, there will be a net increase in the productivity ratio.

Simultaneous increase in output and decrease in input: Let us assume that there are advanced automated technologies like robots and automated guided vehicle systems (AGVS), available in the market which can be employed in the organization we are interested in. If we employ these modern tools, then:

- There will be a drastic reduction in the operation cost. Initially, the cost on equipment would be very high. But, in the long run, the reduction in the operation cost would break-even the high initial investment and offer more savings on the input.
- These advanced facilities would help in producing more products because they do not experience fatigue. The increased production will yield more revenue.

In this example, in the long run, there is an increase in the revenue and a decrease in the input. Hence, the productivity ratio will increase at a faster rate.

38.2.2 Definition and Scope of Engineering Economics

As stated earlier, efficient functioning of any business organization would enable it to provide goods/services at a lower price. In the process of managing organizations, the managers at different levels should take appropriate economic decisions which will help in minimizing investment, operating and maintenance expenditures besides increasing the revenue, savings and other related gains of the organization.

Definition

Engineering economics deals with the methods that enable one to take economic decisions towards minimizing costs and/or maximizing benefits to business organizations.

Scope

The issues that are covered in this book are elementary economic analysis, interest formulae, bases for comparing alternatives, present worth method, future worth method, annual equivalent method, rate of return method, replacement analysis, depreciation, evaluation of public alternatives, inflation adjusted investment decisions, make or buy decisions, inventory control, project management, value engineering, and linear programming.

38.3 ELEMENTS OF COSTS

Cost can be broadly classified into variable cost and overhead cost. Variable cost varies with the volume of production while overhead cost is fixed, irrespective of the production volume.

Variable cost can be further classified into direct material cost, direct labour cost, and direct expenses. The overhead cost can be classified into factory overhead, administration overhead, selling overhead, and distribution overhead.

Direct material costs are those costs of materials that are used to produce the product. Direct labour cost is the amount of wages paid to the direct labour involved in the production activities. Direct expenses are those expenses that vary in relation to the production volume, other than the direct material costs and direct labour costs.

Overhead cost is the aggregate of indirect material costs, indirect labour costs and indirect expenses. Administration overhead includes all the costs that are incurred in administering the business. Selling overhead is the total expense that is incurred in the promotional activities and the expenses relating to sales force. Distribution overhead is the total cost of shipping the items from the factory site to the customer sites.

The selling price of a product is derived as shown below:

(a) Direct material costs + Direct labour costs + Direct expenses = Prime cost
(b) Prime cost + Factory overhead = Factory cost
(c) Factory cost + Office and administrative overhead = Costs of production
(d) Cost of production + Opening finished stock – Closing finished stock
= Cost of goods sold
(e) Cost of goods sold + Selling and distribution overhead = Cost of sales
(f) Cost of sales + Profit = Sales
(g) Sales/Quantity sold = Selling price per unit

In the above calculations, if the opening finished stock is equal to the closing finished stock, then the cost of production is equal to the cost of goods sold.

38.4 OTHER COSTS/REVENUES

The following are the costs/revenues other than the costs which are presented in the previous section:

- Marginal cost
- Marginal revenue
- Sunk cost
- Opportunity cost

38.4.1 Marginal Cost

Marginal cost of a product is the cost of producing an additional unit of that product. Let the cost of producing 20 units of a product be Rs. 10,000, and the cost of producing 21 units of the same product be Rs. 10,045. Then the marginal cost of producing the 21st unit is Rs. 45.

38.4.2 Marginal Revenue

Marginal revenue of a product is the incremental revenue of selling an additional unit of that product. Let, the revenue of selling 20 units of a product be Rs. 15,000 and the revenue of selling 21 units of the same product be Rs. 15,085. Then, the marginal revenue of selling the 21st unit is Rs. 85.

38.4.3 Sunk Cost

This is known as the past cost of an equipment/asset. Let us assume that an equipment has been purchased for Rs. 1,00,000 about three years back. If it is considered for replacement, then its present value is not Rs. 1,00,000. Instead, its present market value should be taken as the present value of the equipment for further analysis. So, the purchase value of the equipment in the past is known as its sunk cost. The sunk cost should not be considered for any analysis done from now onwards.

38.4.4 Opportunity Cost

In practice, if an alternative (X) is selected from a set of competing alternatives (X,Y), then the corresponding investment in the selected alternative is not available for any other purpose. If the same money is invested in some other alternative (Y), it may fetch some return. Since the money is invested in the selected alternative (X), one has to forego the return from the other alternative (Y). The amount that is foregone by not investing in the other alternative (Y) is known as the opportunity cost of the selected alternative (X). So the opportunity cost of an alternative is the return that will be foregone by not investing the same money in another alternative.

Consider that a person has invested a sum of Rs. 50,000 in shares. Let the expected annual return by this alternative be Rs. 7500. If the same amount is invested in a fixed deposit, a bank will pay a return of 18%. Then, the corresponding total return per year for the investment in the bank is Rs. 9000. This return is greater than the return from shares. The foregone excess return of Rs. 1500 by way of not investing in the bank is the opportunity cost of investing in shares.

38.5 BREAK-EVEN ANALYSIS

The main objective of break-even analysis is to find the cut-off production volume from where a firm will make profit. Let S = selling price per unit, v = variable cost per unit, FC = fixed cost per period and Q = volume of production.

The total sales revenue (S) of the firm is given by the following formula:

$$S = s \times Q$$

The total cost of the firm for a given production volume is

$$TC = \text{Total variable cost} + \text{Fixed cost} = v \times Q + FC$$

The linear plots of the above two equations are shown in Fig. 38.2. The intersection point of the total sales revenue line and the total cost line is called the break-even point. The corresponding volume of production on the X-axis is known as the break-even sales quantity. At the intersection point, the total cost is equal to the total revenue. This point is also called the no-loss or no-gain situation. For any production quantity which is less than the break-even quantity, the total cost is more than the total revenue. Hence, the firm will be making loss.

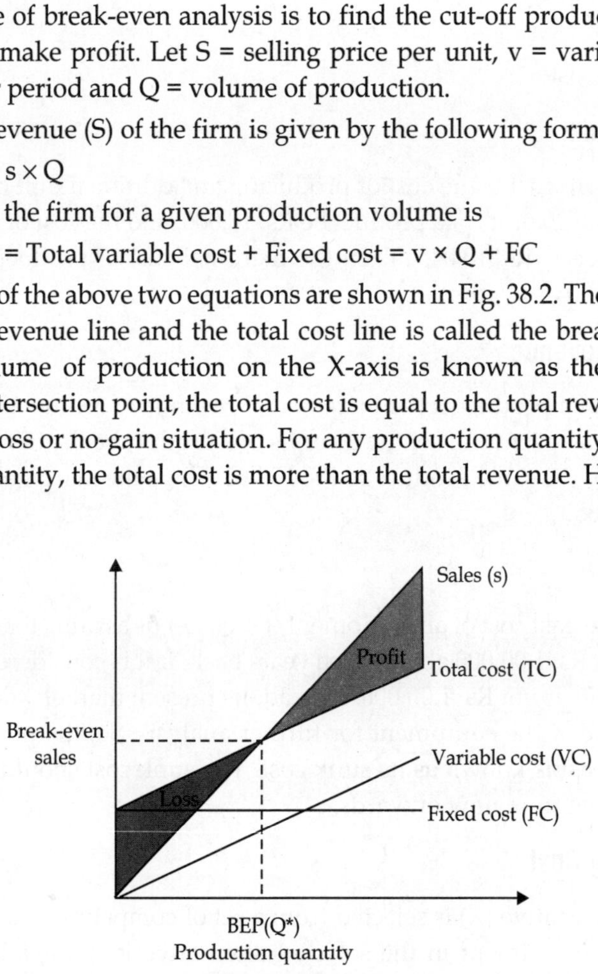

Fig. 38.2: Break-even chart.

For any production quantity which is more than the break-even quantity, the total revenue will be more than the total cost. Hence, the firm will be making profit.

Profit = Sales – (Fixed cost + Variable costs)= $s \times Q - (FC + v \times Q)$

The formulae to find the break-even quantity and break-even sales quantity

Break-even quantity = {(Fixed cost)/(Selling price/unit) – (Variable cost/unit) × (Selling price/unit)}

= (FC)/(s-v) (in units)

Break-even sales = {(Fixed cost)/(Selling price/unit) – (Variable cost/unit)} × Selling price/unit

= FC/ (s – v) × s (Rs.)

The contribution is the difference between the sales and the variable costs. The margin of safety (M.S.) is the sales over and above the break-even sales. The formulae to compute these values are:

Contribution = Sales – Variable costs Contribution/unit

= Selling price/unit – Variable cost/unit

M.S. = Actual sales – Break-even sales

= (Profit/Contribution) × Sales

M.S. as a per cent of sales = (M.S./Sales) × 100

Example 1: Delta Ltd. has the following details:

Fixed cost = Rs. 20,00,000

Variable cost per unit = Rs. 100 Selling price per unit = Rs. 200

Find

(a) The break-even sales quantity;

(b) The break-even sales;

(c) If the actual production quantity is 60,000, find

(i) contribution and

(ii) Margin of safety by all methods.

Solution:

Fixed cost (FC) = Rs. 20,00,000

Variable cost per unit (v) = Rs. 100

Selling price per unit (s) = Rs. 200

(a) Break-even quantity = FC/(s-v)= 20,00,000/(200-100)

= 20,00,000/100 = 20,000 units

(b) Break-even sales = FC/(s – v) × s (Rs.)

= {20,00,000/(200 – 100)} × 200

= (20,00,000/100) × 200 = Rs. 40,00,000

(c) (i) Contribution = Sales – Variable cost

= s × Q – v × Q

= 200 × 60,000 – 100 × 60,000

= 1,20,00,000 – 60,00,000

= Rs. 60,00,000

(ii) Margin of safety

Method I:

M.S. = Sales – Break-even sales

= $60,000 \times 200$ – 40,00,000

= 1,20,00,000 – 40,00,000 = Rs. 80,00,000

Method II:

M.S. = (Profit/Contribution) $\times$ Sales

Profit = Sales – (FC + v $\times$ Q)

= $60,000 \times 200$ – (20,00,000 + $100 \times 60,000$)

= 1,20,00,000 – 80,00,000

= Rs. 40,00,000

M.S. = (40,00,000/60,00,000) $\times$ 1,20,00,000 = Rs. 80,00,000

M.S. as a per cent of sales = (80,00,000/1,20,00,000) $\times$ 100 = 67%

38.6 PROFIT / VOLUME RATIO (P/V RATIO)

P/V ratio is a valid ratio which is useful for further analysis. The different formulae for the P/V ratio are as follows:

P/V ratio = Contribution/Sales = (Sales - Variable costs)/Sales

The relationship between BEP and P/V ratio is as follows:

BEP = Fixed cost/P/V ratio

The following formula helps us find the M.S. using the P/V ratio:

M.S. = Profit/P/V ratio

Example 2: Consider the following data of a company for the year 1998:

Sales = Rs. 1,20,000

Fixed cost = Rs. 25,000 Variable cost = Rs. 45,000

Find the following:

(a) Contribution

(b) Profit

(c) BEP

(d) M.S.

Solution:

(a) Contribution = Sales – Variable costs

= Rs. 1,20,000 – Rs. 45,000

= Rs. 75,000

(b) Profit = Contribution – Fixed cost

= Rs. 75,000 – Rs. 25,000

= Rs. 50,000

(c) BEP

P/V ratio = Contribution/Sales

= $(75{,}000/1{,}20{,}000) \times 100 = 62.50\%$

BEP = Fixed cost/ P/V ratio = $(25{,}000/62.50) \times 100$ = Rs. 40,000

(d) M.S. = (Profit/P/ V ratio) = $(50{,}000/62.50) \times 100$ = Rs. 80,000

39
Replacement and Maintenance Analysis

39.1 INTRODUCTION

Several facilities are used by organisations providing goods and services. Machinery and equipment are required directly by service oriented organisations to carry out their operations effectively. To ensure that the quality of service provided is not poor, a continuous monitoring of all such facilities is required. Besides the quality of service of the facilities, the cost of their operation and maintenance would increase with the passage of time. Hence, it is an absolute necessity to maintain the equipment in good operating conditions with economical cost. Thus, we need an integrated approach to minimize the cost of maintenance. In certain cases, the equipment will be obsolete over a period of time.

If a firm wants to be in the same business competitively, it has to take decision on whether to replace the old equipment or to retain it by taking the cost of maintenance and operation into account.

There are two basic reasons for considering the replacement of an equipment – physical impairment of the various parts or obsolescence of the equipment.

Physical impairment refers only to changes in the physical condition of the machine itself. This would lead to a decline in the value of the service rendered, increased operating cost, increased maintenance cost or a combination of these.

Obsolescence is due to improvement of the tools of production, mainly improvement in technology.

So, it would be uneconomical to continue production with the same machine under any of the above situations. Hence, the machines are to be periodically replaced.

Sometimes, the capacity of existing facilities may be inadequate to meet the current demand. Under such situation, the following alternatives will be considered.

- Replacement of the existing equipment with a new one.
- Augmenting the existing one with an additional equipment.

39.2 TYPES OF MAINTENANCE

Maintenance activity can be classified into two types: preventive maintenance and breakdown maintenance. Preventive maintenance (PM) is the periodical inspection and service activities which are aimed to detect potential failures and perform minor adjustments or repairs which will prevent major operating problems in future. Breakdown maintenance is the repair which is generally done after the equipment has attained down state. It is often of an emergency which will have associated penalty in terms of expediting cost of maintenance and downtime cost of equipment. Preventive maintenance will reduce such cost up to a point. Beyond that point, the cost of preventive maintenance will be more when compared to the breakdown maintenance cost. The total cost, which is the sum of the preventive maintenance cost and the breakdown maintenance cost, will go on decreasing with an increase in the level of maintenance up to a point. Beyond that point, the total cost will start increasing. The level of maintenance corresponding to the minimum total cost is the optimal level of maintenance. The concepts are demonstrated in Fig. 39.1.

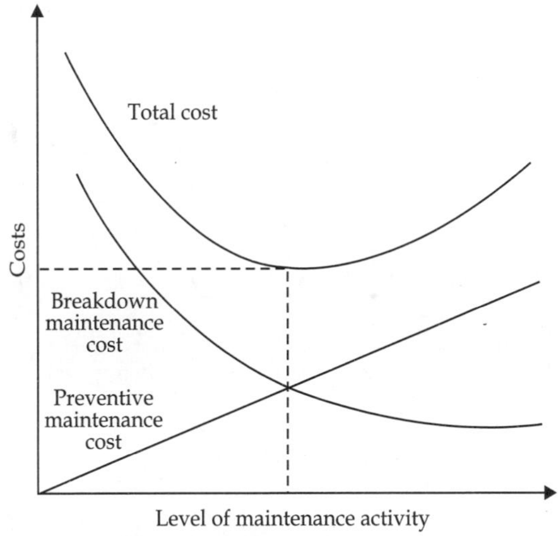

Fig. 39.1: Maintenance costs.

39.3 TYPES OF REPLACEMENT PROBLEMS

Replacement study can be classified into two categories:

(a) Replacement of assets that deteriorate with time (replacement due to gradual failure, or wear and tear of the components of the machines).

This can be further classified into the following types:

(i) Determination of economic life of an asset.

(ii) Replacement of an existing asset with a new asset.

(b) Simple probabilistic model for assets which fail completely (replacement due to sudden failure).

39.4 DETERMINATION OF ECONOMIC LIFE OF AN ASSET

Any asset will have the following cost components:

- Capital recovery cost (average first cost), computed from the first cost (purchase price) of the machine.
- Average operating and maintenance cost (O & M cost)
- Total cost which is the sum of capital recovery cost (average first cost) and average maintenance cost.

A typical shape of each of the above costs with respect to life of the machine is shown in Fig. 39.2.

From Fig. 39.2, it is clear that the capital recovery cost (average first cost) goes on decreasing with the life of the machine and the average operating and maintenance cost goes on increasing with the life of the machine. From the beginning, the total cost continues to decrease up to a particular life and then it starts increasing. The point where the total cost is minimum is called the economic life of the machine.

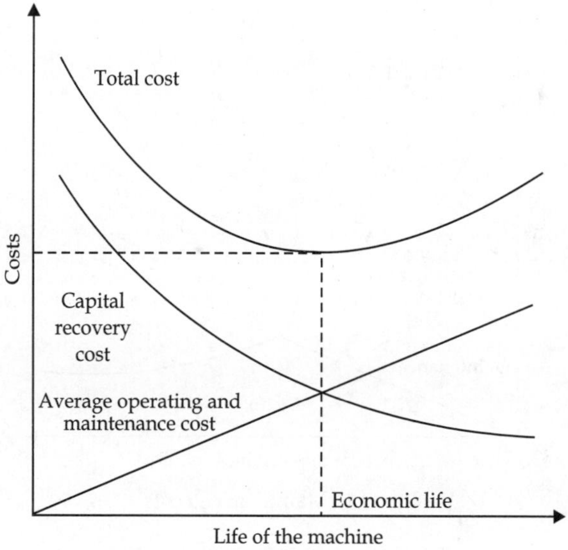

Fig. 39.2: Chart showing economic life.

If the interest rate is more than zero per cent, then we use interest formulas to determine the economic life.

The replacement alternatives can be evaluated based on the present worth criterion and annual equivalent criterion.

Example 1: A firm is considering replacement of an equipment, whose first cost is Rs. 4000 and the scrap value is negligible at the end of any year. Based on experience, it was found that the maintenance cost is zero during the first year and it increases by Rs. 200 every year thereafter.

(a) When should the equipment be replaced if i = 0%?

(b) When should the equipment be replaced if i = 12%?

(a) When i = 0%.

(i) First cost = Rs. 4000

(ii) Maintenance cost is Rs. 0 during the first year and it increases by Rs. 200 every year thereafter.

This is summarized in column B of Table 39.1.

Table 39.1: Calculations to determine economic life (First cost = Rs. 4,000, Interest = 0%).

End of year (n)	**Maintenance cost at end of year**	**Summation of maintenance costs**	**Average cost of maintenance through year given**	**Average first cost if replaced at year end given**	**Average total cost through year given**
		ΣB	C/A	4,000/A	D + E
A	B (Rs.)	C (Rs.)	D (Rs.)	E (Rs.)	F (Rs.)
1	0	0	0	4,000.00	4,000.00
2	200	200	100	2,000.00	2,100.00
3	400	600	200	1,333.33	1,533.33
4	600	1,200	300	1,000.00	1,300.00
5	800	2,000	400	800.00	1,200.00
6	1,000	3,000	500	666.67	1,166.67*
7	1,200	4,200	600	571.43	1,171.43

*Economic life of the machine = 6 years.

Column C summarizes the summation of maintenance costs for each replacement period. The value corresponding to any end of year in this column represents the total maintenance cost of using the equipment till the end of that particular year.

Replacement period

Average total cost = {First cost (FC) + summation of maintenance cost}/Replacement period

= FC/n + Column C/n

= Average first cost for the given period + Average maintenance cost for the given period

Column F = Column E + Column D

The value corresponding to any end of year (n) in Column F represents the average total cost of using the equipment till the end of that particular year.

For this problem, the average total cost decreases till the end of year 6 and then it increases. Therefore, the optimal replacement period is six years, i.e., economic life of the equipment is six years.

(b) When interest rate, i = 12%. When the interest rate is more than 0%, the steps to be taken for getting the economic life are summarized with reference to Table 39.2.

Table 39.2: Calculations to determine economic life (First cost = Rs. 4,000, Interest = 12%).

End of year (n)	Maintenance cost at end of year	P/F, 12%, n	Present worth as of beginning of year 1 of maintenance costs	Summation of present worth of maintenance costs through year given	Present worth of cumulative maintenance cost and first cost	A/P, 12%, n	Annual equivalent total cost through year given
			(B × C)	ΣD	E + Rs. 4,000		F × G
A	B (Rs.)	C	D (Rs.)	E (Rs.)	F (Rs.)	G	H (Rs.)
1	0	0.8929	0.00	0.00	4,000.00	1.1200	4,480.00
2	200	0.7972	159.44	159.44	4,159.44	0.5917	2,461.14
3	400	0.7118	284.72	444.16	4,444.16	0.4163	1,850.10
4	600	0.6355	381.30	825.46	4,825.46	0.3292	1,588.54
5	800	0.5674	453.92	1,279.38	5,279.38	0.2774	1,464.50
6	1,000	0.5066	506.60	1,785.98	5,785.98	0.2432	1,407.15
7	1,200	0.4524	542.88	2,328.86	6,328.86	0.2191	1,386.65*
8	1,400	0.4039	565.46	2,894.32	6,894.32	0.2013	1,387.83
9	1,600	0.3606	576.96	3,471.28	7,471.28	0.1877	1,402.36
10	1,800	0.3220	579.60	4,050.88	8,050.88	0.1770	1,425.00
*Economic life of the machine = 7 years							

The steps are summarized below:

1. Discount the maintenance costs to the beginning of year 1.

   Column D = Column B × $1/(1 + i)^n$

   = Column B × $(P/F, i, n)$ = Column B × Column C.

2. Find the summation of present worth of maintenance costs through the year given (Column E = Σ Column D).

3. Find Column F by adding the first cost of Rs. 4,000 to Column E.

4. Find the annual equivalent total cost through the years given.

   Column H = Column F × I $(1 + i)^n/(1 + i)^n - 1$

   = Column F × (A/P, 12%, n) = Column F × Column G

5. Identify the end of year for which the annual equivalent total cost is minimum.

For this problem, the annual equivalent total cost is minimum at the end of year 7. Therefore, the economic life of the equipment is seven years.

39.5 REPLACEMENT OF EXISTING ASSET WITH A NEW ASSET

In this section, the concept of comparison of replacement of an existing asset with a new asset is presented. In this analysis, the annual equivalent cost of each alternative should be computed first. Then the alternative which has the least cost should be selected as the best alternative. Before discussing details, some preliminary concepts which are essential for this type of replacement analysis are presented.

39.5.1 Capital Recovery with Return

Consider the following data of a machine. Let

P = purchase price of the machine,

F = salvage value of the machine at the end of machine life,

n = life of the machine in years, and

i = interest rate, compounded annually

The corresponding cash flow diagram is shown in Fig. 39.3.

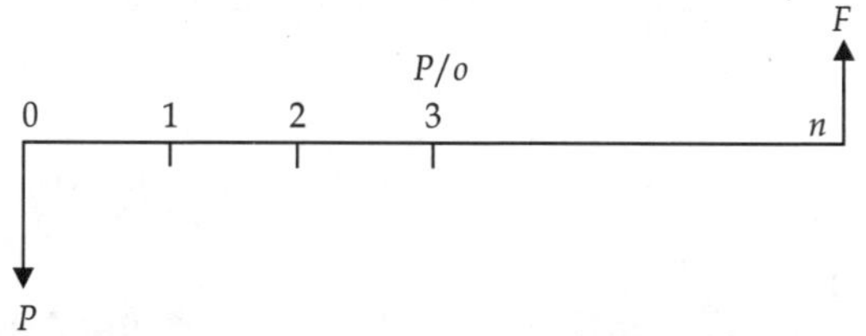

Fig. 39.3: Cash flow diagram of machine.

The equation for the annual equivalent amount for the above cash flow diagram is

$$AE\ (i) = (P - F) \times (A/P, i, n) + F \times i$$

This equation represents the capital recovery with return.

39.5.2 Concept of Challenger and Defender

If an existing equipment is considered for replacement with a new equipment, then the existing equipment is known as the defender and the new equipment is known as challenger.

Assume that an equipment has been purchased about three years back for Rs. 5,00,000 and it is considered for replacement with a new equipment. The supplier of the new equipment will take the old one for some money, say, Rs. 3,00,000. This should be treated as the present value of the existing equipment and it should be considered for all further economic analysis. The purchase value of the existing equipment before three years is now known as sunk cost, and it should not be considered for further analysis.

Example 2: Two years ago, a machine was purchased at a cost of Rs. 2,00,000 to be useful for eight years. Its salvage value at the end of its life is Rs. 25,000. The annual maintenance cost is Rs. 25,000. The market value of the present machine is Rs. 1,20,000. Now, a new machine to cater to the need of the present machine is available at Rs. 1,50,000 to be useful for six years. Its annual maintenance cost is Rs. 14,000. The salvage value of the new machine is Rs. 20,000. Using an interest rate of 12%, find whether it is worth replacing the present machine with the new machine.

Solution:

Alternative 1 – Present machine

Purchase price = Rs. 2,00,000

Present value (P) = Rs. 1,20,000

Salvage value (F) = Rs. 25,000

Annual maintenance cost (A) = Rs. 25,000

Remaining life = 6 years

Interest rate = 12%

The cash flow diagram of the present machine is illustrated in Fig. 39.4.

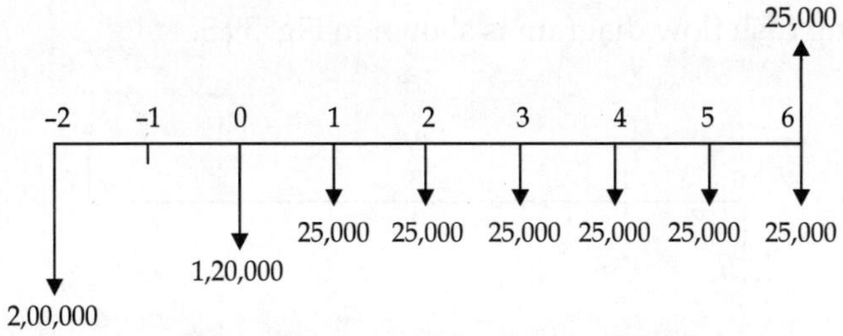

Fig. 39.4: Cash flow diagram for alternative 1.

The annual maintenance cost for the preceding periods are not shown in this figure. The annual equivalent cost is computed as

$$AE\ (12\%) = (P - F)(A/P, 12\%, 6) + F \times i + A$$

$$= (1{,}20{,}000 - 25{,}000)\ (0.2432) + 25{,}000 \times 0.12 + 25{,}000$$

$$= \text{Rs. } 51{,}104$$

Alternative 2 – New machine

Purchase price (P) = Rs. 1,50,000

Salvage value (F) = Rs. 20,000

Annual maintenance cost (A) = Rs. 14,000

Life = 6 years

Interest rate = 12%

The cash flow diagram of the new machine is depicted in Fig. 39.5.

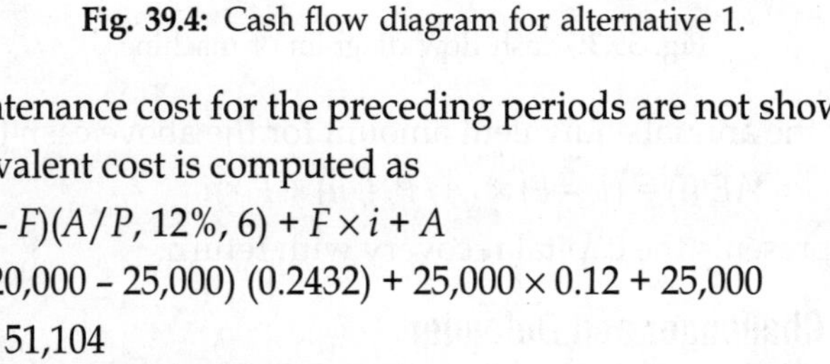

Fig. 39.5: Cash flow diagram for alternative 2.

The formula for the annual equivalent cost is

$$AE(12\%) = (P - F)(A/P, 12\%, 6) + F \times i + A$$
$$= (1{,}50{,}000 - 20{,}000)(0.2432) + 20{,}000 \times 0.12 + 14{,}000$$
$$= \text{Rs. } 48{,}016$$

Since the annual equivalent cost of the new machine is less than that of the present machine, it is suggested that the present machine be replaced with the new machine.

Example 3: A steel highway bridge must either be reinforced or replaced. Reinforcement would cost Rs. 6,60,000 and would make the bridge fit for an additional five years of service. If it is reinforced, it is estimated that its net salvage value would be Rs. 4,00,000 at the time it is retired from service. The new prestressed concrete bridge would cost Rs. 15,00,000 and would meet the foreseeable requirements of the next 40 years. Such a bridge would have no salvage value. It is estimated that the annual maintenance cost of the reinforced bridge would exceed that of the concrete bridge by Rs. 96,000. If the bridge is replaced by a new pressurised concrete bridge, the scrap value of the steel would exceed the demolition cost by Rs. 4,20,000. Assume that the money costs the state 10%. What would you recommend?

Solution:

There are two alternatives:

1. Reinforce the existing bridge.
2. Replace the existing bridge by a new prestressed concrete bridge.

Alternative 1 – Reinforce the existing bridge

Cost of reinforcement (P) = Rs. 6,60,000

Salvage value after 5 years (F) = Rs. 4,00,000

The excess annual maintenance cost over prestressed concrete bridge (A) = Rs. 96,000

Life (n) = 5 years

Interest rate (i) = 10%

The cash flow diagram of alternative 1 is illustrated in Fig. 39.6.

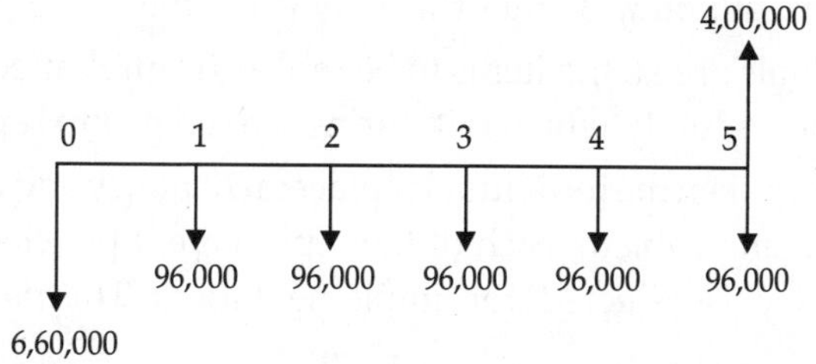

Fig. 39.6: Cash flow diagram for alternative 1.

The annual equivalent cost of alternative 1 is computed as

$$AE\ (10\%) = (P - F)\ (A/P, 10\%, 5) + F \times i + A$$
$$= (6{,}60{,}000 - 4{,}00{,}000)\ (0.2638) + 4{,}00{,}000 \times 0.10 + 96{,}000$$
$$= \text{Rs. } 2{,}04{,}588$$

Alternative 2—Replace the existing bridge by a new prestressed concrete bridge

Cost of prestressed concrete bridge (P) = Rs. 15,00,000

Excess scrap value of steel over the demolition cost of the current bridge (X) = Rs. 4,20,000

Life (n) = 40 years

Interest rate (i) = 10%

Note that the excess maintenance cost of the reinforced bridge over the prestressed concrete bridge is included in alternative 1.

The annual equivalent cost of alternative 2 is calculated as

$$AE\,(10\%) = (P - X)\,(A/P, 10\%, 40)$$
$$= (15{,}00{,}000 - 4{,}20{,}000) \times 0.1023$$
$$= \text{Rs. } 1{,}10{,}484$$

The annual equivalent cost of alternative 2 is less than that of alternative 1.

Based on equal lives comparison over 40 years, alternative 2 is selected as the best alternative.

Thus, it is suggested to go in for prestressed concrete bridge.

39.6 SIMPLE PROBABILISTIC MODEL FOR ITEMS WHICH FAIL COMPLETELY

Electronic items like transistors, resistors, tubelights, bulbs, etc., could fail all of a sudden, instead of gradual deterioration. The failure of the item may result in complete breakdown of the system. The system may contain a collection of such items or just one item, say a tubelight. Therefore, we use some replacement policy for such items which would avoid the possibility of a complete breakdown.

The following are the replacement policies which are applicable for this situation.

(i) Individual replacement policy. Under this policy, an item is replaced immediately after its failure.

(ii) Group replacement policy. Under this policy, the following decision is made:

At what equal intervals are all the items to be replaced simultaneously with a provision to replace the items individually which fail during a fixed group replacement period?

There is a trade-off between the individual replacement policy and the group replacement policy. Hence, for a given problem, each of the replacement policies is evaluated and the most economical policy is selected for implementation. This is explained with two numerical problems.

Example 4: The failure rates of transistors in a computer are summarized in Table 39.3.

Table 39.3: Failure rates of transistors in computers.

End of week	1	2	3	4	5	6	7
Probability of failure to date	0.07	0.18	0.30	0.48	0.69	0.89	1.00

The cost of replacing an individual failed transistor is Rs. 9. If all the transistors are replaced simultaneously, it would cost Rs. 3.00 per transistor. Any one of the following two options can be followed to replace the transistors:

(a) Replace the transistors individually when they fail (individual replacement policy).

(b) Replace all the transistors simultaneously at fixed intervals and replace the individual transistors as they fail in service during the fixed interval (group replacement policy).

Find out the optimal replacement policy, i.e., individual replacement policy or group replacement policy. If group replacement policy is optimal, then find at what equal intervals all the transistors should be replaced.

Solution: Assume that there are 100 transistors in use.

Let, p_i be the probability that a transistor which was new when placed in position for use, fails during the *i*th week of its life. Hence,

$p_1 = 0.07,\quad p_2 = 0.11,\quad p_3 = 0.12,\quad p_4 = 0.18,$

$p_5 = 0.21,\quad p_6 = 0.20,\quad p_7 = 0.11$

Since the sum of p_is is equal to 1 at the end of the 7th week, the transistors are sure to fail during the seventh week.

Assume that

(a) Transistors that fail during a week are replaced just before the end of the week, and

(b) The actual percentage of failures during a week for a sub-group of transistors with the same age is same as the expected percentage of failures during the week for that sub-group of transistors.

Let

N_i = The number of transistors replaced at the end of the *i*th week

N_0 = Number of transistors replaced at the end of the week 0 (or at the beginning of the first week).

$= 100$

N_1 = Number of transistors replaced at the end of the 1st week

$= N_0 \times p_1 = 100 \times 0.07 = 7$

N_2 = Number of transistors replaced at the end of the 2nd week

$= N_0 \times p_2 + N_1 \times p_1$

$= 100 \times 0.11 + 7 \times 0.07 = 12$

$N_3 = N_0 \times p_3 + N_1 \times p_2 + N_2 \times p_1$

$= 100 \times 0.12 + 7 \times 0.11 + 12 \times 0.07$

$= 14$

$N_4 = N_0 \times p_4 + N_1 \times p_3 + N_2 \times p_2 + N_3 \times p_1$

$= 100 \times 0.18 + 7 \times 0.12 + 12 \times 0.11 + 14 \times 0.07$

$= 21$

$$N_5 = N_0 \times p_5 + N_1 \times p_4 + N_2 \times p_3 + N_3 \times p_2 + N_4 \times p_1$$
$$= 100 \times 0.21 + 7 \times 0.18 + 12 \times 0.12 + 14 \times 0.11 + 21 \times 0.07$$
$$= 27$$
$$N_6 = N_0 \times p_6 + N_1 \times p_5 + N_2 \times p_4 + N_3 \times p_3 + N_4 \times p_2 + N_5 \times p_1$$
$$= 100 \times 0.2 + 7 \times 0.21 + 12 \times 0.18 + 14 \times 0.12 + 21 \times 0.11 + 27 \times 0.07$$
$$= 30$$
$$N_7 = N_0 \times p_7 + N_1 \times p_6 + N_2 \times p_5 + N_3 \times p_4 + N_4 \times p_3 + N_5 \times p_2 + N_6 \times p_1$$
$$= 100 \times 0.11 + 7 \times 0.2 + 12 \times 0.21 + 14 \times 0.18 + 21 \times 0.12 + 27 \times 0.11 + 30 \times 0.07$$
$$= 25$$

Calculation of individual replacement cost

Expected life of each transistor $= \sum_{i=1} i \times p_i$

$$= 1 \times 0.07 + 2 \times 0.11 + 3 \times 0.12 + 4 \times 0.18 + 5 \times 0.21 + 6 \times 0.2 + 7 \times 0.11$$

$= 4.39$ weeks

Average no. of failures/week $= 100/4.39 = 23$ (approx.)

Therefore,

Cost of individual replacement = (No. of failures/week × Individual replacement cost/transistor)

$= 23 \times 9 =$ Rs. 207.

Determination of group replacement cost

Cost of transistor when replaced simultaneously = Rs. 3

Cost of transistor when replaced individually = Rs. 9

The costs of group replacement policy for several replacement periods are summarized in Table 39.4.

Table 39.4: Calculations of cost for preventive maintenance.

End of week	Cost of replacing 100 transistors at a time	Cost of replacing transistors individually during given replacement period	Total cost (B + C)	Average cost/week (D/A)
A	B (Rs.)	C (Rs.)	D (Rs.)	E (Rs.)
1	300	7 × 9 = 63	363	363.00
2	300	(7 + 12) × 9 = 171	471	235.50
3	300	(7 + 12 + 14) × 9 = 297	597	199.00
4	300	(7 + 12 + 14 + 21) × 9 = 486	786	196.50*
5	300	(7 + 12 + 14 + 21 + 27) × 9 = 729	1,029	205.80
6	300	(7 + 12 + 14 + 21 + 27 + 30) × 9 = 999	1,299	216.50
7	300	(7 + 12 + 14 + 21 + 27 + 30 + 25) × 9 = 1,224	1,524	217.71

*Indicates the minimum average cost/week.

From Table 39.4, it is clear that the average cost/week is minimum for the fourth week. Hence, the group replacement period is four weeks.

Individual replacement cost/week = Rs. 207

Minimum group replacement cost/week = Rs. 196.50

Since the minimum group replacement cost/week is less than the individual replacement cost/week, the group replacement policy is the best, and hence all the transistors should be replaced once in four weeks and the transistors which fail during this four-week period are to be replaced individually.

40
Inventory Control

40.1 INTRODUCTION

Inventory is essential to provide flexibility to the operating a system. Inventory can be classified into raw materials inventory, in-process inventory, and finished goods inventory. The raw material inventories obviate the need for dependency between suppliers and plants. The work-in-process inventories eliminate dependency between machines of a product line. The finished goods inventory removes dependency between plant and its customers/market.

The main functions of inventory are:

1. Smoothing out irregularities in supply
2. Minimizing the production cost
3. Allowing organizations to cope with perishable materials

Inventory Decisions

Two basic inventory decisions are generally taken by managers:

1. When should the inventory of an item be replaced?
2. How much of an item is to be ordered when the inventory of that item has to be replenished?

Costs Trade-off

If we place frequent orders, the cost of order will be more, but the inventory carrying cost will be less. On the other hand, if we place less frequent orders, the ordering cost will be less, but the carrying cost will be more. These are shown in Fig. 40.1. In the figure, for an increase in Q (order size), the carrying cost increases and the ordering cost decreases.

In Fig. 40.1, the total cost curve represents the sum of the ordering cost and carrying cost for each order size. The order size at which the total cost is minimum is called the Economic Order Quantity (EOQ) or Q^* (optimal order size).

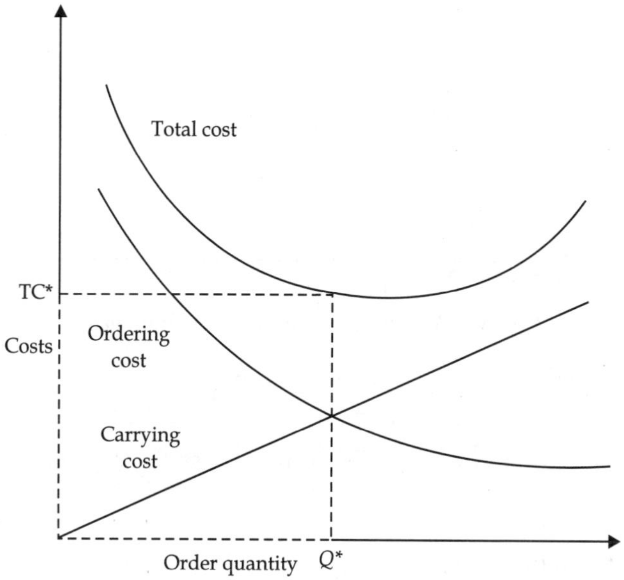

Fig. 40.1: Trade-off between costs.

There are different models of inventory. The inventory models can be classified into deterministic models and probabilistic models. The various deterministic models are as follows:

1. Purchase model with instantaneous replenishment and without shortages
2. Manufacturing model without shortages
3. Purchase model with instantaneous replenishment and with shortages
4. Manufacturing model with shortages

These models are explained in the following sections.

40.2 PURCHASE MODEL WITH INSTANTANEOUS REPLENISHMENT AND WITHOUT SHORTAGES

In this model of inventory, orders of equal size are placed at periodical intervals. The items against an order are replenished instantaneously and they are consumed at a constant rate. The purchase price per unit is same irrespective of order size. Let

D = annual demand in units

Co = ordering cost/order

Cc = carrying cost/unit/year

P = purchase price/unit

Q = order size

Then, the corresponding model is shown in Fig. 40.2.

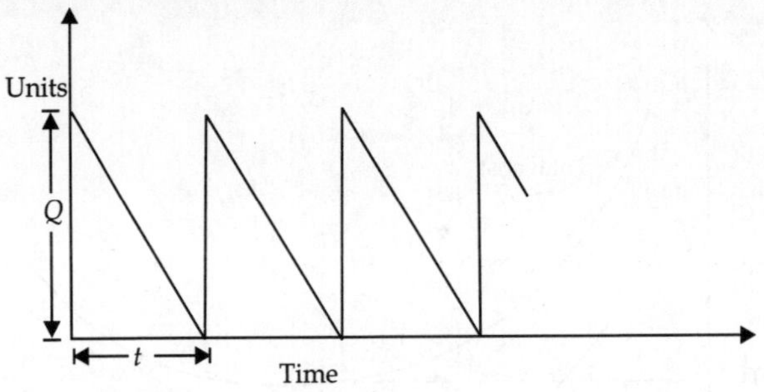

Fig. 40.2: Purchase model without shortages.

For this model, the formula for the EOQ is as follows:

$$Q^* = \sqrt{\frac{2C_O D}{C_C}}$$

$$\text{No. of orders} = D/Q^*$$

$$\text{Time between orders} = Q^*/D$$

Example 1: Krishna Industry needs 24,000 units/year of a bought-out component which will be used in its main product. The ordering cost is Rs. 150 per order and the carrying cost per unit per year is 18% of the purchase price per unit. The purchase price per unit is Rs. 75. Find

(a) Economic order quantity
(b) No. of orders per year
(c) Time between successive orders

Solution:

(a) D = 24,000 units/year
Co = Rs. 150/order Purchase price/unit = Rs. 75.
Cc = Rs. 75 × 0.18 = Rs. 13.5/unit/year

Therefore,

$$\text{EOQ} = \sqrt{\frac{2C_o D}{C_c}} = \sqrt{\frac{2 \times 150 \times 24{,}000}{13.50}} = 730 \text{ units}$$

No. of orders/year = D/Q^* = 24,000/730 = 32.88

Time between successive orders = Q^*/D = 730/24,000
= 0.0304 year
= 0.37 month
= 11 days

40.3 MANUFACTURING MODEL WITHOUT SHORTAGES

If a company manufactures its component which is required for its main product, then the corresponding model of inventory is called the "manufacturing model". This model will be with or without shortages. The rate of consumption of items is uniform throughout the year. The cost of production per unit is same irrespective of production lot size. Let

r = annual demand of an item

k = production rate of the item (No. of units produced per year)

Co = cost per setup.

Cc = carrying cost per unit per year.

p = cost of production per unit

$t1$ = period of production as well as consumption satisfying requirement for the period

$t2$ = period of consumption only.

Q = production size

The operation of the manufacturing model without shortages is shown in Fig. 40.3.

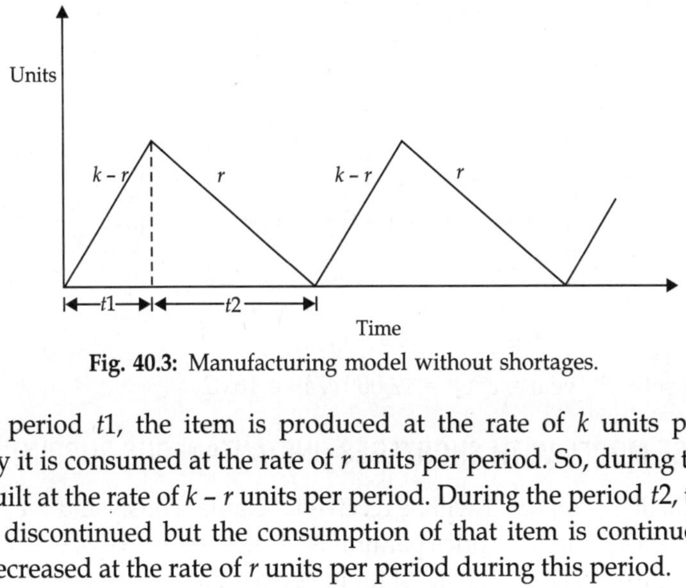

Fig. 40.3: Manufacturing model without shortages.

During the period $t1$, the item is produced at the rate of k units per period and simultaneously it is consumed at the rate of r units per period. So, during this period, the inventory is built at the rate of $k - r$ units per period. During the period $t2$, the production of the item is discontinued but the consumption of that item is continued. Hence, the inventory is decreased at the rate of r units per period during this period.

The various formulae for this situation are as follows:

$$Q^* = \text{EOQ} = \sqrt{\frac{2C_o r}{C_c(1 - r/k)}}$$

$$t1^* = Q^*/k$$

$$t2^* = \frac{Q^*[1 - r/k]}{r} = \frac{(k - r)t1}{r}$$

$$\text{Cycle time} = t1^* + t2^*$$

$$\text{No. of setups/year} = r/Q^*$$

Example 2: If a product is to be manufactured within the company, the particulars are:

$r = 12{,}000$ units/year

$k = 24{,}000$ units/year

Co = Rs. 175/setup

Cc = Rs. 15/unit/year

Find the EOQ and cycle time.

Solution:

$$Q^* = \text{EOQ} = \sqrt{\frac{2C_o r}{C_c(1 - r/k)}}$$

$$= \sqrt{\frac{2 \times 175 \times 12{,}000}{15(1 - 12{,}000/24{,}000)}}$$

$$= 749 \text{ units}$$

$$t1^* = Q^*/k = 749/24{,}000$$

$$= 0.031 \text{ year} = 0.372 \text{ month} = 11 \text{ days}$$

$$t2^* = \frac{Q^*}{r}(1 - \frac{r}{k}) = \frac{749}{12{,}000}(1 - \frac{12{,}000}{24{,}000})$$

$$= 0.031 \text{ year} = 0.372 \text{ month} = 11 \text{ days}$$

Therefore,

$$\text{Cycle time} = t1^* + t2^*$$

$$= 11 + 11 = 22 \text{ days}$$

$$\text{No. of set-ups/year} = r/Q^* = 12{,}000/749 = 16.02$$

40.4 PURCHASE MODEL WITH SHORTAGES (INSTANTANEOUS SUPPLY)

In this model, the items on order will be received instantaneously and they are consumed at a constant rate. The purchase price per unit is same irrespective of order size. If there is no stock at the time of receiving a request for the items, it is assumed that it will be satisfied at a later date with a penalty. This is called back ordering. The operation of this model is illustrated in Fig. 40.4.

The variables which are used in this model are

D = Demand/period

Cc = Carrying cost/unit/period

Co = Ordering cost/order

Cs = Shortage cost/unit/period

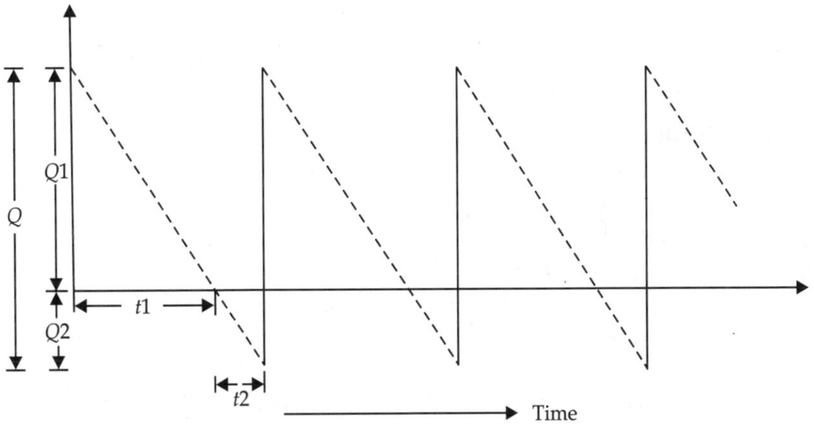

Fig. 40.4: Purchase model of inventory with shortages.

In the above model,

Q = Order size,

$Q1$ = Maximum inventory,

$Q2$ = Maximum stock-out,

$t1$ = Period of positive stock,

$t2$ = Period of shortage

$$Q^* = \text{EOQ} = \sqrt{\frac{2C_oD}{C_c}\frac{(C_s + C_c)}{C_s}}$$

$$Q1^* = \sqrt{\frac{2C_oD}{C_c}\frac{C_s}{C_s + C_c}}$$

$$Q2^* = Q^* - Q1^*$$

$$t^* = Q^*/D$$

$$t1^* = Q1^*/D$$

$$t2^* = Q2^*/D$$

No. of orders/year = D/Q^*

Example 3: The annual demand for a component is 30,000 units. The carrying cost is Rs. 2.00/unit/year, the ordering cost is Rs. 100.00/order, and the shortage cost is Rs. 12.00/unit/year. Find the optimal values of the following:

(a) Ordering quantity

(b) Maximum inventory

(c) Maximum shortage quantity

(d) Cycle time

(e) Inventory period ($t1$)

(f) Shortage period ($t2$)

Solution:

D = 30,000 units/year

Cc = Rs. 2.00/unit/year

Co = Rs. 100/order

Cs = Rs. 12/unit/year

$$Q^* = \text{EOQ} = \sqrt{\frac{2C_oD}{C_c}\frac{(C_s + C_c)}{C_s}}$$

$$= \sqrt{\frac{2 \times 100 \times 30{,}000}{2}\left(\frac{12+2}{12}\right)}$$

$$= 1871 \text{ units}$$

$$Q1^* = \sqrt{\frac{2C_oD}{C_c}\frac{C_s}{C_s + C_c}}$$

$$= \sqrt{\frac{2 \times 100 \times 30{,}000}{2}\left(\frac{12}{2+12}\right)}$$

$$= 1604 \text{ units}$$

$$Q2^* = 1{,}871 - 1{,}604 = 267 \text{ units}$$

$$t^* = Q^*/D = (1{,}871/30{,}000) \times 365 = 23 \text{ days (approx.)}$$

$$t1^* = Q1^*/D = (1{,}604/30{,}000) \times 365 = 20 \text{ days}$$

$$t2^* = t^* - t1^* = 23 - 20 = 3 \text{ days}$$

$$\text{No. of orders/year} = D/Q^* = 30{,}000/1{,}871 = 16.03$$

40.5 MANUFACTURING MODEL WITH SHORTAGES

In this model, the items are produced and consumed simultaneously for a portion of the cycle time. During the remaining cycle time, the items are only consumed. The cost of production per unit is same irrespective of production lot size. In this model, stock-out is permitted. It is assumed that the stock-out units will be satisfied from the units which will be produced at a later date with a penalty. This is called back ordering. The operation of this model is shown in Fig. 40.5. The variables which are used in this model are given now.

Let

r = Annual demand of an item per period

k = Production rate of the item (No. of units produced per period)

Co = Cost per set-up.

Cc = Carrying cost per unit per period, Cs = Shortage cost per unit per period; p = cost of production per unit

$t1$ = Period of production as well as consumption satisfying period's requirement

$t2$ = Period of consumption only

$t3$ = Period of shortage

$t4$ = Period of production as well as consumption satisfying back order

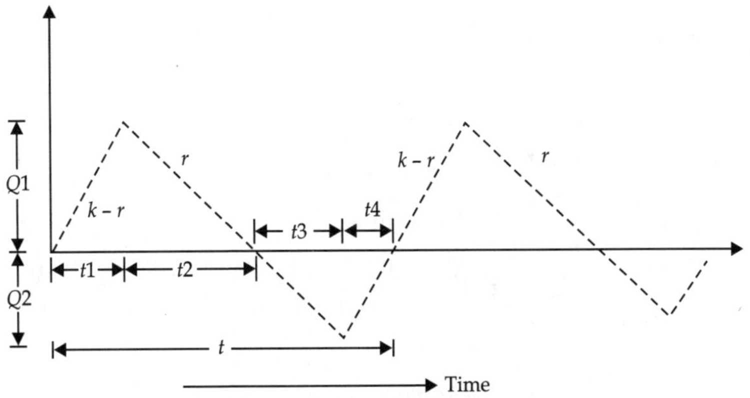

Fig. 40.5: Manufacturing model of inventory with shortages.

In the above model,

Q = Production size

$Q1$ = Maximum inventory

$Q2$ = Maximum stock-out

The formulae for the optimal values of the above variables are presented below.

$$Q^* = EOQ = \sqrt{\frac{2C_o}{C_c}\frac{kr}{k-r}\frac{C_c+C_s}{C_s}}$$

$$Q1^* = \sqrt{\frac{2C_o}{C_c}\frac{r(k-r)}{k}\frac{C_s}{C_c+C_s}}$$

$$Q2^* = \sqrt{\frac{2C_oC_c}{C_s(C_c+C_s)}\frac{r(k-r)}{k}}$$

$$Q1^* = \sqrt{\frac{k-r}{k}}Q^* - Q2^*$$

$$t1^* = Q1^*/r$$

$$t2^* = Q1^*/(k-r)$$

$$t3^* = Q2^*/r$$

$$t4^* = Q2^*/(k-r)$$

Example 4: The demand for an item is 12,000/year. Its production rate is 2000/month. The carrying cost is Re. 0.20/unit/month and the setup cost is Rs. 400/setup. The shortage cost is Rs. 15/unit/year. Find the various parameters of the inventory system.

Solution:

$r = 12{,}000$ units/year

$k = 2{,}000 \times 12 = 24{,}000$ units/year

$Co =$ Rs. 400/set-up.

$Cc =$ Rs. $(0.20 \times 12) =$ Rs. 2.40/year

$$Q^* = \text{EOQ} = \sqrt{\frac{2 \times 400}{2.40}\,\frac{24{,}000 \times 12{,}000}{(24{,}000 - 12{,}000)}\,\frac{(2.40 + 15)}{15}}$$

$$= 3{,}046 \text{ units}$$

$$= \sqrt{\frac{2 \times 400 \times 2.40}{15(2.40 + 15)}\,\frac{12{,}000(24{,}000 - 12{,}000)}{24{,}000}}$$

$$= 210$$

$$Q1^* = \sqrt{\frac{24{,}000 - 12{,}000}{24{,}000}}3{,}046 - 210$$

$$= 1{,}313$$

$t^* = [Q^*/r]365$ days $= [3{,}046/12{,}000]365$ days $= 93$ days

$t1^* = [Q1^*/(k - r)]365$ days $= [1{,}313/(24{,}000 - 12{,}000)]365$ days $= 40$ days

$t2^* = [Q1^*/r]365$ days $= [1{,}313/12{,}000]365$ days $= 40$ days

$t3^* = [Q2^*/r]365$ days $= [210/12{,}000]365$ days $= 7$ days

$t4^* = [Q2^*/(k - r)]365$ days $= [210/(24{,}000 - 12{,}000)]365$ days $= 7$ days

Review Questions

SECTION II: PRODUCTIVITY AND WORK STUDY

1. Define: i) Method study; ii) Work measurement.
2. Outline the factors that affect productivity.
3. State the advantages of work study.
4. Briefly outline the basic procedure of the method of study.
5. You have been assigned the task of carrying out method study of robot construction in your college in preparation for robot competition among colleges. During examination of the facts recorded in the preliminary stages, what should you bear in mind?
6. A gear production company produces gears either through hobbing, milling or shaping. Customers place their orders with the sales department where they pitch their products once completed. Most of the jobs have to go through design and drawing using AutoCAD before being machined.
   (a) From the above information, list the main activities carried out on customers gear order from the sales until the finished product is delivered to the sales after production.
   (b) Prepare a process chart showing the main activities.
   (c) What is the importance of work measurement?
7. Outline the procedure of work measurement.
8. Why is it important for the management to know how long it should take to carry out various kinds of work in production?
9. Outline five types of allowances that may be applied during work measurement.
10. Explain objectives of work study.
11. Define ergonomics.
12. What is human machine system?
13. What are stress and fatigue?
14. What is meant by applied physiology in workplace?
15. What is control-response ratio?

SECTION III: METHOD STUDY & SECTION IV: WORK MEASUREMENT

1. Explain steps in conducting method study.
2. Explain the procedure for making flow process chart.
3. Define objectives and concepts of work measurement.
4. i) Explain work sampling, ii) What is work factor system?
5. Explain the principles of motion economy.
6. Explain the features of design for standing workers, and seated workers.
7. Write notes on the following: a) Fatigue allowance, b) Heat stress, c) Learning curves, d) Industrial Noise
8. Describe the principles for design of visual and auditory displays.
9. Define: i) Method study, ii) Work measurement, iii) Time study, iv) Work sampling, v) Process charts.
10. Describe four indications of a possible need for a method study.
11. Explain the following in connection with the time study: i) Selection of job, ii) Breaking the job into elements, and iii) Qualified worker.
12. Outline the users of work study.
13. Describe i) Micromotion study and ii) Memo motion technique.
14. The following data showed the activities to be carried in production of a batch of donor brackets in a manufacturing industry.

    Activities

    (1) Order placed by the customer to sales.
    (2) Order is put in the in-try.
    (3) The order is transferred to the design department.
    (4) Specification of the brackets are verified.
    (5) Design of the bracket is developed.
    (6) Design is verified by the design manager.
    (7) Design is transferred to the production.
    (8) Design is verified against available raw materials.
    (9) A batch of brackets are produced.
    (10) The batch is stored, awaiting customer to collect them.

    Draw a flow process chart for the job described above.
15. Outline the steps to be undertaken in work measurement for standardization by stopwatch method.
16. Calparks Company has been in operation for five years. The establishment work has never been effectively done. There seems to be bottlenecks and an explained delay in production, the wages paid to the workers cannot be justified. The company has invited a consultant to advise her on the way forward. As a consultant, advise

the company management highlighting the importance of measuring work and how it can be done.

17. Outline five types of allowances that may be applied during work measurement.
18. Outline the following work measurement techniques. i) Synthesis from elemental data, ii) Predetermined motion time systems, iii) Analytical estimating and iv) Activity sampling.
19. Define the method study. What are its objectives? How is job selected for the method study?
20. What is meant by incentives? What do you understand by negative incentives plans?

SECTION V: ENTREPRENEURIAL DEVELOPMENT

1. Who is an entrepreneur? Define entrepreneurship.
2. Discuss productivity as a master key of social prosperity.
3. Discuss the role of Industrial Engineer in improving productivity of any organization.
4. What is the influence of environment on the growth of entrepreneurship?
5. State important attributes and skills of successful small business owners.
6. Discuss role of identifying and evaluating business opportunity in success of a business venture.
7. What are the main reasons to lower down productivity in any organization? How can one overcome this problem?
8. What do you mean by 'techno-preneur'?
9. Discuss the role of 'techno-preneurs' in world's emerging economy like India.
10. How does creativity play an important role for success of any entrepreneur?
11. What do mean by a business plan?
12. Discuss guidelines for preparing an effective business plan.
13. Write note on "Entrepreneurial Support System".
14. "Productivity is an attitude of mind" - Explain.
15. Discuss the importance of agricultural productivity in development of national economy of India.
16. Explain various kinds of productivity measurement.
17. What is entrepreneur and entrepreneurship? State the factors influencing entrepreneurship.
18. Discuss labour productivity as a key concern in Indian context to improve manufacturing productivity.
19. Discuss "Funding of financial needs of entrepreneurs".
20. Discuss entrepreneur as an innovator.
21. Discuss the significance of IT in national productivity enhancement.

22. Discuss how use of appropriate technology and flexible production can improve the productivity.
23. Discuss entrepreneur as a risk bearer.
24. Write a note on the "role of productivity councils in India".
25. Explain your views on how to improve productivity in service sector.

SECTION VI: INSPECTION AND STATISTICAL QUALITY CONTROL

1. How can quality be quantified?
2. What are the benefits of TQM?
3. What are the important habits of quality leader?
4. Name a few barriers to team's progress?
5. What are the benefits of benchmarking?
6. Describe the six basic concepts of TQM.
7. What are the duties of a quality council?
8. Discuss the Deming's philosophy for TQM.
9. What are the suggestions to improve the appraisal system?
10. Explain the seven-step plan to establish the TPM in an organization.
11. Explain the ISO control cycle.
12. Explain the strategic planning.
13. Discuss the need, construction and applications of control charts for variables.
14. Discuss the implementation of ISO:9000:2000 quality systems.
15. Explain the need for quality systems in an organization.
16. Write short notes on a) Principles of TQM; b) Kaizen; and c) SQC.
17. What is S.Q.C.? Explain in brief how P chart and C chart are constructed?
18. Compare between control charts for variables and control charts for attributes.
19. Describe how the quality of facial tissue paper can be defined in operations and give some examples of the quality measures that can be used to assess the tissue paper's quality. If Kleenex (a major manufacturer of facial tissue products in North America) were to launch a new advertising campaign that emphasizes "improved quality," which quality definition would be useful for Kleenex?
20. Which process type is most suitable for planning an Olympic game? Justify your answer briefly.
21. Is the JIT system suitable for all companies? Explain your answer briefly.
22. Discuss how a JIT system contributes to quality improvement.
23. An automotive-part manufacturer started using kanban two months ago in its effort to become a "just-in-time" company. The company expected to see some reduction in its inventory by now, but the level of inventory has not gone down at

all. Speculate as to why the inventory level has not changed at this manufacturing plant.

24. If you were in charge of a startup company with shipping service as the core business, how would you implement the philosophy of TQM?
25. Explain why TQM may be difficult to achieve in a short period of time for a company that has placed a low priority on the quality initiatives over the years.

SECTION VII: PRODUCTION PLANNING AND CONTROL

1. What is the meaning of production planning?
2. What is the cycle of production?
3. What does a production planner do?
4. What is production control?
5. What is production planning and control?
6. What are the types of production control?
7. What is PPC in production?
8. What are the objectives of production planning?
9. What are the benefits of production planning?
10. What are the strategies taken care of by production planning?
11. What are the factors of production control?
12. What are the advantages of robust production control?
13. What are the objectives of production control?
14. What are the stages of production planning and control?
15. What are the main elements of production planning and control?
16. What are the types of production systems?
17. Explain job production.
18. Explain batch production.
19. Explain mass production.
20. Explain product design.

SECTION VIII: LOCATION SELECTION AND PLANT LAYOUT

1. Discuss the various factors that affect the plant location.
2. Differentiate between product layout and process layout by taking suitable examples.
3. Compare urban area and rural area for site selection of plant.
4. Enlist any two applications where combination layout is preferred
5. Explain fixed position layout with suitable example. List advantages and disadvantages of the same.
6. Differentiate between open and closed job shop.

7. Give the advantages of a multi-storied building over a single storey building for a factory.
8. Define the various types of plant layout in brief with suitable examples of each.
9. Explain the factors to be considered for selection of site in manufacturing environment.
10. Explain in detail the scientific step-by-step procedure that must be followed in order to achieve sound plant layout.
11. Which are the major factors affecting plant location?
12. Discuss the factors to be considered for the selection of the site for a thermal power plant.
13. Discuss the types of plant layout.
14. A company is to decide on the location of a new plant. It has narrowed down the choice to 3 locations A, B, and C; data in respect of which is furnished below: Use suitable criterion and advise the company on the best choice.

Data	Location A	Location B	Location C
Wages & salaries	Rs.20,000	Rs.20,000	Rs.20,000
Power & water supply expenses	Rs.20,000	Rs.30,000	Rs.25,000
Raw material & other supplies	Rs.80,000	Rs.75,000	Rs.60,000
Total initial investment	Rs.2,00,000	Rs.3,00,000	Rs.2,50,000
Distribution expenses	Rs.50,000	Rs.40,000	Rs.60,000
Miscellaneous expenses	Rs.40,000	Rs.25,000	Rs.30,000
Expected sales per year	Rs.2,25,000	Rs.2,50,000	Rs.2,25,000

15. Discuss the factors to be considered for the selection of the site for textile industry.

SECTION IX: JOB EVALUATION AND WAGES

1. Define wages and explain in detail various types of incentive plans.
2. Explain different types of wages briefly.
3. List any four factors affecting wages of workers.
4. Give equation of bonus and wages earned by workers using Halsey incentive plan.
5. Define rating. Why it is required?
6. Describe the following methods of job evaluation: i) Ranking method and ii) Job classification method.
7. Differentiate between job evaluation and merit rating. Discuss in brief any one method of merit rating.
8. Describe the characteristics of good wage plan. Discuss any one wage plan.
9. State various methods of job evaluation.
10. Differentiate between minimum wage, fair wage and living wage.

SECTION X: INDUSTRIAL LEGISLATION

1. Explain the Factories Act, 1948? What are the major provisions for safety and health?
2. What are industrial disputes? Discuss the process of resolving the industrial disputes through the Industrial Dispute Act.
3. What is industrial legislation and why it is required?
4. Name the different Acts which are helpful in resolving the industrial disputes. Discuss any one Act in detail.
5. Explain Workmen Compensation Act 1923.

SECTION XI: VALUE ANALYSIS

1. Define value, value analysis and value engineering. Discuss in detail.
2. Discuss aesthetic, ergonomics, technical and economic factors with illustrations for value determination.
3. Explain questionnaire technique used in value analysis.
4. How do applications of value engineering/analysis enhance total productivity?
5. Discuss the phases of value analysis procedure in details.
6. What is value? Explain the reasons for poor value.
7. Explain the importance of leadership, teamwork and communication in value engineering.
8. Discuss considerations of human aspects in value engineering.
9. List and explain the advantages of value engineering.
10. Explain the value standards.
11. Explain project selection and methods selection with reference to selection of evaluation of value engineering projects?
12. Explain the different phases of value engineering job plan in brief.
13. What is meant by value engineering methodology? Give its application.
14. Discuss value engineering training plan.
15. Discuss value engineering team structure.
16. Explain the relationship between product development and value engineering. Also explain the advantages of value engineering.
17. Explain the value engineering job plan. Also explain the advantages of value engineering.
18. Explain the selection of evaluation of value engineering projects.
19. Define value, value engineering and value analysis. Discuss with illustrations.
20. Discuss the different phases of value analysis job plan.
21. Explain the procedure of value engineering and value analysis.

22. Discuss the various types of value with illustrations.
23. Explain the meaning of value and worth. How is present worth calculated?
24. Explain in brief different costs to be considered in value engineering.
25. How can value engineering programme be initiated?

SECTION XII: LEADERSHIP

1. Explain the multidisciplinary nature of organisational behaviour.
2. Differentiate between the roles of a manager and a leader.
3. Explain charismatic and transformational styles of leadership.
4. Explain meta-communication and its implications for a leader.
5. Describe the skills needed for effective communication.
6. Explain power-play, bargaining and collaboration as strategies of conflict management.
7. Describe the process of organisational communication. Identify the factors that affect the fidelity of communication in your organisation.
8. Describe the measures you would take to increase the effectiveness of your organisational communication.
9. Differentiate between leader and manager.
10. Give the detailed account on emergence of informal leader.
11. What are all the factors affecting leadership styles?
12. Discuss the theories of leadership.
13. What are the different factors and characteristics that influence leadership in organizations?
14. Distinguish between formal and informal leadership.

SECTION XIII: OPERATIONS RESEARCH

1. What are the components of formulation of linear programming problems?
2. What is an assignment problem? How will you deal with assignment problem where some assignments are prohibited?
3. Name any three methods of finding initial basic feasible solution for transportation problems. Which one of them is best and why?
4. Distinguish between PERT and CPM network. Give one application of CPM network.
5. What are the objectives of project crashing?
6. Write down three differences between PERT and CPM in brief?
7. Give three advantages of linear programming.
8. Name the important techniques of operations research.

9. Define time estimates in network analysis.
10. What do you mean by assignment problem?
11. Enumerate the role of operations research in decision making.
12. What do you understand by unbalanced transportation problem? How would you convert it into a balanced problem?
13. What do you mean by operations research? Discuss its scope in various areas.
14. Give three variations in transportation problems. How are these resolved?
15. Explain the concept of dynamic programming. What are the demerits of dynamic programming?

SECTION XIV: INDUSTRIAL SAFETY

1. How did the concept of safety in industry evolve?
2. What are the impediments in implementation of safety functions?
3. Describe an ideal safety organization for a large company.
4. Describe various work-related operations that attract safety precautions.
5. Discuss the occupational health problems.
6. What is confined space standard?
7. Explain the concept of record keeping.
8. What are incidence rates?
9. Explain the impact of government responsibilities in occupational safety.

SECTION XV: ENGINEERING ECONOMICS

1. Define economics. Also discuss the flow of goods, services, resources and money payments in a simple economy with the help of a suitable diagram.
2. Illustrate the effect of price on demand and supply with the help of a diagram.
3. Discuss the factors which influence demand and supply.
4. Distinguish between technical efficiency and economic efficiency by giving examples.
5. What are the ways by which the economic efficiency can be improved?
6. Give the definition and scope of engineering economics.
7. Clearly explain the method of deriving the selling price of a product.
8. Define the following costs with examples:
   (a) Sunk cost
   (b) Opportunity cost
   (c) Marginal cost
   (d) Marginal revenue.

9. Define break-even point. Draw a break-even chart and explain its components.
10. Consider the following data of a company for the year 1999. Sales = Rs. 2,50,000
    Fixed cost = Rs. 40,000 Variable cost = Rs. 65,000
    Find the following:
    (a) Contribution
    (b) Profit
    (c) BEP
    (d) Margin of safety
11. List and explain the different types of maintenance.
12. Discuss the reasons for replacement.
13. Define 'economic life' of an equipment.
14. Distinguish between breakdown maintenance and preventive maintenance.
15. A firm is considering replacement of an equipment, whose first cost is Rs. 1750 and the scrap value is negligible at any year. Based on experience, it was found that the maintenance cost is zero during the first year and it increases by Rs. 100 every year thereafter.
    (a) When should the equipment be replaced if $i = 0\%$?
    (b) When should the equipment be replaced if $i = 12\%$?
16. The following table gives the operation cost, maintenance cost and salvage value at the end of every year of a machine whose purchase value is Rs. 20,000.
    (a) Find the economic life of the machine assuming interest rate (i) of 0%
    (b) Find the economic life of the machine assuming interest rate of 15%.

End of year (n)	Operation cost	Maintenance cost	Salvage value
1	2,000	200	10,000
2	3,000	300	9,000
3	4,000	400	8,000
4	5,000	500	7,000
5	6,000	600	6,000
6	7,000	700	5,000
7	8,000	800	4,000
8	9,000	900	3,000
9	10,000	1,000	2,000
10	11,000	1,100	1,000

17. A manufacturer is offered two machines A and B. A is priced at Rs. 8000 and maintenance costs are estimated at Rs. 500 for the first year and an equal increment of Rs. 100 from year 2 to year 5, and Rs. 1500 for the sixth year and an equal increment of Rs. 500 from year 7 onwards.

Machine B which has the same capacity is priced at Rs. 6000. The maintenance costs of the machine B are estimated at Rs. 1000 for the first year and an equal yearly increment of Rs. 200 thereafter.

If the money is worth 15% per year, which machine should be purchased? (Assume that the scrap value of each of the machines is negligible at any year.)

18. Three years back, a machine was purchased at a cost of Rs. 3,00,000 to be useful for 10 years. Its salvage value at the end of its estimated life is Rs. 50,000. Its annual maintenance cost is Rs. 40,000. The market value of the present machine is Rs. 2,00,000. A new machine to cater to the needs of the present machine is available at Rs. 2,50,000 to be useful for 7 years. Its annual maintenance cost is Rs. 14,000. The salvage value of the new machine is Rs. 20,000. Using an interest rate of 15%, find whether it is worth replacing the present machine with the new one.
19. A steel highway bridge must either be reinforced or replaced. Reinforcement would cost Rs. 8,60,000 and would make the bridge adequate for an additional seven years of service. If it is reinforced, it is estimated that its net salvage value would be Rs. 5,00,000 at the time it is retired from service. The new pressurised concrete bridge would cost Rs. 18,00,000 and would meet the foreseeable requirements of the next 35 years. Such a bridge would have no salvage value. It is estimated that the annual maintenance cost of the reinforced bridge would exceed that of the concrete bridge by Rs. 1,00,000. If the bridge is replaced by a new prestressed concrete bridge, the scrap value of the steel would exceed the demolition cost by Rs. 5,20,000. Assume that the money costs the state 12%. What would you recommend?
20. What are the reasons for stocking items in inventory?
21. List and explain different types of costs in the inventory system.
22. What are the types of model of inventory system? Explain them in brief.
23. Explain the cost trade-off of the purchase model of inventory system without shortage.
24. Alpha Industry estimates that it will sell 12,000 units of its product for the forthcoming year. The ordering cost is Rs. 100 per order and the carrying cost per unit per year is 20% of the purchase price per unit. The purchase price per unit is Rs. 50. Find:

    (a) Economic order size

    (b) No. of orders per year

    (c) Time between successive orders
25. A product is to be manufactured within the company whose details are as follows:

    $r = 24{,}000$ units/year, $k = 48{,}000$ units/year, $Co =$ Rs. 200/setup, $Cc =$ Rs. 20/unit/year.

    Find the EOQ and cycle time.
26. The annual demand for an automobile component is 24,000 units. The carrying cost is Re. 0.40/unit/year, the ordering cost is Rs. 20/order, and the shortage cost is Rs. 10/unit/year. Find the optimal values of the following:

(a) Economic order quantity
(b) Maximum inventory
(c) Maximum shortage quantity
(d) Cycle time
(e) Inventory period ($t1$)
(f) Shortage period ($t2$)

27. The demand for an item is 18,000 per year. Its production rate is 3000/month. The carrying cost is Re. 0.15/unit/month, and the setup cost is Rs. 500.00/setup. The shortage cost is Rs. 20.00/unit/year. Find various parameters of the inventory system.

Index

W